VADIM **ZELAND**

PRIESTESS ITFUT

Saint-Petersburg
Ves Publishing Group
2020

Translation by *Joanna Dobson*
Cover design: *Irina Novikova*
Photographer: *Maria Taykova*
Makeup artist: *Galina Zhelenkova*

Zeland V.
Priestess Itfut. — SPB.: PG Ves, 2020. — 450 p.
ISBN 978-5-9573-3547-4

Everyone's watching Tufti. Everyone's reading Tufti. Everyone's talking about Tufti. Some shout, "We can't stand Tufti!" Others shout, "We want Tufti!" So who is she Priestess Itfut, who goes by the second name Tufti?

Tufti is not a made up character. She used to exist and in some sense she still does. This book describes the amazing adventures of the priestess and her friends in metareality. What happens there is not entirely fiction.Truth be told, it is not fiction at all. The reader will have to decide for themselves how much of it they wish to believe.

This book does not promise a magic wand and you will not absorb the superpowers of its fabulous characters by reading it, but you can take Tufti's techniques away with you, as many others have done already.

UDK 159.9
BBK 86.30

Topic: Esoteric teachings

ISBN 978-5-9573-3547-4

Zeland Vadim

PRIESTESS ITFUT

Ves Publishing Group, OJSC
Saint Petersburg, 197101, RU, PO Box 88
e-mail: info@vesbook.ru
http://www.vesbook.ru

Подписано в печать 29.07.2020.
Формат 60 × 90 1/16. Тираж 300 экз.

Налоговая льгота — общероссийский классификатор продукции ОК-005-93, том 2;
953130 — литература по философским наукам, социологии, психологии

Издательская группа «Весь»
197101, Санкт-Петербург, а/я 88.
E-mail: info@vesbook.ru

Посетите наш сайт: http://www.vesbook.ru

Вы можете заказать наши книги:
по телефону 8-800-333-00-76
(ПО РОССИИ ЗВОНКИ БЕСПЛАТНЫЕ)

Отпечатано в АО «Т8 Издательские Технологии» (АО «Т8»)
109316, Москва, Волгоградский проспект, дом 42, корпус 5

CONTENT

TIME COMES TO A STANDSTILL

It all took place in the distant past roughly 100 million years ago. No-one knows the precise date but that does not matter. When it comes to events that happened so long ago that it is impossible to conceive of their remoteness in time, it ceases to be relevant whether they took place eons ago or relatively recently.

When we look up at the stars, we don't consider the fact that their light has taken millions of years to reach us. As far as we are concerned, the stars simply exist in the here and now. It is the same with events of the past, even those lost in the depths of millennia. In the moment that they are recalled, either in memory or in storytelling, it is as if they were here right now.

Although, in truth, they are not fully here right now. So how far do the depths of millennia stretch? The earth and the sea extend downwards, and the sky stretches upwards but in what direction does time go? And where does it come from?

Space is quite straightforward. It approaches from up ahead and ends up behind us. When it comes to time, things are just as straightforward, at least until you start to really think about it: what has already happened is gone and what is yet to happen is yet to arrive. But where did what happened yesterday go, and where does what will happen tomorrow come from?

As soon as you start trying to understand the nature of time, things get much more complicated. When you stop to think about it, if you cannot say where yesterday went and where tomorrow will come from, you have to conclude that yesterday and tomorrow might not exist after all and contemplate the possibility that only today exists — the present.

So, if yesterday no longer exists and tomorrow has not yet come into being, time cannot be anything at all as it doesn't go anywhere and it doesn't come from anywhere. Are we to assume then that time is simply an abstract notion or might not be a physical phenomenon after all?

Future time is an ephemeral concept. The past, however, must be real not least because archaeological excavations testify to its existence. Yet shards of pottery and human remains are really just another obsolete present. When we talk about the past, we are usually referring to a series of events and in this regard, the question is, where are those events now? Where are they stored?

However unlikely it sounds; you can actually see the past. The starry sky is visual proof of that. We see the stars light up, shine and burn out in the present moment, however long ago those events took place. When it comes to the stars, we can see what happened on Earth millions of years ago, so, should we assume that the past is preserved in rays of light and nothing more?

Mysteries such as these are best left to the philosophers. Some things in life are not meant to be explained. They are better recounted in stories... And so, once, something mysterious happened. Time froze and the world came to a standstill.

Until this particular moment, everything had carried on as normal: one royal dynasty replaced another, one civilization followed another and the statues of forgotten gods became riddled with cracks and veiled in layers of sand... Things came and went but nothing ever stood still.

Although, who knows? Maybe this was not the first occasion that time came to a standstill and the Universe assumed a state of limbo. After all, if time was set in motion for a reason, then maybe there is a reason for its coming to a standstill. And the pause itself could have lasted for a single moment and it could just as easily have lasted for an eternity because without movement, there can be no time.

So, in that limitless moment of non-existence, when nothing was supposed to happen, strangely, there was one place where something did happen.

* * *

Priestess Itfut was trailing the boundless blue desert talking to herself. An eccentric figure, it was impossible to tell which country or era she belonged to or even how old she was. She could have been twenty, but she could just as well have been forty. She was dressed in an ankle-length, dark-blue, black velvet dress with a neck collar studded in diamonds. On her left hand, she wore a ring inlaid with a crystal with the same dark-blue sheen. Her face was covered in scarlet ritual paint, her cheeks bones dotted with white spots. She had green eyes and black hair cut into a bob. What else could one say about her? For all the harshness of her appearance, she was beautiful.

How she was able to move through frozen reality was a mystery. Indeed, it was a mystery to the priestess herself, as she had not the faintest idea where she was, nor could she remember how she had ended up there.

“Oh, Gods, rulers of the world! Take me home!” Itfut’s protest was expressed more in capricious indignation than a helpless wail. “Where are my servants, my subjects? If you don’t show yourselves right now, I’ll order you to have everyone beheaded!”

These words were probably spoken for effect as the priestess did not have the reputation of a cruel or bloodthirsty ruler.

“Right, if this is some sick joke everyone will suffer for it! And believe me, suffer they will!” Itfut was exhausted but she still had the spirit to behave like a capricious princess, at least in some circumstances! One had to admit, the priestess had a brave heart. Anyone else finding themselves in her shoes would already have become hysterical or fallen into trance, not least because the landscape was frighteningly surreal. Everywhere, the same, monotonous, blue waves of sand stretched as far as the horizon. There was not the slightest whiff of a breeze in the air. It was neither hot nor cold. The sky that held no sun glowed with a yellow shimmer and in contrast the sand was blue.

"Okay, okay, get with it, thinking — what is this, a nightmarish horror or a horrible nightmare?" Itfut had the habit of repeating herself.

"This kind of thing shouldn't be happening to me. I'm the one who creates the nightmares and the horrors that make everyone else tremble! This is your last warning! If I'm not returned to my temple this instant, I'll get angry, and you know how terrifying that can be!" Itfut fell to her knees in despair. "Oh no, I think I'm going to cry."

Then it suddenly came to the priestess that she could barely remember who she was or where she was from. Vague fragments of memory were tangled in her mind. She recalled that she was a High Priestess and ruler... she had a temple, ministers, a Teacher but she could not recall the details. She could not even remember her name.

"Oh! Gods, who am I?"

No sooner had she spoken than a whisper appeared in the emptiness flicking from one direction to another like an unsettled wind:

"Itfut, Itfut! Priestess Itfut! Priestess, priestess!"

"Strange, that is kind of like my name, and at the same time, it isn't..." the priestess muttered while looking around for the source of the voice. "Who's there?"

"Threshold, Threshold!" the whisper responded.

"Threshold of what?"

"Time, time!"

"Where are you? Show yourself!"

But the whisper faded just as suddenly as it had appeared and did not respond.

“Right...” sighed Itfut, not waiting for a reply. “This must be a bad dream. Either I’m about to wake up, or I’m going mad. Either way, I can’t take this anymore.”

Then, she suddenly remembered something her Teacher had taught her: to return to reality from a dream you have to be consciously aware of who you are, who you really are.

“That’s not me,” the priestess declared. “This is me!” But the priestess’s incantation did not help. Nothing happened. ‘So, who am I? What will happen if I never remember myself fully?’ thought the priestess. ‘Even the name the whisper spoke somehow did not quite feel like it was her real name. And what did that mean, it did not quite feel real?’

“So, what are we going to do, Itfut?” the priestess asked herself. “Ok, my name is Itfut, my name is Itfut. What next? There is no point in walking any further. There’s just sand and nothing but sand as far as the eye can see. Hang on a minute. What else did the Teacher say?”

The fresh memory gave the priestess a glimpse of hope. ‘Wake up in the dream and you can take control of the dream. To do this you have to look very carefully at all that surrounds you and then ask yourself whether everything is as it should be, or whether something is wrong, and if so, what exactly. Learn to see your reality.’

“No, everything is wrong with me and my surroundings. Everything is wrong! And what is there to see here except sand? And, by the way, why is it blue?" Itfut sat down and began pouring sand from one hand to the other.

"Sand, this is not sand. Sand is sand!" she said trying to see the unusual essence in ordinary things as her Teacher taught her to. "What is unusual about it aside from the color? It consists of grains and pours like sand."

In that moment, the sand in front of the priestess began to rise up like smoke turning into a huge vortex and charging up into the sky. The priestess screamed at the terrifying spectacle and tried to run away but it was futile. Wherever she ran, the sandy spiral appeared in front of her. The shoes Itfut was wearing were not meant for running in and she stumbled and fell.

The priestess was almost on the verge of great despair, but she pulled herself together again and managed to calm herself a little, telling herself that the whirlwind was not doing her any harm at least.

"Okay, okay. I'm really scared now; I couldn't be any more scared. So, if things can't get any worse, then that's good — they're about to get better. But I've seriously had enough of all this. My fear is now separate from me, and I am separate from it. I don't want to be with it anymore. I'm going and leaving my fear in my shoes. They're no good here anyway. Away, away, get away from me!" The priestess kicked off her shoes and flung them straight into the whirlwind.

"That's it. I've gone and I've left my fear here!"

The shoes disappeared into the whirlwind which twisted even more powerfully now with an increasing roar.

'This is bad,' thought Itfut. 'I need to take more effective measures otherwise this is not going to end well.'

"Right, Itfut, Itfut, priestess, priestess, you need to see this damn reality, work out what it is, or this is the end. This isn't just sand and that isn't just any old whirlwind. What is it? Think, quickly, quickly now, hurry, hurry!"

And then it dawned on her.

"It's a sand-timer!" she exclaimed. "It's a sand-timer! I see you, devilish reality!"

In that moment, the whirlwind stopped twisting, the roar was replaced with a glassy chime, and the gigantic funnel came crashing to the ground. The sand acquired a natural yellow color, and the sky shone blue again. The sun was the one thing still absent from the sky.

SYNTHETIC MAID

At the same time but in a different era and in a different place...

How it is possible for something to be 'at the same time but in a different era' - we will explain later. Movement through time and space is not always linear, at least within the limits of what can be seen and understood. And just because something lies beyond the limits of our comprehension does not mean that it does not exist.

In order to move from the point in time and space where we left priestess Itfut to the new place of action, the observer is required to undertake a rather elaborate journey.

Imagine that you are flying up through the sky. Itfut transforms from a figure on the sand to a tiny speck. The earth appears to move further and further away until it resembles the lines on a map, and you are lifted higher and higher until eventually, the blue of the sky is replaced by the black of the cosmos.

Now you are flying through the black abyss, but it is not dark because of the stars and Earth is still visible like a blue ball moving away in the distance. And soon Earth is nothing more than a dot and your movement is no longer visible. There comes a point when you are frozen in this position, surrounded by stars in the blackness, nothing but stars.

Then, one of those stars suddenly transforms into a tube. It draws you inside a glowing tunnel, pulling you through it for what feels like an infinity and at the same time you are travelling incredibly fast.

Finally, the speed slows down, you are pushed out of the other end of the tube and again find yourself floating in black space filled with stars. One star begins to increase in size, and you realize that you are no longer hanging there suspended, you are moving.

Then the star transforms into a ball which gradually expands before you into a blue planet. It is the Earth but in a different epoch. You enter the Earth's atmosphere and blackness is replaced by blueness; it is as if you are drowning, falling through the clouds. You find yourself floating in a gray fog for a while before being plunged back into darkness this time because, in this epoch, the sun has already set.

Below you can see the lights of the city at night. You plane downwards drawing ever closer to the flickering lights. You fly across motorways with cars whizzing past, squares filled with people, rivers, bridges, luminous apartment blocks, houses, until finally, you dart in through a random window.

Now we can say that it is the same time only we are in a different epoch and a different place, specifically a theater, in which a film is being made of the musical 'Finished Clown'.

Why a clown and in what way 'finished'? Finished as in passed away or finished in the sense of hopeless, incorrigible, done-for? The film crew did not appear to know either as they were still in the so-called 'creative process'.

The auditorium was immersed in half-light. Abandoned belongings and coats lay thrown across chairs. A handful of people were sitting in the auditorium, one dozing and another staring at the brightly lit stage, where theatre types rushed about busy preparing for a rehearsal. The stage was set up as a semi-cylindrical transformer with images and lighting effects projected onto the floor and walls.

The director was standing in the middle of the stage, an emotional figure cursing wildly.

"It won't do. None of you will do! Are we shooting a musical or a funeral? Get lost, fools! Get lost! Come back different!" What he meant by this and in what way they should return different, the director did not bother to explain. But the members of the film crew, a motley crowd dressed up to the nines, were not going to hang about to find out and fled in all directions.

"Right, where is my diva? She's the only one who inspires me. Bring me my diva! Max, will she be long?" he asked turning to his operator. "Go and find out."

The operator ran behind the wings and quickly returned. Max was a young man with a stutter, and he had the habit of taking a long time to prepare before saying anything:

"Victor, we... We-e..."

"We what? Who we are and what we are is a complex philosophical question. Spit it out!"

"Matilda is being difficult again." Max finally managed to say.

"Just get her here!" yelled Victor (which was what they called the director) in an intimidating voice.

"Victor!" A woman's voice could be heard behind the wings. "Here she is, I'm here!" Following on from the voice the woman herself appeared. The instantly created the impression of being a highly eccentric individual dressed as she was in a dark-green jumpsuit and huge pink platforms, as well as donning a shock of light-blue hair strewn with light-purple highlights. You could say she was a 'blue blonde'.

"Come here, Tili, my darling, my angel!" Victor approached the eccentric woman throwing his arms wide open. "Ok, turn around. Aren't you beautiful!" and abruptly changing the tone of his voice, he said, "What are you doing here still not made up! Skedaddle back to the dressing room, quick!"

"I don't want to. It takes so lo-o-o-ong!" Matilda had the habit of extending her vowels. "It's only a rehearsal anyway!"

"I'm the one who decides whether it's a rehearsal or a film shoot. Get out of my sight!"

"I want a sweet! You promised me chocolate-coated cherries."

"What a b..." Max stuttered, trying to join the conversation. "B, b..."

"You're saying I have such a beautiful what? Hurry up!"

"What a banal choice — chocolate-coated cherries!" said Max, finally managing to finish his sentence.

"Oooh, but I want some!"

"Diva, you know the rules. If you don't do a take, you don't get a treat," said Victor. "Do it, and you'll have your treat. Now get lost all of you! No, wait, let's rehearse your curtsy again."

Matilda stepped to one side and gave an affected curtsy.

"Oh, how vulgar!" shouted Victor. "Come on, again. Do it as you were taught to, hands to the chest and ... not on the chest, to the chest, and with feeling, with dignity! It should be light, not buffoon-like! What am I going to do with her? That's it, get out of here, you monster, or I'll shoot you myself!"

Matilda turned on her platforms and was about to make a run for it.

"No! Stop! Tili, darling! Come back here!"

Matilda turned again and waited expectantly.

"Sometimes, you say something, out of the mouth of a babe. Seriously, what would be the best dance to use in this shot, street or house?"

"It needs the twist. The twist is what's needed." the diva answered him.

"What, what, what? Why?"

"Because all your go-go and R&B totally sucks. It's all old hat."

"What? What? What do you mean, old hat, it's contemporary dance."

"Because it's all so boring! Boring - that's why!"

"Right, great explanation. But why the twist? That's retro."

"New is the forgotten old. You can make a new fashion out of anything that's been forgotten."

"That's a th... th-th... That's a thought." said Max.

"Agreed. We should try it." said Victor. "Ok, go and get made up, there's a smart girl."

"I'm clever with or without my makeup!" Matilda retorted and ran backstage with a happy skip.

Victor beckoned the wardrobe-mistress and whispered something in her ear, after which she disappeared.

"Right, now the rest of you talentless, retards, take a good look at yourselves and quickly assume a genius state. Go on, go on, I can see you beginning to shine already! Max, you and the other bird-brains! We need to decide on the music and effects. Time, time! We're running out of time! Let me know as soon as Matilda is ready."

The stage was once again a whirl of bustling preparations. After some time that as always, 'was and was not', Victor began giving directions.

"Right, all set! Max, where is Matilda? Ah, here she comes, all happy and radiant."

Matilda made for an impressive sight. In addition to her turquoise colored hair, her face was covered in blue face paint and her eyes were made up so that there was no doubt, the diva was a total diva.

"Okay, come on! Come here, my darling! Turn around!"

Victor beckoned to the wardrobe-mistress, who was holding a huge pink bow, the kind those women used to wear on the backs of old-fashioned dresses.

"Just a second! We're just going to dress you up a bit!"

Scarcely having glimpsed the bow, Matilda jumped backwards waving her hands about.

"No, no! Are you mad?"

"You don't understand! Look at it! It's huge, pink and beautiful!" said Victor admiring his invention. "It matches the color of your shoes. It is perfect!"

"I'm not wearing that ... gaudy thing!"

"But we're dancing the twist. Now you'll have something to twirl!"

"It stinks! What am I, a doll?"

"Of course! You're my living doll!"

"Stand still." Paying no attention to the diva's moans, the wardrobe-mistress fastened the bow to the belt just above her bottom. The other actors surrounded Matilda, trying to calm her down.

"Don't worry Matilda, it really suits you!"
"It looks really interesting!"
"It's fantastic!"
"Gorgeous!"

Eventually, they managed to convince her.

"Tili, sweetheart, you look very, very beautiful!" Victor said, still trying to persuade her.

"Very, super-very?"

"Yes, yes. And you're so clever!"

"What is it you want from me now?"

"We're having a teeny-weeny problem. We can't decide on the special effects for the floor and walls. Nothing is quite right. Any ideas?"

Despite the fact that the diva gave the impression of being frivolous by nature, she had an extraordinary mind and saw many things from her own unique point of view, sometimes too much so.

"You don't need any special effects. Let's just have a mirror floor and make the walls mirrors, too. They'll give a reflection of the whole dance group ..."

"Your bow too!"

"Stop it. That was not what I meant. If everything is in mirrors, something interesting might happen."

"Ok, we'll try it. Max, run the transformer, we're turning the whole stage into a mirror."

"A... A-all of it?"

"Yup. the floor, the walls, everything. Ok, attention people, in your places!" said Victor turning to the others. "Ready? Jugglers, acrobats, go! Music, go! Cameras, let's go!"

And at that, the previously chaotic, motley crowd suddenly came together transformed, moving smoothly and stylishly, as if the scene had been rehearsed a thousand times before. And of course, the diva was at the very center of the action, charmingly twirling her bow.

La-la, lalalala-la, lalalala-la, lalala.
If you've never been
To our bright city,
Never dreamed till dawn
Above the evening river,
If you have never strolled with friends
Down the vast avenues,
You have never seen
The best city in the world.
Ta-tada-tada-da!
The song sets sail, and my heart sings,
These words are about you, Moscow...*

In that moment, all the mirrors seemed to sparkle simultaneously and Matilda, on whom the camera was focused, was lit up in a flash of bright light. She continued moving to the beat of the music as a green mist engulfed her from all sides. Dumbfounded, Matilda stopped dancing. The mist quickly dissipated but the space around her was filled with a mirage of blue sand and yellow sky. Matilda's eyesight

---

* Song "The Best City in the World", music by A. Babadzhanyan, lyrics, L. Derbenev

seemed to go dim. She was alone inside the mirage which was slowly floating right through her. She could hear music playing somewhere in the distance. Then the mirage dissolved and in its place, Matilda was surrounded by gray figures, moving about as if dancing the same dance that was being performed on the stage just moments ago. The figures were dressed in gray, shapeless, hooded robes, their faces obscure and blurred. The music faded and was replaced by a glassy chime. The figures froze and stared at Matilda perplexed. Matilda looked back at them in horror.

* * *

Emerging from their stupor, the gray figures rushed at the poor woman shouting.

“Synthetic maid! Synthetic maid!”

“Eat heo! Eat heo!”

Matilda’s legs buckled and she fainted before the figures had time to pounce.

THE GLAMROCKS

Matilda regained consciousness and found herself tied to a pole. She was not so much tied to it as firmly wound with rawhide straps, her legs dangling above the ground. The figures in the gray hooded robes circled the pole in a ring mumbling some kind of mantra.

Mana-veda, mana-sana, mana-una, mana-mana.
Mana-oma, ata-mana, mana-okha, mana-dana.

From time to time they would stop, turn to the center of the circle and shout out.

"Synthetic maid! Eat heo!" Then they would resume their sinister circle dance.

"Mana-oga, makha-mana, mana-osha, mana-shana."

The ground around the pole was desert-like and stony. Not far from the pillar a large fire burned, and a little further off, Matilda could make out primitive-looking buildings. The sky glowed with a dim, gray light but there was no sun. The overall picture was completely colorless, like a black and white film. Against this background, Matilda's vivid figure looked like an alien from some distant world. As the reader may recall, Matilda had turquoise hair, and a blue painted face and she was wearing a dark-green jumpsuit, pink platforms and a bow of the same color attached to her lower back.

The unfortunate diva was in a state of shock. She could not understand where she was or what was happening. Even worldly-wise priestess Itfut would no doubt have paled finding herself in such a situation. What was the poor thing to feel, as one accustomed to pampering, home comforts and universal adoration? In other circumstances, she would have complained in her usual manner: "Everything is horrible, very, very ho-o-rrible!" But this was not the time to be capricious. For some reason there was only one thought going through her mind at that moment and oddly enough that thought was 'now my bow will get squashed.' This was very strange indeed taking into account what had happened to her and what awaited her now.

Meanwhile, the savages, who had spent plenty of time in a circle mumbling began arguing amongst themselves over what to do next with their captive. Some cried, "We'll f'y heo!"

Others, "No, b'ew heo!"

They appeared either not to be able to pronounce the letter 'r', or not to want to because it wasn't just that they spoke with an uvular 'r'; they swallowed the sound instead. Far from being comical, this created a creepy effect.

They continued arguing huddled in a group before splitting into two groups which started yelling at each other.

"F'y!"

"B'ew!"

The argument eventually escalated into a messy brawl.

The savages (or whoever else they were, as their faces were all the same, gray, genderless, lifeless and waxlike), were fighting not for life but for death. They had no weapons, but they made use of the stones lying at their feet. Soon, they were no longer standing but rolling around in the dust tearing their robes to shreds. It turned out that they had no hair.

Matilda observed the wild medley with horror and understood that even if they all killed each other, bound to the post unable to move her arms or legs, she stood no chance. She wanted to scream but there was a lump in her throat, and anyway, what was the point? There was not anyone else from whom she could expect help. This was not a dream.

Who knows how long the mindless mayhem would have continued had it not been for a powerful, deep sound like a trumpet. As if waking up, the gray numbskulls picked themselves up reluctantly and still staggering a little managed to arrange themselves in a circle around the pole. Dirty, their clothes in tatters, they once again started stamping their feet in the same circle dance, murmuring what might have been spells or mantras.

Sometime later, as if on cue, they stopped, turned to the center of the circle and angrily shouted in one voice as if they had come to agreement.

"B'ew heo!"

And having spoken these words as one, they began running about. Some threw logs into the flames of the fire. Others dragged a huge cauldron that had appeared as if out of nowhere. A third group leapt closer to Matilda, stuck out their tongues, and stared right at her, shaking their heads and mumbling. They shook and they mumbled and then they shouted.

"Synthetic maid!" All the others joined in unanimously. "Eat heo! Eat!"

Then, mumbling, baring their teeth and sticking out their tongues, they untied their victim and dragged her towards with fire.

It made for a truly surreal scene. Nothing like this could ever happen in reality. A girl with a doll-like appearance and a pink bow... treated with such foul intent... No, it was all too unreal. And yet, it was actually happening.

In this moment, Matilda, who was scared to death just seconds before, suddenly regained her self-control as sometimes happens to a person who, condemned to death, finally has nothing to lose and realizes that things cannot get any worse. Gathering all her strength, Matilda began to shout.

"Get lost, you fools! Get your filthy hands off my bow!"

She cried out instinctively not understanding why she should shout these phrases specifically or why she should be concerned about a thing so trifling, when she was about to breathe her last. All she felt was an intense desire to be left alone. She also noticed that this desire was accompanied by an unusually wearying feeling in the area of her lower back. Whether the sensation arose because of the bow or for some other reason, Matilda was suddenly aware that the feeling was giving her an inexplicable power over the gray breed.

They stopped dead in their tracks and stared at her in complete amazement. Matilda freed herself from their clutches and even managed to push some of them away. She knew intuitively that she must not run, so she froze in expectation of what might happen next. 'Anything but run,' thought the diva, who was ready for whatever might happen next, experiencing the same weary feeling in her back.

"Get away from me, you freaks!"

The freaks did in fact start to back off, making sounds of astonishment.

"Did she say the lette'?"

"Is she allowed?"

"Is she mana?"

"Does she have full?"

"She can say the lette'!"

The gray ones huddled together whispering occasionally casting glances at the diva who tried as best she could to assume a posture of pride and dignity. Then, they gathered round Matilda nonetheless keeping a wary distance. One of them took a step forward and asked, "Who are you?"

Matilda answered more calmly, realizing that the immediate threat had passed, at least for now.

"I'm a glamorous diva-a-a! And who are you, freaks?"

Then she stopped short, as if forgetting for a moment where she was, and all about the freaks, who she probably should not be insulting considering that they had almost boiled her alive. 'Where am I?' was the huge question that naturally followed. The freaks, meanwhile, paid no attention and began shouting again.

"The synthetic maid!"

"She can say the lette'!"

"Why are you calling me synthetic maid?" asked Matilda.

They silently exchanged glances. The question clearly confused them.

"We don't know."

"Ok, and who are you?"

"We glam'ocks!" The grays clamored and interrupted one another. "We 'ead gibb'ish! We ain't allowed to 'ead the lette'!

It's aboo! It's aboo!"

"I see," said Matilda. "You are glamrocks and you read gibberish."

"Full! Full!" They shouted noisily. "She can say ou' name! She can!"

It would appear that the alien stranger's ability to freely pronounce the letter 'r' and experience no terrible consequence as a result had made a huge impression on the savages. The grays discussed it amongst themselves again, after which, one of them stepped forward with a question.

"A you mana?"

"I'm Matilda, get it?" said the diva.

"Mana-tida! Mana-tida!" shouted the glamrocks. Matilda's answer caused them to become terribly excited again.

"Why don't you pronounce the letter?" she asked.

"We ain't allowed! Not allowed! It's aboo!" they shouted. "A c'ash will happen!"

"But I say the letter and I don't have a crash."

"You mana! Mana-tida!"

"You see! And you wanted to brew me and eat me. Do you know what would have happened if you had?" Matilda was beginning to live into the role assigned to her. "There would have been a total crash!"

On hearing these words, the wretches raised a howl clearly filled with reverential awe.

"Who taught you to read gibberish? And what do you need it for?"

"The Glamo'c taught us! Mana-glamo'c! Theah! Theah!" The grays began gesticulating in an animated fashion and pointing in the direction of the buildings.

"We have to 'ead gibb'ish, so that we will be full.We must not say the lette'. We not allowed to fight. We not allowed to eat each othe'. It's aboo! We have to 'ead gibb'ish."

"Right, but you are allowed to eat me?"

"Not ou' own. You not one of us."

"That's not true. I am one of you!" said Matilda, thinking on her feet. In situations like this, you tend to think on your feet quite well. "I am your mana!"

Before the glamrocks had time to react, the same trumpet noise sounded from afar. The sound was evidently a kind of signal for them because the savages became alarmed and started shouting.

"Sac'ed hlevjun! We must take heo to sac'ed hlevjun!"

"What hlevjun is that?" Matilda asked.

"The glamo'c is there! Mana-glamo'c! We'll show you! Let's go!"

Matilda was gripped with anxiety. If this glamorc was their leader then he might well have his own ideas about who was or wasn't the real mana. And then the process of cooking and subsequently eating the synthetic maid might be resumed with renewed appetite.

Matilda had no choice. She had not the slightest idea where she could run to. She had to go with them. So, the entire procession set off in the direction of the buildings.

THE DEAD HEAD

The glamrocks walked in silence encircling Matilda in a tight crowd but still keeping some distance from her. It was a strange sight. The gray figures with their wax faces and among them a blue blonde wearing a pink bow. It was a truly phantasmagorical procession consisting of a living doll surrounded by mannequins.

You would never say of Matilda that she was just a barbie doll. Some people are pretty, and others are beautiful. It is the difference between form and content. Matilda was one of those people who just have something about them.

But the main thing distinguishing her from the overall picture was not so much her colorful silhouette against the 'black and white cinema' background, so much as her lifeforce. Everything else including the gray figures was not so much dead as lifeless if one could put it that way. The other world probably looked much like this - not that different from our own - it was just different because it was 'on the other side'. The question is, on the other side of what?

That question remains unanswered for now. Matilda was not concerned about the physics of such phenomena right in this moment. Her mind was filled with anxious thoughts about what would happen next. By virtue of some fated coincidence, she had ended up in a foreign world and it was not yet clear how she might escape. She could see nothing on which to pin any hope. What should she expect from her sinister companions? She dared not imagine.

The glamrocks' faces expressed grim determination to find out for themselves something that could cost Matilda her life. Although the glamrocks were not touching Matilda, they looked at her with suspicion. One of those walking in front turned around, stuck out his tongue and cried out, "Synthetic maid!", no doubt out of habit. But then he got a slap. The maid was supposed to be left untouched until it had finally been determined who she really was: 'mana' or simply an edible maid.

Matilda's situation was aggravated by the fact that she was desperate to go to the toilet. 'At least I only want a number one for now', she thought. 'But there's the thing. How to go about it? What sex are they, I wonder?' She had not observed any outward indication of gender. And then she was struck by a terrible thought. They might not only eat her but abuse her body to their hearts' content, who knows in what awful ways.

She trotted along hurriedly in her platform shoes and stubbed her toe against a rock. The poor girl would have given anything to be back in her own world again. 'I'll never be capricious again.' she thought. 'I'll be obedient in everything. I'll never take off my wonderful bow ever again. I'll do anything, just send me back!'

Remembering the bow, she experienced again that same weird feeling in her back. It was not clear why, but it seemed to give her strength and for some reason caused Matilda to feel that she had the ability to control events. It was as if she could choose what came into being and what did not.

She suddenly realized that she was separate from everything that surrounded her and all that was happening to her. She was the reality in which she found herself. She existed of herself, independently just as reality did. Matilda suddenly understood, not with her mind but with all her being, that here, she had ended up in a book and she was supposed to wander through the pages playing out the plot.

It was like a movie, which you watch as you immerse yourself in a fictional reality. If you concede and give yourself over to what is happening, you have no other choice than to play the role assigned to you. But what if Matilda chose not to? What if she remained separate and the movie separate from her?

'Can this really be my reality?' thought Matilda. 'No, this is not my reality. Something is wrong. This kind of thing happens in dreams, but this is not a dream. Although what difference does it make, for God's sake? Everything will be all right with me, whatever happens. I don't know how, but I know I'll be ok. I have no other choice. What other option is there? That's what I've decided, period!'

Immediately after this thought, something happened. To her surprise, Matilda noticed a slanting black strip flash from the sky down to the ground as if some unknown force had turned the page on reality. The gray ones seemed to pay no attention to it and continued their same grim procession as if nothing had happened. Matilda, however, suddenly felt much better and was confident that from now on everything would be all right.

Meanwhile, they reached the buildings they had been heading towards. It was not a town or a village but something quite odd. Everywhere, there were simple, cubic houses with smooth, gray walls made from a material Matilda did not recognize. The houses were interspersed with empty recesses with the same cubic frame. And there were stairways everywhere, some leading up to the rooftops, others down into pits, and still others twisting senselessly and disappearing into nowhere. The fanciful intertwining of cubic structures and niches along with the many stairways created an absurd scene.

By an indirect route, crossing from one stairway to another, they exited onto what looked to be the only open space, a square, in the middle of which stood a construction, no less strange than anything else in this peculiar place. The construction was a black monolith with an oval perimeter enclosed by protruding columns, which bent gently upwards to form a ribbed dome.

By all appearances, this was the very same 'sacred hlevjun' although its sinister form was more reminiscent of a spaceship. The glamrocks could not have built such a structure themselves, or the rest of the city for that matter.

In the same moment that the procession approached the megalith, the construction produced a startlingly powerful trumpet sound in a low tone, which permeated the surrounding space. As soon as the sound reached the glamrocks' ears, they began to fuss and rushed inside. Matilda followed them with a mixture of curiosity and fear.

The megalith had the same form inside as it did on the outside. The black pillars that extended outwards from the walls rose smoothly upwards into a high dome. A green glow emanated somewhere from a niche near the floor. The floor was black and as smooth as a mirror. The place was empty except for a single element at the center which looked to be a rectangular-shaped altar or plinth made of the same material as the floor. A head was growing up out of the plinth, bald and gray like the glamrocks.

The head writhed with grimaces not making a sound. The glamrocks surrounded the altar, shoved Matilda inside the circle, fell to their knees and with raised hands began making invocations.

"Glamo'c! Mana-glamo'c!"

Without changing its expression from a grimace, the head spoke in a low bass tone.

"Read gibberish. You must not read the letter. I am mana. I can. But you can't.

Mana-veda, mana-sana, mana-una, mana-mana.
Mana-oma, ata-mana, mana-okha, mana-dana."

The glamrocks muttered the mantra obediently repeating the words the head spoke.

"Mana-oga, makha-mana, mana-osha, mana-shana," continued the glamorck (obviously, this was him). "Read gibberish.Then you will be full. Don't do the things that aren't allowed, otherwise there'll be a crash!"

The savages put their heads in their hands and groaned.

"Aboo! It's aboo!"

"Who is mana here?" asked the head. "Who do you need to kiss around here?"

"Glamo'c! Mana-glamo'c!" they responded and began rubbing their faces along the floor, mercilessly squashing their noses.

"Praise me!" the glamorc shouted ominously, accompanying the words with horrible grimacing and sending out a monotonous murmur. "O-a-oo-khomm, o-a-oo-homm."

"O-a-oo-khomm!" the glamrocks repeated.

They droned on for a while longer following the head's lead but then gradually became quiet and turned their gaze to the maid inside the circle. Matilda stood completely at a loss not knowing what to do with herself. They clearly expected her to do something. It was time to take urgent action and as she correctly surmised, it had to be something extraordinary as her authority had diminished rapidly in the presence of the glamorc.

She was also desperate for the toilet. Matilda could not understand what kind of head this was, whether it was alive, and if so, why it was growing out of the monolith. As she watched, it continued to mumble and grimace. Then Matilda spotted something mechanical about the head. It was periodically repeating the same movements over and over again in a cycle.

She had nothing to lose. It was now or never. If she did not take the situation into her own hands this very second, she was finished. Without further hesitation, Matilda climbed up onto the altar, undid the zipper on her jumpsuit, crouched down and relieved herself right on top of the talking head.

The glamrocks stared at her completely dumbfounded, a look of indescribable horror appearing on their faces, formerly devoid of any facial expression. They observed the entire spectacle without making a single sound. Having completed the sacrilege, the diva rose and calmly zipped herself back up again. In that moment, the head began sending out sparks, then it twitched and with a fading mumble stalled, completely paralyzed in a pitiful grimace.

Matilda understood now. Standing on the plinth, she gave the savages a triumphant look. Their glamorc was defeated. After an initial pause, Matilda asked them the sacred question they had already heard before.

"Who is mana here?"

"Mana-tida! Mana-tida!" the glamrocks cried out. The sound of their voices faded and then again, they cried. "You are our new mana!"

In this instant, the glamrocks fell to their knees wiping their faces across the floor as before. Matilda climbed down from the plinth and began to give orders.

"Stop! Get up! Really, get up, I tell you!"

The glamrocks rose to their feet and surrounded her still keeping a respectful distance. The diva was finally herself again and asked, "So, what are we going to do?"

"...'ead gibb'ish! ...'ead gibb'ish!" the gray ones shouted. The dead head did not seem to interest them anymore. They stared in awe at their new mana ready to follow any order she might give them.

Matilda stopped and thought for a moment. She had just escaped a terrible fate, finding a way out of what she had assumed to be a hopeless situation. She had never experienced anything like this ever in her life before, and naturally, could never have imagined herself capable of coping with such a crisis. But events were developing so rapidly, she did not have time to be surprised or celebrate.

As before, Matilda faced a multitude of unresolved questions: what was the head? What was this building, this town? Who built it all and why? What was this world in which she found herself? Whoever the architects were, it definitely was not the glamrocks. Judging from what she had seen, the head was an electrical mechanism that served as a means of shackling these primitive people. Now the head was broken but the source of energy that had fed it was clearly still active as the monolith continued to emit its green glow.

The main thing was to work out what on earth Matilda was going to do next. If these people were primitive, there was no telling what they might come up with. That meant she had to occupy their minds with something resembling a ritual, otherwise they might become disobedient to her. Having considered the circumstances, clever Matilda (and she was undoubtedly very clever) decided to start by establishing some kind of bond with the gray ones.

LETKAJENKHA

"Listen, why don't you learn to pronounce the letter?" asked Matilda.

"We ain't allowed!" the glamrocks answered. "A c'ash will happen if we say it!"

"Well, I'm telling you that there won't be a crash. I'm your new mana. I decide! Understand?"

The glamrocks were shaken with indecision.

"But we ain't allowed! It's aboo!"

"Yes, you can! Repeat after me, 'we are glamrocks'."

The glamrocks exchanged glances and whispered to each other for a while, not yet ready to take such a decisive step. Finally, one of them stepped forward and said,

"We glam'o-o-ocks."

"We glam'o-o-ocks." The others followed on, no longer swallowing the letter 'r' but trying to pronounce it, at first, however, with little success.

"Repeat after me: crocodiles!"

"C'okodiles! C'okodiles!"

"Cheburashkas!"

"Chebuaashkas! Chebuaashkas!

"Brownie!"

"B'ownie! B'ownie!" the glamrocks said, trying hard to get it right.

"Go on, go on, you can do it! Ok, again: Leningrad rock-n-roll!"

The glamrocks were enlivened by these words and tried even harder. It is unlikely that they understood what they were saying but they obviously liked the words. And then a miracle happened. They did it!

"Leningrad! Leningrad!" they cried with enthusiasm. "Leningrad rock-n-roll!"

"You see!" said Matilda pleased with herself. "Well done! Now, repeat after me,

'May the drizzling rain today fall from morrrning,
but you and I are dancing again like yesterrrday.
From Moscow to Leningrad, and returrrning to Moscow,
The lines, rrrailings and bridges dance.'*"

The glamrocks were clearly capable students. They easily repeated the unfamiliar words. But it didn't matter to them that the words were unfamiliar. They just really enjoyed it because now they could say the letter too and there was no crash.

"Aba! Aba!" they shouted in delight. "We are glamrocks! We read gibberish! And we read the letter!"

The savages became excessively excited by the new opportunities now opening up before them and Matilda wondered how to calm them down before went seriously out of control.

"Stop, stop! Listen to me!" Matilda was only just able to make herself heard above the noise they were making. "Why do you read this gibberish?"

The glamrocks calmed down a little and then one of them replied,

---

* Song by pop group 'Bravo' - 'Leningrad Rock-n-Roll'

"We must read gibberish." and then they started up again. "Aba! I am reading the letter."

The exclamation 'aba' appeared to be the glamrocks way of expressing delight. But Matilda interrupted the enthusiast.

"Yes, I understand, you read gibberish. But what is the point of it?"

The glamrocks seemed puzzled by the question.

"What is point'?" he asked, and then without waiting for an answer, added, "there does not need to be a point. There needs to be full!"

Matilda was beginning to realize that weaning them off their silly habit was beyond her and that it probably was not worth the effort anyway. After a little thought, she turned to them with the words,

"Right, so you don't need there to be a point. In that case, I will teach you some new, magical gibberish. If you read it regularly and continuously, you won't just be full, you'll be wonderful. That's more. That's better.

The glamrocks seemed to be intrigued. Matilda gathered her thoughts and began to recite a chorus not yet wanting to overwhelm them with the song's melody.

"Listen:

Mamma-mia, here I go again,
My, my, how can I resist you?
Mamma-Mia, does it show again?
My, my, just how much I missed you.
Yes, I've been brocken hearted,
Blue since the day you parted.
Why, why, did I ever let you go?*

---

* A free transcription of Abba song, 'Mamma Mia'.

The glamrocks listened spellbound, and after Matilda had finished, they were silent for a few moments more. Then they burst into ecstatic exclamations:

"Mana-mia! Mana-mia! We have new gibberish! Wonder-ful! That's more. That's better. Aba! Aba!"

"Yes, it's Abba," Matilda said. "Now calm down, all of you! Listen, I'll repeat it for you so that you can learn it by heart."

"Mana-mia! We remember!" the glamrocks responded, then repeated it word for word in an out of tune chorus, only replacing 'mama' with the usual 'mana'. Clearly their minds were unburdened with excess information, and so they could memorize and reproduce any word or phrase with ease.

"Well, what do you know!" said Matilda, surprised. "Okay, let's go outside. It's stuffy in here. Let's go!"

The glamrocks obeyed and flocked behind Matilda who led them outside. But they could not calm down outside either. Overcome with emotion and very excited, they arranged themselves according to their custom in a circle and started stamping their feet, muttering their new gibberish.

"Mana-mia, hir a go egen..."

This time, they confidently uttered the letter, but the cheerful song had turned into a gloomy chant, like soldiers mechanically singing a boring drill song.

"Ma-na, dast ha mach a mist yu..."

Observing the stomping and mumbling, Matilda thought, 'No, this is just another kind of frenzy. This won't do. I need to get them going with something more positive.'

“Right, listen up!” commanded Matilda. “Stop where you are. Now we’re going to learn some new gibberish. In fact, it’s not just gibberish, it’s a song-dance. That’s even more! Even better! You will feel wonderful! Grip onto each other and repeat the movements and the words after me.”

The glamrocks were surprised, but obeyed, nonetheless. Matilda stood at the front of the line, placed the hands of the glamrock immediately behind on her waist warning him, ‘Don’t touch my bow!’, and began to sing, beginning the steps of a once fashionable dance.

Once late at night on an empty street,
I returned from a romance sad again.
Believe it or not, for some reason my feet
started dancing this dance themselves.
Again, the path led to my sweetheart,
again, I was at her door,
tapped at the window, waited a little.
Listen dear, come out quickly.
One, two, put on your shoe!

Still asleep? Shame on you!
Wonderful, sweet, funny jenka
Invites us to dance.’*

Awkwardly out of time at first, the glamrocks copied Matilda’s movements, becoming increasingly coordinated and merry as they went along. It turned out that they were even capable of reproducing the melody. Even though it was new to them, it was clear that they loved the song-dance.

---

* Song-dance ’Letkajenkha’, author unknown.

Anyone who has ever seen the letkajenkha performed with dancers jumping back and forth making funny movements with their feet can imagine what a spectacle it was to see the same dance performed by the glamrocks. The diva knew how much the good old dance had been made trite by the glamorous divas of today. But she was not quite as trivial as her 'fellow tradeswomen'. Matilda valued everything that was real, which was why she sang and danced like they did in the good old days, which she loved, just as much as she loved the twist.

The glamrocks quickly mastered the melody and words, and were happily singing along, jumping about enthusiastically and throwing their legs out from under their robes. They were engulfed in an unfamiliar feeling they had never experienced until now — happiness.

'One, two, put on your shoe!
Still asleep? Shame on you!
Wonderful, sweet, funny jenka
Invites us to dance.'

Having danced to their heart's content, they gathered around Matilda, and brimmingover with delight began to praise her in their own fashion.

"Mana-tida-enka! Mana-tida-enka! Invites us to dance!"

They would have gone on shouting for much longer, but Matilda waved her hands at them.

"Stop, that's enough! I'm tired. I need a rest."

As if filled with understanding, the glamrocks took her by the hands and walked her in the direction of the buildings shouting all the while.

"Mana-tida! Mana-tida-enka! You are our mana!"

They escorted her into the nearest house, carefully sat her down on something resembling a bed and left, respectfully stepping backwards as they went. The bed area was covered with hay. There was a table and a chair in the room, as well as some kind of toilet. The rest of the premises were empty and extremely austere. Round windows were positioned high up on every wall and there was just one door. Everything was made of the same unfamiliar, smooth material with which all the other buildings were trimmed. Despite being primitive, the construction of the dwelling was quite technically advanced, the only exception being the hay, who knows where that had come from here in the desert.

Matilda sighed with relief. They had left her alone at last. But not for long. Soon the door opened and a glamrock entered the house without knocking of course, (such were their manners), although carrying an offering. Only now did Matilda realize how hungry she was. The glamrock placed a tray on the table on which there was a cup, a spoon and a dish.

"What's this?" asked Matilda.

"Food!" he answered concisely.

The cup contained water and the bowl, something that looked like beans. It did not smell too bad. Matilda tried the beans cautiously. Oddly enough the dish turned out to be quite tasty.

"Where did you get this?" she asked.

"Hlevjun gives it to us. There is lots of food!"

'Bastards' thought Matilda. 'Why did you want to eat me then if you have shit loads of grub?' But she did not say anything. The glamrock did not say much and she did not have the slightest desire to start interrogating him. He left, walking backwards away from her and closing the door behind him. Finally, it seemed, the ceremonies for today were complete.

Matilda ate quickly, climbed onto the simple bed and covered herself in the hay. The bed was not up to much but in circumstances like these, there was no point in hoping for comfort. The poor thing was so tired from the events and emotions of the day that she could not fall asleep and instead burst into tears. Yes, everything had turned out well in the end. The glamorous diva had become the glamrocks' goddess. But what next? What could Matilda do here in the city of glamrocks? Why should she stay?

Matilda was overcome with deep sorrow. 'Was she really not destined to return home? Would life really never be again as it was before? Her old life remained in a carefree past that had not been valued and might now be lost forever. And no-one would ever put her to bed in clean sheets, kiss her little forehead and affectionately call her 'Tili, darling'. She could remember her mother doing that. How was she now? She must be worried. And what about the others? Were they looking for her?'

With these sad thoughts, now totally exhausted, Matilda fell asleep.

MANNEQUIN CITY

Priestess Itfut looked around her frantically. She was not easily surprised by anything these days, but recent events and her surrounding reality were simply outrageous. After the sand timer or whatever it was had been turned over and started pouring sand again, reality had calmed down. The sky turned blue and the sand turned yellow but there was still no sun in the sky. 'Where is that light coming from?' thought the priestess.

"My shoes flew away, away" said the priestess, who continued talking to herself. "Okay, okay, we'll assume I have paid for my fear. But if this goes on for much longer, I'll soon have nothing left to pay with."

All Itfut had left was her gorgeous dark-blue, velvet dress with the diamond-studded collar, and the crystal ring that she wore on her left hand.

"You won't get anything more out of me, you, half-wit reality you! Just because you've lost the plot, doesn't mean that I have to. I'm not afraid of you anymore. Give me back my shoes! You hear?"

Meanwhile, after the tilting of the hourglass, the landscape acquired a new detail. In the distance, Matilda began to make out the contours of a city.

"You see, Itfut, priestess, you priestess, now you have somewhere to go. So, let's go. Let's get a move on. It is high time we put an end to all this nonsense. I just hope it isn't a mirage."

She shook the sand from her dress and strode in the direction of her goal. The sand creaked beneath her bare feet like glass although it was soft to the touch. To the priestess it felt like she was walking on cotton wool. But she was more puzzled by a phenomenon, no less peculiar. It seemed to her as if, rather than her walking ahead, the landscape was coming forwards to meet her, while she had barely placed one foot in front of the other. Moreover, the goal was approaching with unnatural speed.

"What kind of trick is this?" said Matilda indignantly. "Do you want to shock me or frighten me again?" she said, talking to reality. "That's not possible! And there is no point in being afraid of something that is not possible. I'm not afraid, I'm not afraid! Not at all, at all! Get it?"

Reality meanwhile continued to change ignoring the priestess. Within a few minutes the sky was gray. The waves of sand turned into a rocky wasteland and the outlines of the city grew larger before her eyes. For some reason Itfut could not feel the stones beneath her feet. Strangely, they did not bother her at all despite walking barefoot. It was surprising but she was tired of being surprised by now.

The priestess entered the city, if you could call it that, an abstract conglomeration of cubic structures and niches, and wherever you looked, endlessly interweaving flights of stairs. A sepulchral silence reigned, only occasionally interrupted by the sound of falling drops as if an invisible, giant clepsydra was measuring intervals of time.

“What awful quiet. It’s just a-a-awful quie-e-t-t.” repeated Itfut, lost in a maze of structures and formations. ‘It gets worse by the hour. Surely this isn’t a nightmare that’s only just beginning?’

“Hey, is there anybody there?!” she shouted, and a resonant echo carried her shout into a multiple ‘body-body-body’.

“Ts-s-s,” she hissed, switching to a whisper. “When the awfulness is quiet, you have to quiet, too.”

She gingerly opened the door to one of the houses and peeped inside. There was no one there. The interior consisted solely of a table, a chair and a bed of boards. Nothing more. The same scene was repeated in each of the houses Itfut looked in. She examined them one by one but there was not a soul to be seen.

Itfut plucked up the courage to climb a high stairway from where she could get a better view. It turned out that the stairs did not lead anywhere but just hung in midair after several turns. Itfut did not bother climbing right to the top of the stairs because her head was already spinning from the height. She stopped somewhere halfway up and looked about her in both directions. Between identical roofs, she spotted a black, ominous-looking structure towering close by.

The priestess went back down the flight of stairs and decided to make for the megalith, as far as that was possible wandering through the bizarre maze. She went from one house to another, from stairway to stairway being mindful of where she placed her feet, until she almost collided with a gray figure.

She leapt backwards in surprise, her heart beating furiously. The figure stood motionless but in such a posture that suggested it might be just about to take another step. Clothed in a shapeless, hooded robe that hid the face, it was not clear whether the figure was a human being or a statue. Recovering her breath, Itfut walked to the side of the figure and took a peep under its hood.

Glassy eyes burned in the shadows staring into nowhere. Itfut thought as if the eyes reflected signs of life but the rest of the face was a deathly gray, frozen in an indifferent expression. “Hey!” Itfut called quietly.

The figure did not move an inch. The priestess warily touched the hood which was sewn from a rough material. She ran her fingers up the figure’s arm and touched its cheeks... At that moment, something unnatural happened. The priestess’ fingers passed freely through the skin on the face as if it were a ghost.

Deciding to test her hunch, Itfut tried passing her hand through the figure’s body and sure enough, her hand passed right through. The priestess took a step back in complete amazement, and suddenly found herself falling through the staircase behind her as if it were made of air.

Panicking, the priestess zig-zagged from side to side, falling through walls and stairways like a phantom. She could no longer tell what was ghost-like and immaterial here, herself or everything that surrounded her. This was too much. Reality was continuing to weave an ominous web of illusion in a game that the priestess appeared to be losing.

Itfut eventually managed to calm down a little and began to explore new properties in herself and her surrounding reality.

"Wonderful, super-wonderful! I'm dead! No, I've gone mad! Which is better, to be dead or to have lost my mind? Or which is worse?"

She felt along the wall. It was solid and smooth to the touch but as soon as she pushed her hand forward, it passed through as if the wall did not exist.

"Reality, which one of us is transparent, you or I?"

But she was not able to determine the answer, the illusion was complete. Or maybe it was not an illusion at all.

In the square where the gray statue was standing Itfut noticed a spring equipped with a small, stone-laid pool. The water in it seemed to pour forth and, at the same time, it looked as if it were not pouring at all. A jet of water hung frozen mid-air like a freeze frame. The priestess approached the spring and touched the water. It felt like water to the touch, but she could not scoop it up in her hand. Itfut tried to drink it but soon realized that would not work.

And then she saw that the jet of water was not actually motionless but flowing slowly, barely noticeably. Then the priestess took a half guess at something. She ran up to the statue and examined it again. The figure was standing in a slightly different position now, with one leg halfway into taking another step forward.

"Right" the priestess said and began pacing up and down. "There's something weird going on with time here."

As if to confirm her thoughts, the invisible clepsydra continued to measure the deathly silence with occasional, loud drops.

“What quiet, shush and quiet awfulness!” repeated Itfut. “Have I finally gone mad or am I still in the process of losing my mind?”

Matilda had already forgotten which direction she was moving in and had to climb up the stairs again to get her bearings. The black building was not far away but getting to it through the maze was not easy. The priestess passed down winding streets trying to keep her sense of direction. Along the way, she came across another statue, then another and another. They are all were identical, just frozen in various transitional positions. Some were standing in half-step, others were sitting down, and others frozen leaning forwards.

“Can somebody tell me what on earth is going on here?” Itfut exclaimed. “Somebody!”

Then she remembered that in the sandy desert she had engaged with a certain “interlocutor”.

“Hey, Threshold, are you there?”

No sooner had she spoken these words than a whisper rose out of the silence and swished from one direction to the other like wind.

“I am here and everywhere, here and everywhere...”

“Oh, you really are here,” said Itfut, delighted that at least someone living had appeared. “I am not going to ask who you are and where you are this time. Can you tell me where I am and what all this is about?”

“Meta-reality,” the whisper replied, no longer darting about but appearing to come from all directions at the same time.

“What meta-reality?”

"A prototype reality."

"Oh, the Gods, could you be a bit clearer? What's a prototype?"

"It's where everything starts, where everything is born, and where everything originates."

"What city is this?"

"It is a model of what could be."

"And who are these people frozen here?"

"They aren't people. They're mannequins, models of people."

"Why are they so slow? And what am I doing here? How come I can pass through walls?"

"Too many questions. I'm disappearing."

"Wait, wait, just tell me how to get back."

"You'll find out, find out, find out..." The whisper faded and evaporated in the silence.

Evidently Threshold was not inclined to having long conversations. Itfut tried to shout after him but to no avail. An echo was the only response. Her dialogue with Threshold left her with more puzzles than answers. There was nothing the priestess could do except keep moving.

She wandered for a long time through the convolutions of the labyrinth occasionally bumping into 'mannequins' until she finally reached a small platform. And there she saw a spectacle that sent chills down her spine. In the middle of the platform, a figure was hanging in midair clothed in a dark-blue dress, the same as her own. Itfut noted the fact that in this gray environment they were the only two in color.

The figure hung in an unnatural pose: bare feet stretched back and out to the sides, arms reaching upwards, head thrown back, black hair spread out like a fan. Holding her breath, the priestess crept up to the figure from behind, walked around and then looked the figure in the face... She trembled at what she saw. It was she.

Itfut darted away from the figure letting out a wild cry. The huge echo amplified her cry repeating it many times. Never in her life had she screamed so much or experienced such animal fear as she did right now, although you would think that meeting a mannequin of yourself was no more frightening necessarily than anything else, she had witnessed here. But for the priestess this was a sight all too infernal.

And still, she could not run away from the scene. She tried with all her might, but her legs barely moved as if paralyzed and she was fixed to the spot. In that moment, an unknown force caught hold of her, lifted her up into the air, drew circles in a spiral, and then squeezed her in a sharp action into the hanging figure.

A moment later, Itfut's body, now one with the priestess collapsed onto the ground. The priestess lay there motionless for a while but finally came round, shook her head and examined her body. Everything was where it should be. And now she and her body were united again. In that instant, her shoes crashed down beside her from somewhere up above.

"Oh, my shoes!" the priestess moaned in a weak voice.

She was still having difficulty coming back to her senses. Itfut crawled towards her shoes, sat down, put them on and stood up, although her entire body felt unusually heavy. It seemed her body had acquired its material form once again.

She walked up to one of the buildings and tried to put her hand through the wall, but it was hard and would not yield. Itfut gave a sigh of relief. At least one problem had been solved. 'Thanks to the Gods, I am me again', thought Itfut and walked with bold strides towards the black construction, which was now visible behind the roofs. Her heels clicked confidently and sharply along the rocky soil.

She finally reached the square, in the middle of which stood the monolithic, black monument.

"Wow, what's this?" exclaimed the priestess in surprise, a Temple of the Supreme Creator no less!"

She approached the construction, and there an equally strange scene appeared before her. Next to the monolith, a girl with light-blue hair, a blue face and a pink bow at the back was sitting on a stone.

The girl sat motionless, just like the gray statues although she was strikingly different to them, not only in her overall image and colorfulness but the presence of life. Itfut walked past her several times looking at her from all sides. She might be alive, or she might not. She just sat there without moving. It could be a mannequin or something else more ungodly. The girl's entire appearance was highly exotic.

Itfut moved away to one side and then turned back sharply. She was sure she saw the girl blink or maybe she just imagined it. Itfut approached again and began peering carefully into the girl's face. She remained motionless. Then the priestess pretended to be leaving and set off from the square in the direction of the buildings.

Once out of the girl's sight, she took off her shoes, carrying them in her hands and quickly ran around the megalith approaching from the opposite side. Carefully looking out from behind the pillars, she saw that the girl was standing up and looking about her. Itfut quietly sneaked up behind her and shouted.

"Hey!"

Matilda (it was, of course her) jumped in shock and also gave a shout.

For a few moments, they stood looking back at each other in silence. Finally, Itfut spoke.

"What kind of a pantomime have you got going on here?"

"Nothing. You just really scared me."

"Why would you be afraid of me?"

"Why are you all red?"

"Why are you all blue?"

Both fell silent again.

"Who are you?" asked Itfut.

"I'm a diva," answered Matilda.

"Great, a miraculous miracle, a marvelous marvel," Itfut commented, a note of irony in her voice.

"And who are you?" asked the diva.

"I'm a priestess. So, what's your name?"

"Matilda, but you can call me Tili."

"How touching. Tili-games, Tili-games, the cat's house went up in flames."

"Why are you mocking me?" asked Matilda, offended. "You could say that you're the first living soul I've met, and you're poking fun at me. You have no idea what I've been through here!"

"Sorry," replied the priestess. "I hardly know myself what I just said. I'm having a kind of breakdown. I'm Itfut. And I've been through a lot here too."

They looked at each other as if they were both feeling the same thing. And then, without even asking, they gave each other a hug and burst into tears.

THE MEETING

"Oh, now my makeup will run!" Matilda suddenly realized.

They immediately stopped crying, blinked and wiped beneath their eyes. Seeing that they were both doing the same thing, they laughed. It is not unusual for women to find themselves crying one minute and laughing the next without rhyme or reasonbut for extraordinary individuals such as the diva and the priestess everythingwas unpredictable, since they never knew what they might create from one moment to the next.

"Look at me, it has all run, hasn't it?"

"No, you're fine," answered Matilda, "what about mine?"

"You're fine, too. Strange."

They touched each other and then themselves, once again making the same movements, like twins, although they were strikingly different.

"My stage make-up hasn't smeared at all," said Matilda in surprise.

"Very strange things are happening here," said Itfut.

"Yes, more than. What's that war-paint you're wearing?"

"It's ritual paint. What about you?"

"Theatrical."

"Which, which?"

“It’s a long story. You know, when I first saw you, I thought Death itself had come for me.”

“Ha, ha! Well, I’ve never seen anyone like you before either.”

They laughed again and started looking at each other and holding on to one another, as if they had met at a party and there was nothing to do and nothing to worry about except for discussing their appearance and giggling. This was no doubt down to nerves after all they had been through and mutual delight at finding themselves no longer alone.

“Have a look. Is my bow squashed?” asked Matilda, turning her back to Itfut as if she were in a dressing room.

“No, it’s fine. Your bow is quite something.”

“Oh yes! I was fussy about it at first and did not like it at all! But I think it helped me with something.”

“What with?”

“I’m not sure exactly. Another time.”

“For some reason, my dress has not creased at all.”

“Yes, that’s remarkable,” said Matilda.

“It’s as if here nothing gets creased or stained here,” said Itfut.

“And make-up does not run. Maybe we should go and wash it off?”

“That’s unlikely to happen. I could not even drink the water here.

“Ah, that must have been after everything stopped.”

“After what? What was it like before then?”

“I don’t know, I don’t get it. I don’t even know where I am or how I got here. Do you?”

“No, it’s the same for me.”

In that moment, reality began to change as if reminding the new-found friends that it was time to start considering more serious matters. The invisible clepsydra, which was still measuring equal intervals of silence, began to speed up. The sound of falling drops was repeating even faster until there was a crack, like the sound of breaking glass. The diva and priestess jumped. Immediately afterwards, the clepsydra went quiet and the sky split into two hemispheres.

On one side, there was a wavering haze, and on the other, the sky was lined with glowing meridians which stretched out as far as the horizon.

"We need to split!" Matilda exclaimed.

"What's 'split'?" asked Itfut.

"Run for it! We've got to run for it!"

"But where to? We're surrounded by desert."

"Something's changed. Something's happening. Have you seen the sky? We've got to sling our hooks!"

"What, what hooks?"

"Futi, have you dropped off the moon or something? You don't seem to understand half of what I say... Oh God, I did not ask you. Where are you from?"

"I... so, where am I from, where? Not from the moon, that's for sure. What did you call me?"

"Futi. Is that okay?"

"I don't think anyone has ever called me that but... it sounds familiar somehow... It's strange."

"Never mind, later, there's no time now! Run!"

"No, stop! Tili, come back!" Itfut shouted after her.

Matilda stopped as if rooted to the spot, spun round on her platforms and froze in surprise. She had heard those

words before, and on more than one occasion: "No, stop, Tili, darling, come here!"

"What is it?" asked Matilda. At some point she had lost the habit of over-extending her vowels. Local reality was not especially conducive to diva ways.

"Why did you decide that we should make a run for it?" asked Itfut. "What if where we run to is even worse?"

"Nothing could be worse than what's happened to me so far. I was almost eaten alive."

"Well I almost died. Or rather, I died and then kind of 'undied'. But we are still alive, aren't we!"

"You can see that something is happening! Whenever anything happens here, you know nothing good will come of it!"

"Okay, then where do we run, to the left or to the right? That way, there's something swaying, and the other way, there are those strange lines."

"Good question. Let's go that way, where nothing is wavering."

The diva and the priestess ran in the direction of the converging meridians. It was easy to maintain their course through the city maze now just by looking at the sky. On the way, they had time to talk.

"Futi, why do you call yourself a priestess?"

"Because that's what I am."

"You mean, a true, real-life one?"

"What other kind is there?"

"We don't have priestesses in our country."

"I'm not from your country and you aren't from mine, otherwise you would recognize me and I you."

"So why do we speak the same language? Oh, I'm such a twit! The glamrocks spoke the same language as me for some reason too!"

"Glamrocks?"

"Yes, they were the ones who were going to eat me. And then I became their goddess. And then they all froze for some reason. There is one over there, you see?"

Along the way, they came across a gray statue.

"You mean these mannequins? And you became their goddess? How?"

"I'll tell you later. Let's walk for a bit, these platforms aren't made for running in."

"Mine aren't either. I don't get it. You said they spoke the same language as you?"

"Yes."

"What do you mean yours? We're talking my language."

"No, I'm talking mine."

"So am I."

They looked at each other in surprise.

"I see and I don't see," said Matilda.

"Neither do I. And yet, I kind of do," said Itfut. "It must be one of the same order of miracles as the clothes not getting creased or dirty and our makeup not running."

"This place is nothing but miracles, only they aren't so miraculous as monstrous!" Matilda said decisively.

While they were talking, the diva and the priestess reached the outskirts of the city. The desert landscape was considerably changed. Fluorescent green lines ran along the ground and across the sky stretching far into the distance. There they curved forming a tunnel, at the end of which, there was a black spot.

"Futi, I'm scared," said Matilda.

"We don't have to go," said Itfut.

"But what if that's the only way out of this world?"

"And what if that world is even more frightening than this one?"

"We need to get out of here somehow!"

"Let's go then."

"We'll just take a quick look inside and if it looks dodgy, we can turn back straight away."

"Okay, okay, quick, quick!"

The diva and the priestess joined hands and set off to meet with uncertainty. As they moved forward, the earth and the sky narrowed, and the tunnel became increasingly dark. Only the lines were visible, glowing in the half-light. But their passage did not last long. Having reached the narrowest, darkest point, the tunnel mouth began to expand and finally unfolded into a wide, open vista. Our heroines found themselves astounded once again as they took in the scene.

The earth and the sky had changed places. The diva and the priestess were standing in an emptiness that seemed to descend into nowhere, and above their heads hung the same glamrock city, only now it was upside-down. But that was not all.

"Itfut, where are you?" yelled Matilda.

"Matilda! I can't see you! I am seeing myself again!"

"I see myself too! Itfut, where are you?"

"Where are you?"

They shouted standing side by side but the whole time turning and looking to the sides. In the end, they turned to face each other and started studying each other as if looking in a mirror making different movements with their hands, head, legs and watching what appeared to be their reflection.

"Futi, I'm scared!" Matilda shouted again. "When I look at you, I only see me and yet this is not a mirror!"

"Tili, is that really you?!" exclaimed Itfut, looking at the figure opposite her trying to work out whether it was a reflection or her double.

"Is that you? Is it you answering me?"

"Tili, have you turned into another me?"

"No, no, that's impossible. Am I you?"

They examined the other version of themselves and gasped in one voice. Itfut was in Matilda's body and Matilda was in Itfut's.

"You were right!" said Matilda. "Things are really, really, super ba-a-ad here!"

"Run, run back before it closes!" shouted Itfut and taking each other by the hand they rushed back into the tunnel.

RANDOM THOUGHTS

Having escaped the 'inside' and returned to the 'frontal side' of reality, the diva and the priestess confirmed with relief that everything was as it should be. With no other option, they set off back towards the square.

"This is sheer mockery!" shouted Matilda. "We're on a complete hiding to nowhere."

"Hiding what?" asked Itfut. "I don't always understand your expressions."

"I said that things don't look good for us."

"Either the Gods are angry about something, or we are being sent a test or initiation of some kind."

"You'll be telling me next that we've got to placate these Gods of yours and make them a sacrifice!"

"No, that's what primitive peoples do. We're more inclined to strive towards the perfection of the Gods, to reach their level, so that we can command the laws of reality as they do."

"Futi, then command this reality to take us home!"

"I don't know how to yet. There's something wrong with my memory. The past is all a blur."

"Well, my reality is currently one continual nightmare."

Exhausted, they finally returned to the spot where they first met beside the megalith in the square.

"So, what do you think? Shall we go and test our fate on the other side, where everything is wavering?" Itfut suggested.

"No. I've had enough. We need to rest and at least have something to eat," said Matilda.

"Is there anywhere here that we can get something to eat?"

"Are you hungry, Futi? I don't know how, but the glam-rocks said that hlevjun gives them food."

"What hlevjun?"

"Um, the megalith, at least that's what they called it. Come on, let's go take a look."

They went inside and looked around.

"Oh! The head's disappeared!" Matilda exclaimed in surprise.

"Head? What head?"

"There was a head here on that plinth, the glamorc, their kind of God, but now it's gone!"

The altar had in fact disappeared and, in its place, stood a cylinder about three meters high and one-and-a-half meters in diameter made from a tinted glass-like material. The diva and the priestess wandered round the cylinder touching its smooth surface which was devoid of the slightest detail or embellishment.

"Look, it does not reflect anything," said Itfut.

"And you can't see through the sides either," said Matilda.

"Interesting, what is it and what's it for?"

"Let's take a look around and explore."

They walked around the megalith's entire interior space but did not find anything exceptionally unusual. Along the walls there were half-protruding columns, which, curving upwards, turned into a high-reaching arch. From somewhere below, a green light was streaming out of an enclave. There was not a single detail that could have suggested the presence of a device or control panel.

"You said there might be food here?" said Itfut.

"Well, that's what they said."

They approached the cylinder again.

"I think this thing has some kind of function," said Matilda. "We just need to understand how it works. There must be a button or something somewhere."

"What is a button?" asked Itfut.

"It's a thing you press and then something happens, like food appears."

"Does that kind of thing really happen?"

"Yes, in my world there are machines like this, only you have to put money in first, then you press the button and it gives you food or water."

"Tili, I don't really get what you're talking about, anyway, there isn't any button here."

"There must be. Then what are we going to do?"

"As far as I know, you don't always have to do something in order to receive."

"What do you mean?"

"Well, there is nothing you can do to make it rain for example or make the sun come out. And you can't force it to rain or the sun to shine. But if you want something very badly, they can want the same thing with you."

"Wow! Matilda stared at the priestess in complete amazement. "I have never heard anyone talk like that!

But there is something in what you say... Wait! I have had success with something here already!"

The diva straightened her bow and started whispering something while pacing back and forth.

"What are you doing?" asked Itfut.

"It's not working. Damn!"

At that moment, something started buzzing inside the cylinder and a segment emerged, on top of which lay a small box.

"I don't believe it!" Matilda exclaimed.

She opened the box to find it contained sweets. Matilda took one to try. And instantly started jumping about and squealing.

"Tili, you're mad!" said Itfut, scared for her friend.

But Matilda continued to jump and squeal. Then she grabbed the box and presented it to the priestess.

"Futi!" she said with a shout. "It's chocolate-coated cherries! Try one!"

"What, what?" The priestess took a sweet, chewed and melted into a smile. "How did you manage that? What did you do?"

"I did not do anything, just like you said! I wanted it, that's all. It's my bow! It's my bow!"

"Wait, wait wait. What's any of this got to do with your bow? Would you calm down!"

"Sometimes I get a strange feeling in my back." Matilda explained, gesticulating enthusiastically. It's happened here a couple of times before. I remember about my bow, then I want something really badly, and then I get this strange sensation and then whatever I wanted actually materializes!"

"What did you feel exactly?"

"A kind of heavy feeling, as if there were something between my shoulders, something..."

"Hey! I know what that is!" Now it was Itfut's turn to get excited only she instantly began to doubt herself. "Or maybe not... I definitely know what I know! But it's a bit of a blur. I can't quite recall exactly..."

"So, tell me what you know about it!" said Matilda impatiently.

Reality is controlled by random thoughts that originate somewhere at the back of the mind. If you want something with a burning, unstoppable desire, then you have to make your desire one of those random thoughts. Something like that."

"I don't quite catch your meaning," said Matilda. "What is it, that thing behind?"

"I only vaguely recollect," said Itfut. "As I say, I've lost my memory. My entire past is like a dream. Just glimpses."

"Futichka, you have to remember! Our lives may depend on it, do you understand?"

"I'll try. Tell me what you did. Whatever you did, it worked!"

"I focused on my bow, waited until I could sense that feeling behind me and imagined a box of chocolates."

"And that's it?"

"That's it. Do you get the feeling of something behind you, on your back?"

Itfut raised her head thinking of something and said,

"No, but I have the feeling that I used to know what it was and how to use it. I can't make it work anymore though for some reason."

"I am sure you will remember, and when you do, it'll work for you too. The most important thing to know is that whatever it is, this thing works. I'm going to give it another go. What do you want?"

"Something to drink."

Matilda touched her bow again, worked some kind of magic, and the miracle repeated itself. The cylinder made the same buzzing sound and the flat segment extended outwards delivering two cups of water.

"You're practically a priestess yourself!" said Itfut.

They took the glasses and drank the water looking at each other, their eyes shining with delight.

"Cool! What delicious water!" said Matilda.

They put the glasses down.

"Interesting. I wonder how these little tables go back in." Matilda touched the edge of the segment and it slid back in together with the glasses, which passed through the cylinder wall as if it did not exist. Then she closed the other segment.

"Nothing can surprise me now," said Itfut. "There is some kind of other-planetary technology at work here. Unbelievable!"

"Tili, you're using incomprehensible words again."

"La-la-la! It doesn't matter! Right now, we need to eat. What's your favorite dish?"

"Flamidi."

"Now that's a word I don't know. What is it?"

"It's a kind of baked fish."

"I love fish, too. I can't guarantee it'll be the exact same dish, but we'll conjure something up for sure."

Matilda did her magic for a moment and then, one segment after another started emerging from the cylinder carrying all kinds of dishes.

"It's nothing short of a miracle! And you imagined all this?" asked Itfut surprised although she had sworn, she would not be any more.

"It's a buffet!"

"A what, what?"

"Never mind. Ah, I forgot something."

As soon as she had finished speaking another segment emerged delivering cutlery. Then, a table and two chairs rose up unexpectedly right out of the ground almost knocking the diva and the priestess over.

"Ooh! Now that wasn't me!" Matilda exclaimed.

"I think this time it was me," said Itfut. "It just occurred to me that all we need now is a table and chairs."

"Wow! A random thought? You see, you can do it!"

"Accidentally."

"It looks like it is not just the column that works but the floor too."

"We probably ought to be careful of our thoughts."

"You've got to remember what it is we have behind us, and how to work with it."

"Okay, okay. I get the impression that everything is working so easily here because we are in this temple. Nothing is that easy in reality."

"So get on with remembering, Futichka. Now, let's eat!"

They dug into the food and began sharing stories of their adventures. When the diva told the priestess of how she had managed to tame the glamrocks, Ifut jumped up and began to spin about laughing uncontrollably, and then Matilda joined her. The new-found friends were chatting away without a care in the world enjoying their happiest moment since their arrival in this strange, frightening world. At least for now, things were not turning out too badly. Most importantly, they were no longer alone. They had each other. What they would experience next only the world around them knew.

THOSE WHO SEE REALITY

"There, at least we have fed ourselves," said Matilda. "Wonderful! Do you want anything else, Futi?"

"No, it was all delicious," replied Itfut. "I've never eaten anything like this before. What would I do without you?"

"I would have gone crazy here without you. I was on the verge of losing it."

"Let's get rid of these dishes, shall we and leave the chairs and table?"

"Sure." One by one, Matilda pushed the edges of the segments which slid back into the cylinder together with their contents. "Cool machine. We won't go hungry now."

Relaxed, they carried on chatting for a while as if they were sitting in a cafe and not at all at the edge of time and space where they had mysteriously ended up.

"Futi, tell me, what country are you from?" asked Matilda.

"From the land of the Gods," replied Itfut.

"And what do you do with your gods?"

"We praise them."

"And what do they do?"

"Rule."

"I see."

"What country are you from?" asked Itfut.

"Me? Oh, I'm from the land of fools," replied Matilda.

"And what do you do with them?"

"With them? There is no distinction between the 'fools' and 'us'."

"So, you're saying that everyone there is a fool?"

"Exactly!"

"We just strive to feel closer to our Gods."

"With us it's the opposite. One group of fools shouts at the other, 'get lost, you fools!' And the other group replies, 'no, you get lost!'"

"Really?" asked Itfut.

"No, I was joking," replied Matilda. "What country am I from... how can I put it. Well, you could say, for example, that I am from the land of mushrooms."

"And what do you do with them?"

"We gather them. Then we boil them, dry and marinate them. And then we eat them."

What else do you do?"

"We sing and we dance. That's how we live."

"How strange."

"Well, it's just that when there's so much to tell you, I don't always know what to say."

They fell silent for a few minutes, each lost in her own thoughts.

"Futi, do you miss home?" asked Matilda.

"Yes," replied Itfut with sadness in her voice. "And you?"

"Yes, me too. Do you believe that we can return home?"

"Yes, I think we can. There must be a way out."

"You know, what worries me," said Matilda "is that if you return to your world and I return to mine, we won't be together anymore."

"Yes, the truth is that we can either go home or we can stay together," said Itfut.

"I can't imagine what it would be like parting with you now."

"Me neither."

"Would you like to come to us? It's not bad."

"I don't know. What if you were to come to us?"

"I don't know either. All I know is that I don't want to lose you."

"Then we need to decide what's better, to be together or to go back home," said Itfut rationally.

"I hate dilemmas like this!" Matilda exclaimed. "Why do we always have to choose one or the other, why not both?"

"Tili, Tili, we don't have any choice to make at all yet."

"It's just that I hate situations that force you into a box like that."

"Like what?"

"Situations that pressurize and coerce! It's like milk soup. They made me eat milk soup when I was a child. I hate milk soup! Why should I have to eat it? Or when people love each other and need one another or want to be together, why must they part, why? There isn't any good reason for it! You wouldn't believe the kind of dramas we play out on this score. Oh, they love each other so much, can't live without each other, they suffer and yet circumstances force them to part. And then it's a major tragedy! And in cases like that, I always think, what the hell, if you don't want to part sod everything and stay together because it's all milk soup! You aren't obliged to gag on milk soup!"

"Tili, Tili! Calm down. What's got you so wound up?" Itfut ran her hand over Matilda's head and straightened her bow and in that moment the entire inner space of the megalith filled with a huge image like a hologram.

Transparent pictures hung in the air, each being replaced by the next: there is a playground, children playing, the teacher calling them, the children gathering in a crowd pattering into the kindergarten taking off their coats at lockers, entering the dinner hall, and taking their places at tables already set for lunch.

A little girl with a pink bow in her hair is sitting at one of the tables, stirring the food in her bowl with a spoon.

"Boiled milk again! What disgusting foam! I don't wa-a-ant it."

"Little Matilda is a good girl. She eats her soup quietly and is never naughty with her food," the teacher is saying to her.

"I'm not being naughty. I just don't like it!"

"Little girls who eat their soup grow up to be strong and beautiful. But girls who don't..."

"I'm already big and beautiful, so there!"

"You must eat it all up, or you won't have any pudding."

"I don't mind not having any pu-u-u-udding!"

"Look, all the other children are eating their soup. Who do you think you are, someone special?"

"Yes, I'm special!"

"Eat your food, this minute, or you'll go and stand in the corner!"

The girl stopped running her spoon around the bowl, turned and looked at the kindergarten teacher directly in the eye. She was noticeably transformed, as if she had just woken up. In a child's voice but with a calm adult tone, she said:

"You're trying to manipulate me. You don't have the right to force me. I am not obliged to eat if I don't want to."

The teacher was stunned. She stood stock-still her jaw dropping in amazement. Then finally, she seemed to wither.

"No little girl should talk like that! Who taught you to say things that like? I shall be speaking with your mother!" With that, the teacher rushed out of the dining hall, confused and on the verge of panicking.

"I'm going to call the head!" she shouted from the other side of the door.

The picture in the air gradually dissolved. Itfut and Matilda had watched silently captivated. The diva was the first to return to her senses.

"Futi, that was me! Those are my memories."

"I thought as much," responded the priestess.

"That's incredible! It is like a movie, no, like a video of my past!

"What is movie, video?"

"Pretty much what we have just seen. Live images, images of things that have either passed or could be."

"That have passed or could be?" repeated Itfut.

"Yes." For example, when that video was shot, well, they captured on camera something that really happened. A movie is when they have performed, or well, acted out something that could potentially happen, and then they filmed it. And then people watch what was filmed. Why do you ask?"

"It vaguely reminds me of something I was once taught."

"What exactly, Futi? Go on, out with it. Nothing is irrelevant here!"

"I was taught that everything that was, is, and could ever be is all the same thing."

"In what sense?"

"They are all things of the same order."

"Futi, now you're making it sound really complicated. I don't understand."

"If I were to explain it in your terms, then everything that was, is and could be is all a movie because it has all been filmed at some primordial outset. First it is filmed and only then does it take place or have the potential to take place. You see?"

"What do you mean, filmed at some primordial outset? Filmed by whom?" asked Matilda, surprised.

"I don't know. I can't quite remember it all. All I know is that these things, 'what was, is and could be' all exist simultaneously."

"Simultaneously how? What on earth are you saying?"

"Imagine, on the one hand there is a model, and on the other, the physical realization of the model - reality. What was, and what could be are both models, one of the past and one of the future and that which is, well, that's physical reality. The models and their physical manifestation can exist simultaneously."

"Wow! I've never considered these kinds of questions before," said Matilda. "I still don't get it."

"Do you remember my telling you about my conversation with the invisible Threshold of Time?"

"What about it?"

"Well, Threshold said that this world is a meta-reality, a reality prototype and that these gray people aren't really people but mannequins, models of human beings."

"Models or not models, they were real enough to almost eat me alive!"

"Tili, I really saw a mannequin of myself here, and I only got my body back after I had entered it!"

"My head's spinning!" Matilda exclaimed. "Can't you simply tell me straight what all this means? How can we use this model-not-model?"

"Tili, I'm sorry, but again, all I can say is that I just don't remember."

"Itfut, priestess, priestess, you're just one big mystery, and I am just one big misunderstanding! What are we to do?"

"Matilda, do you see reality?" asked Itfut.

"What do you mean?"

"That little girl reasoned when she was still a little girl as if she could see the essence of things, the essence of what was happening around her. In my country, those who can see reality are considered enlightened."

"And what does that give them?

"Those who see are free from the inevitable course of events."

"How?"

"Well, circumstances no longer have control over us. Something like that."

"And what about ordinary people?"

"Ordinary people can't see reality. They just live within it."

"Like fish in an aquarium."

"Yes, like fish. They live as they have to and that's it"

"Woot! I'm beginning to get it!" said Matilda pleased with herself. "Or rather, I don't fully comprehend it yet, but I am getting a sense of understanding."

"Yes, getting 'a sense of understanding' is exactly what's happening to me at the moment."

"But it's not enough to feel it. We have to be able to understand it. When you start remembering, then we'll understand."

"So, help me. Tell me. What have you seen here? How do you see this reality?"

"Yeah, I did see something! When they were 'leading me to the slaughter', I clearly remember thinking that this was something that just couldn't happen to me… that this wasn't my reality!"

"What happened after that?"

"I felt as if I existed separately to this reality, as if I had ended up in a book or a movie."

"And then?"

"Then, I decided that everything would be okay. I didn't know how, but I knew for definite that everything would be fine, period. I was totally certain. And after that, I saw a black line flash down from the sky to the earth, as if the page in a book had turned. And there, on the next page, everything really did turn out okay."

"You know what," said Ifut, "let's experiment with the megalith and see if it can shift us through the pages of reality. If your memories conjured up a picture of the past, what might happen if you imagine your present?"

"All I'll probably get is another image. But you're right, we should try it."

"Use that feeling behind your back. And don't just imagine the scene, imagine us inside it too, as if we were in your own personal movie."

"Let's hold onto each other then, so we don't end up flying off in different directions. I don't want to lose you."

The diva and the priestess held onto one another and stood in silence for a few moments. Matilda began mumbling something and then, something happened that neither of them could have foreseen. The figures were laid out flat, first in a horizontal position and then vertically, and then the entire two-dimensional projection bent forwards and split into several fragmented segments that hung in mid-air. Each fragment carried the image of the flat silhouette of the couple stood in embrace. The entire transformation was accompanied by a metallic hum after which there was total silence.

THE FIRST COMMAND

"Futi!" Came the sound of Matilda's voice, only it was not her normal voice but a kind of metallic, digital copy. The projections of the embracing pair began to vibrate and resound with the same metallic, echoing reverberations. Instead of being long and drawn out like the sound of an echo in the mountains, her voice came in short, sharp beats.

"Ti-Ti-Ti-Ti."

"Matilda!" Itfut's voice responded, also breaking into the fragments of an echo.

"Lda, - lda, - lda, - lda."

"Futi, we've frozen!" Matilda shouted again.

"Ozen, - ozen, - ozen, - ozen."

"Ha, ha, ha, ha!" Itfut started to laugh for no apparent reason.

"Ha, ha, ha, ha!" came the echo.

The frozen projected images and surreal voices made for such an ominous scene, that Futi's laughter seemed totally out of place. The priestess appeared to have lost her mind.

"Futi, you're scaring me!" shouted Matilda.

"Me, me, me, me."

"Unglue us!"

"Ueus, ueus, ueus, ueus." Why Itfut used this expression Matilda could not say. It was confusing and weird.

"I can't move!"

"Ove, ove, ove, ove."

"It's hilarious!"

"Ious, ious, ious, ious, ious," Itfut continued in the same good spirits. "Remember your bow!"

"Ow, ow, ow, ow."

On the echo's last reverberation, the projected images suddenly collapsed, and the diva and priestess fell to the floor now in their original form.

"How creepy was that! That was really creepy!" exclaimed Matilda rising to her feet.

"Ious, ious, ious, ious," Itfut twitched like a mechanical doll, and then suddenly stopped still.

Speechless, Matilda looked at her friend in horror, but the priestess suddenly came to life again and laughed at the terrified diva standing before her.

"Futi, stop scaring me!" shouted Matilda. "This is a fine time for making jokes. We barely made it out alive!"

"Ooh-la-la!" The priestess shook her head, frowned and made a small jump as if checking that everything was still working.

"Okay, Tili, okay!" she said reaching out and touching the diva who looked as if she was about to take offence. "The most important thing is that we are ourselves again, and we are together!"

"How can you be so cheerful?" said Matilda, confused. "It didn't work, and we were almost trapped. What if we had got stuck there forever? Weren't you even a little bit scared?"

"No, quite the opposite. When things get really frightening, they might as well be extraordinarily funny."

"Futi, you surprise me. I haven't seen this side of you before."

"I didn't know I had it, either," said Itfut. "I forgot who I am but I'm remembering now."

"What do you mean, you forgot who you are?"

"There is a part of me. I don't know what it is, but I can feel it."

"You can feel something inside that you don't know? That must be a great feeling. I wish I could feel that, but I know everything about myself."

"No, you're wrong. No-one can know oneself completely."

"Futi, sometimes you say things that really do my head in."

"What did I say?"

"You said that I'm the one who should stop and think about the parts of myself I'm not aware of."

"I even surprised myself that I was not afraid and laughed. At first it was just spontaneous and then deliberate." said Itfut.

"What do you mean, at first spontaneous and then deliberate?" asked Matilda.

"It is like when you give in to the first impulse that comes to you from somewhere in the depths of your being, bypassing the thought center."

"Bypassing the thought center...?"

"It's when something comes from within as if by some silent command without needing the words to explain it. It's when you don't have time to work out what it is or why. You just give in to it. Only afterwards do you realize that this command was the right thing to do."

“Interesting. I do actually experience something similar sometimes.” said Matilda.

“Do you also go with that feeling of initial command also?” asked Itfut.

“Yes, sometimes.”

“At first I went with it, and then I understood that the command was showing me a way out of the stupor as well as reminding you of the bow so that you could bring us back, just like you got us there in the first place, only I had no idea where ‘there’ was.”

“So, you were acting. It was all a performance?” asked Matilda, surprised.

“Yep,” said Itfut. “What’s a performance?”

“It’s a movie that is acted out but not filmed.”

“Why? Why isn’t it filmed?”

“So that it will be more like real life.”

“Isn’t a movie real life then?”

“Um, a movie is like a copy of a performance.”

“And a performance is a copy of real life?”

“Yes, to some extent. Futi, are you trying to remember something?”

“Strange, it’s like a chain: life — performance — movie,” said Itfut. “I remember, I was taught that everything is the other way around: first the design is created, then the action turns according to the idea, and only then is the action brought to life. It’s the complete opposite!”

“What design, who creates it?” asked Matilda.

“Do you remember what we were talking about before: what was, what is, and what could be is all a movie? First, it’s filmed, then it happens?”

“Ah, the models or not models, or whatever they are”

"The movie is a model, whereas life, reality, is the embodiment of the model. Right now, we're in a movie."

"In a model of reality?"

"Yes, or in a meta-reality, according to Threshold."

"And we need to get back into reality, into life."

"Exactly."

"But how?"

"I don't know yet," said Itfut. "My intuitive feeling is that we need to somehow walk back up the chain in the other direction: movie, play, life."

"That sounds very abstract." said Matilda. "We need to take action."

"But don't you see, Tili, the idea of traveling through the pages of reality didn't work."

"Yes, somehow pure willpower doesn't work even inside the megalith. We need something else too. Something else."

"What does your first command tell you?"

"There is one option we haven't tried yet."

They glanced at each other.

"Have I guessed?" asked Itfut.

THE MIRROR

"There is still the other side," said Matilda.

"Where everything wavers?" asked Itfut.

"Yes, we need to try it. We should try it."

"Even though it's scary?"

"Everything that happens here is scary!"

Then, as if to confirm what had just been said, the megalith began moving and making a strange noise.

"Something's happening again!" exclaimed Matilda.

"Don't forget, Tili, be careful of your thoughts."

"What am I supposed to do with them? It's impossible for me not to think or say anything!"

"There are simple thoughts and then there are assertions. Assertions have an impact on reality."

"What assertions?"

"Assertions are when you state a judgement that reality is such and such a way."

"A judgement? What did I say that could be a judgement?"

Before Matilda had time to finish, the floor started moving in a circle although it was not entirely clear what was spinning, the floor in relation to the walls, or the walls in relation to the floor. The diva and the priestess instinctively rushed for the exit, but they found the doorway blocked by a black wall. The movement was accompanied by an ominous ticking as if the megalith contained the inner workings of a clock: tick-tock-tick-tock, tick-tock-tick-tock.

In addition to the reverse rotation of the floor and walls, with each stroke of the main beat, the columns changed places in jerking movements like the arrows in a quartz watch. The cylinder at the center of the hall remained still but it was impossible to grasp hold of it, so the diva and the priestess held onto each other not knowing where to hide. Suddenly, everything froze.

Itfut came to her senses first.

"I counted twelve strokes," she said.

"You still had the composure to count!" Matilda exclaimed. "I almost pissed myself!"

"Ha, ha, ha, Tili!" the priestess laughed. "That would hardly help us now!"

"You find everything funny! How do you manage it?"

"Okay, okay, let's take a look and see if the door has opened."

They made for the exit. The doorway was in fact now open. The friends ran outside and there cried out in surprise. Something in the environment had changed. Everything was in the same place as before but the ratio between the length of movements and time was different. The diva and the priestess moved as if in slow motion. Only their voices sounded at the usual speed.

"Futi, what's happening?!" shouted Matilda.

"I don't know. It's like we're under water." replied Itfut.

"God, when will all this end!"

"Tili-Tili! Cheer up. How did you put it? 'We need to split?' Well, we need to split!"

"We do-do! Right now-now! Oh no, I've started talking like you!"

"Then let's go-go!"

And they ran, if you could call it running, for they looked like aquanauts walking through space. The sky was still divided into two hemispheres. One half was lined with luminous meridians, and on the other, there was a swaying haze. The diva and the priestess made in the direction of the latter. What dangers might await them there, they could not say, but they had to do something.

It took them a long time to get out of the city. When they were finally free of the urban setting, an amazing scene unfolded before their eyes. Where previously there was a desert, now there was a real sea with splashing waves, the noise of surf and even grass and palm trees on the shore. The line of vegetation began in an unnaturally sudden, distinct border.

"Woot-laFuti, how amazing, look, the sea!" shouted Matilda.

"Hold off rejoicing. It might be a mirage," suggested Itfut. "See how it's all wavering?"

The scene really did look as if it were floating in streams of hot air. Matilda was impatient though.

"I want to get in! Now! No-o-w!"

They tried to move with renewed vigor, but they were still proceeding slowly, barely getting any closer to their goal. It became even harder to move their legs as if some force was holding them back.

In the end, they stopped no longer capable of taking a step or moving at all. There was a pause. After a few moments, there came the rising sound of a bowstring released and in that same moment both women were thrown backwards like an elastic band that had been stretched and then pinged and let go. They sat down on the sand in complete confusion. The tempting sea and palms were still beyond their reach.

"This is outright mockery!" said Matilda in indignation.

"Yes, reality does have a tendency to be sadistic," said Itfut.

"What are we going to do?"

"We have to find a way of reaching the sea."

"Why, it might not let us in?"

"As far as I remember," said Itfut, "my Teacher taught me that when something does not go right, you have to be able to see reality and yourself within it. So, Tili, what are you seeing?"

"I see the sea and I want to get in it! What else is there to see here?"

"Exactly! You want it too much."

I want it too much? Overmuch? Well, don't you want to?"

"Yes, but excessive desire puts a strain on reality, and it starts to resist."

"Wow, I learned that when I was still in school: any action gives rise to opposition. And what do you suggest — stop wanting? But, how can I?"

"Often it is enough just to come to your senses and be aware of how you are putting a strain on reality. You have to be able to see reality as well as yourself within it. You aren't seeing yourself."

"How am I straining reality? I have wanted a lot of things in my life, but never before have I been kept straight on a leash."

"Don't forget, we are in a meta-reality, and here everything seems to be amplified."

"Okay, so I'll keep telling myself, 'I don't want it, I don't want it'. But is that really going to stop me from wanting it?"

"If you can't give up wanting it, then you can pretend and trick reality."

"Pretend? Now that I can do." Matilda stopped to think for a moment. "I know what we can do. Let's walk towards it backwards."

"Ha, ha, ha! Tili-Tili, that's so stupid it might actually work. Well done!"

"Yes, it might be stupid but it's worth a try." They stood up giggling and made their way forwards with their back to the sea. And then something incredible happened. The field dropped its resistance and they moved at their normal speed.

"Futi!" Matilda exclaimed. "It worked! We're getting there!"

"Yes, even quickly-quickly!"

"But how is that possible? Can you really trick reality? I did not stop wanting to get to the sea!"

"Desire not only slows reality down, it causes us to make mistakes and take the wrong action but if you pretend and behave as if you didn't have the desire at all, reality will release its hold on you."

"Helala, Helala! Now I'm getting it!"

"Hush Tili or you'll startle reality."

"Who is startling who around here?!"

"Come on, let's go, and let's go without looking over our shoulder."

So, the diva and the priestess walked backwards until they bumped up against some kind of barrier. Surprised, they turned and began to fumble along an invisible wall. On one side, there was a sandy desert and on the other, a dramatic shift to tropical vegetation and the sea so near you could reach out and touch it. Yet it was impossible for them to pass through the barrier. And then the friends noticed that they were reflected in the wall, like in a mirror, only the silhouette reflections on the other side were barely distinguishable as if transparent. The seascape was also a little blurry in the wavering haze and yet the sound of the surf could be heard close by and quite clearly.

"Futi, this is punishing! They aren't letting us in!"

"I've got it," said Itfut. "This is the world mirror: reality is on that side. This side is the meta-reality prototype."

"So, we've ended up on the flip side of physical reality?"

"Yes, we should have worked that out ages ago."

"But what is this mirror?"

"I remember now. It borders two aspects of reality: the physical and the imaginary."

"What do you mean, the imaginary?"

"You remember, we talked about the movie being here and life being over there. Here is what was and what could be, and over there is what is. The image is here, the reflection is there. First, it's filmed, then it manifests in physical reality. For now, we're in the movie on the side of images. It's a mirror, only it works the other way around, you see?"

"So that means we are imaginary too?"

"No, we became imaginary on the other side. You see how we are reflected there. No, it is just that our real image and our reflections have changed places. We have jumped from physical reality into the image space."

"But everything here is material too!" retorted Matilda. "And the glamrocks were intending to eat me as a very material maid, although they kept calling me synthetic for some reason..."

"But you feel as if everything is real in a dream too, don't you?"

"Well, yes, but that's a dream. In a dream you only think it's real."

"No, it's more than that. Judge for yourself. Could your mind really have thought up all the quirky things that happen in your dreams? All those worlds you fly through when you are dreaming, do you really think that they are all just in your head?"

"Well, perhaps not. I don't know. I have not really thought about it."

'Well, you're flying here too, or rather, your conscious awareness is flying here in meta-reality. The space of images and the space of dreams are one and the same thing."

"But we aren't sleeping now, are we?" asked Matilda. "Or are we?"

"Unfortunately, this isn't a dream," replied Itfut. "We are here, not only in conscious awareness but in our bodies too. By the way, did you enter your body straight away?"

"Yes, I felt it. I was so tied up my extremities went numb."

"I didn't. Do you remember my telling you that I passed through the wall first and only then found my mannequin?"

"If only we could squeeze through this wall now! As it is, we can't pass through to the other side and we can't leave our bodies either."

"Yes, we need to somehow bring about one or the other."

"Phew, Futi, I'm just so shocked by all this. What are we going to do now?"

LID OF THE WORLD

While Itfut and Matilda were discovering the hitch with the mirror, another movie was playing set in the same time but in a different location.

* * *

Eejit Green was woken up by the sound of the neighbor's dog barking.

Strange, he thought. *The neighbor's house burned down a week ago and the dog was fed to the fish...Maybe I imagined it. Maybe I dreamed it. I should go check my ingenious mind.*

Eejit spent a long time looking for his sneakers, called them dodgy bastards and threatened to throw them out as soon as he found them. The sneakers were afraid and hid from him. In the end, Eejit went barefoot as the elusive sneakers were Eejit's only pair of shoes.

The path, as usual, led through the forest to the sea. The trees turned their branches carefully away from the path as they knew it was better to stay out of Eejit's way. He was in a bad mood as always.

Turning off the path, Eejit came to the edge of the forest where the Stump of Knowledge stood. Eejit often came to this spot to draw on the wisdom of life. He only knew of one place where he could draw on the wise, but one was more than enough.

In short, the Stump of Knowledge stood in the middle of a clearing. There was a hollow in the stump and in this hollow sat a squirrel. Eejit stuck his nose inside the hollow and the squirrel gave Eejit a flick. It was a good one with a slight delay. Having received the flick on the nose, Eejit stated, “It’s the same thing every time. Life is such a bastard.”

With that, Eejit returned to the path and made in the direction of the shore, saying: “Okay, I’ll show you all. I’ll make you dance and sing.” What he meant by this; no-one knows but his intentions were clearly far from benevolent.

Once on the shore, aside from the coastline, he looked around at the sea and the seagulls. Spotting Eejit, the gulls squawked disapprovingly. Eejit picked up a stone out of habit and was about to throw it when he changed his mind, muttering “No-o-o. Never give in to profanity... or how does it go, pro... pro... Ah, whatever. Coordinating profanity, now there’s a principle worth following.”

Pleased with the depth of thought that had occurred to him, he decided to take a walk along the coast. The sea tried to catch Eejit and annoy him, but he did not succumb. “Coordinating profanity, tee-hee... Damn it!” Eejit cursed stumbling over a large snag.

At the same time, Yellow Submarine ran towards him and seemed very anxious about something.

"Oh, Eejit Green!" she exclaimed in surprise.

"I am green, categorically. Why are you so yellow and vague?" he answered, not at all embarrassed.

"Have not you heard?! They've covered the world with a lid!"

"What lid? Who put it there and why? Are you crazy?"

"Just look up, dipstick!"

Eejit lifted his head and indeed, there where the bottomless sky should have been, hung something dark and heavy-looking.

"Orange Cow was the first to notice," Submarine babbled. "She says, it's impossible to fly anymore! I'm so worried, so worried, I'm all itchy! What will become of us? What does it all mean?"

"It means your orange feast is over and now the time has come for deep purple dust, ha, ha."

"But how are we to live? What are we to do?"

Eejit scratched his head with his club, and said: "It's those mammotniks, I know it is. They're the ones to blame. But they've gone too far this time, darn reptiles."

Submarine looked even more alarmed and started running about getting herself in a muddle.

"Oh! Who are they? Are they evil? Are they revolting? Will they eat us?"

"Yes, either they'll eat us, or we'll eat them. I was just about to go hunting. Mammotniks have to be ruffled and then annihilated and you're going to help me."

"Oh no, I can't, I'm afraid!"

"Do you want the lid to crush you completely?"

"No, no!"

“Well, let’s get going then. And stop running about and doing cartwheels around me.”

“Okay. We’re off to save the world!”

They turned off the coastal strip and went deeper into the forest. Submarine would not stop asking questions.

“What’s a mammotnik like? Is he wild? Is he scary?”

“Yes, he’s cunning and crafty.”

“Are we going to catch him?”

“Yes.”

“Is mammotnik-hunting difficult and dangerous?”

“Yes.”

“But we’re going to save the world! Where are we going?”

“Could you shut it, just for a minute?”

They walked and they walked and eventually arrived at a spot where someone had dug a deep pit beneath a wide-branching tree.

“What’s this?” asked Submarine.

“A trap. The mammotnik will run along here, fall in and then we’ll seize him.”

“Oo-oh, how exciting!”

“We need to cover it with branches and leaves.” They quickly disguised the pit, sat down in ambush and waited. They waited and waited but no one seemed to want to run past and fall into the pit.

“And how much longer are we going to sit here?” asked Submarine.

“Hum, we need to somehow lure the mammotnik here,” answered Eejit.

“And what might attract him?”

"More noise, more emotion."

"Well, why did not you say so, dipstick. Let's climb up the tree and make a loud noise."

"Okay, let's." Having scrambled up the tree, they belted out a song for the whole forest to hear.

'Above the border, clouds gloomily pass,
The land is grasped by a silence severe.
Along the high banks of the Amur
Guards of the Homeland stand.'*

They sang and they sang and then they started on a different song.

'I want your love and
I want your revenge.
You and me could write a bad romance.
O-o-o-o-o!
I want your love and
All your lovers' revenge.
You and me could write a bad romance.'**

They sang other songs, too, but no one came.

"Do you think one of us might be an idiot? Or both of us, perhaps?" said Submarine.

"Not enough emotion. But that's all right. We can correct that."

Eejit grabbed Submarine's anchor, hooked it over a branch, and gave her an almighty shove so that she ended up dangling over the pit.

---

* Words by Boris Laskin.

** Lady Gaga.

“What are you doing? Wicked, crafty Eejit! Untie me this minute!”

“Now things should start looking up,” Eejit noted with satisfaction. Then, he climbed back down the tree and hid in the bushes.

“Save me! Help!” cried Submarine hanging from the anchor chain. “Eejit, I’ll kill you for this you bastard!”

At that very moment, a shadow loomed over the edge of the pit. There was the sound of crashing branches and ...

…someone fell into the trap.

QUEEN BRUNHILDA

Queen Brunhilda was pulling carrots in her vegetable garden placing them into the folds of her dress and singing as she worked:

'I am queen, la,la,la,
I am queen, la,la,la!
And you, my carrots,
You are my subjects!
Come to me now,
My carrots, la,la,la!'

Meanwhile, Shaggy Beast was hiding among the beets watching the queen. Shaggy Beast got his name because he was in fact a shaggy beast but also because whenever he stole a carrot from the vegetable garden, the queen would chase after him shouting: "Oh, you! Shaggy Beast!"

Beast did not in fact need the carrot.He had simply fallen in love with the queen and tried everything he could to get her attention, which, it has to be said, was no easy task. Moreover, Brunhilda was a warrior-like individual. Legend had it that her heart could only by won bygaining the upper hand over her in a duel, but very few dared to challenge her since she was a consummate swordswoman.

Beast was afraid of Brunhilda, and did not know how to approach her. He tried teasing her, calling her names, and yanking her skirt surreptitiously but all his efforts were in vain. Brunhilda always repeated the same thing:

"Shaggy Beast, you must fight me."

"If I win," asked Beast, "will you love me?"

"No," answered the queen.

"You see! Then what's the point?"

For some reason, Beast hoped that one day he would so infuriate the queen that she would chase after him, catch him, give him a good beating and then suddenly fall in love. There is a reason they say, 'if they beat you, it means they love you.'

So, Beast waited for the right moment, and when the queen bent down to the ground, he threw a carrot at her which caught her right on the behind.

"Oh, shaggy beast, you!" Enraged, the queen shook the spoilsfrom her skirt folds and chased after the deprived beast, who was already making for the forest full pelt and squealing as he went:

"Brunhilda, I'm going to drag you back to my cave with me!"

But the chase did not last long. Shaggy Beast was unlucky and fell with a loud crack into a pit. Obviously, it was the same pit Eejit Green and Yellow Submarine had dug.

That was when things started to heat up. Eejit jumped up and ran to the edge of the pit cripping his club.

"Got you, you evil mammotnik! Now I'm going to extinguish you!"

"Caught you, caught you! Phenomenal! Eejit you green bastard, get me down from here, now! Do you really think you can save the world without me?!" Submarine squeaked still hanging from the tree.

Meanwhile, the birds and animals of the forest were gathering to see what the noise was all about. Curious, they peered down into the pit. A shaggy creature with sad eyes was sitting on the pit floor. The creature seemed so shocked, it had completely lost the ability to speak.

Eejit gestured for everyone to calm down.

"Ladies and gentlemen, your attention please! The solemn moment has arrived. Yes, our world has been covered with a lid, but this is not the end. We will not lose heart and we will not give up. Friends and colleagues! Now more than ever before, we must closely unite our ranks in the fight for the inalienable right to live as free, conscious individuals in a system that is, so to speak, dominating us with its lid, depriving us of the most valuable thing of all – freedom of choice, the essence of which lies in the right of every individual to decide for themselves whether to live under the lid or above it, whether to boil in the soup of human misconception and base passions or to soar above the gray mass of ignorance and darkness, like a seagull that freely flies over the dump looking from a great height at the essence of all creation, perceiving the illusiveness and frailty, so to speak, of all things, gaining a clear understanding that up there is above and down there is below, thus achieving a state of higher enlightenment and the insight that it can be no other way, because below can never be above nor above below, for such is the immutable order of things..."

At that moment, Orange Cow fell from the sky, or rather, from where the sky should have been and ended up on the ground.

"It's impossible to fly anymore! In short, Eejit..."

"As I was saying," Eejit continued, "the question lies in the fact... Could you please stop interrupting me! You're making me lose the thread! Get down, will you! You're swinging away there completely disrupting my train of thought!" Eejit climbed up the tree and unhooked Submarine.

"I will never forgive you for this!" she said. "You used me!"

"Okay, okay. But how else would we have caught the mammotnik?"

"And who do we have here, all cute and fluffy?" asked Cow.

"I'm not cute or fluffy!" the prisoner finally answered from the bottom of the pit. "I'm Shaggy Beast!! And everyone is afraid of me!"

"Is that right?" answered Cow affectionately. "Would it be okay for me to give you a lick? Come on, get out of there. I'll give you a hand."

"Nobody is getting out of anywhere, and no one is going to help anyone," retorted Eejit. "At the present time, a historical moment is taking place, and you, Cow, are breaking all its solemn, so to speak, pathos and intruding in matters beyond your potency."

"You mean competence?"

"I am most honorably aware of what I meant to say. Don't interrupt. So, I now have the honor of allowing myself to continue. In the depths of this so-called pit, we have the opportunity to observe the embodiment of world evil. It is in fact none other than the very same notorious, odious and sinister mammotnik of whose sophisticated cruelty and cunning I have repeatedly informed you. The real question is the following..."

Once again Eejit had to interrupt his heartfelt speech because those present had started exchanging glances and whispering, "The queen! The queen is here!"

Brunhilda ran into the clearing.At first she looked about in amazement, and then her gaze fell on Beast.

"Get caught, did you?"

"It was us that caught him!" jabbered Submarine. "I pretended I accidentally got stuck in a tree, started calling for help, shouting, and he ran up, all shaggy, and I pretended that I was scared and he was coming towards me, as if about to pounce, and I was above the pit, and in he went ... and, wham! It was tremendous!"

"This is a matter of extreme importance, Your Majesty," Eejit said joining in the conversation. "Our world is in danger. Alas, the threat has thickened in clouds above our heads. It comes from the outcasts of humanity, those we callmammotniks, and now, one of the enemy herd is here right before your eyes and lies at your feet defeated. Allow me to question him with scrupulous contempt and force him to reveal how and why he dared cover our world with a lid."

"Eejit, I appreciate your eloquence, I really do," said Brunhilda, "only that is quite enough tongue-wagging for now. Get Beast out of this pit."

"What do you mean? What beast? I'm not with you? Mammotnik is my prey, and I won't let…"

"What happened to eloquence? This is no mammotnik. This is Shaggy Beast and he's mine. Cow, help him out of there."

Beast was finally brought up to the surface beaming with delight.

"My queen! That's the first time you've ever referred to me as 'my Beast'! I'm so happy!"

"One more word from you and I'll bury you in this pit myself!"

"But allow me…!" Eejit objected. "This is an act of despotism! Are you questioning my theory? That is unheard of! You're hiding in the darkness of ignorance! My theory is airtight!"

"All right, Eejit, calm down.It's quite clear that something does not add up," Submarine remarked.

"No, I won't leave it like this! I wish to object in the strongest manner possible!"

"Instead, let's think about what we're going to do now," suggested Cow.

"Yes, yes, let's!" said all the birds and animals who had gathered in the clearing.

"What is this lid?"

"How did it get there?"

"What threat does itpose?"

"How can we get rid of it?"

"Listen up everyone!" said Brunhilda who had taken the floor. "In order to find out what this lid is, you will have to go to the edge and take a good look at it."

"Yes, yes! That's right! Our wise queen!" the others joined in. "We must equip an expedition!"

"I have to agree. It is a constructive proposal," said Eejit. "But the real question lies in the following..."

"That's enough of your questions!"

"Let me speak! The question is, who will lead the expedition? It's no secret that in difficult times there have always been heroes, whose brave hearts have lit the way for everyone else, like the torch of Danko, leading them through the darkness of yesterday into a brighter tomorrow and who..."

"Enough, enough, Eejit, spit it out!"

"In short, I am willing to sacrifice myself and take this modest mission on my own shoulders..."

"No, no, we don't want you to!" said everyone else present. "You have already mislead us once!"

"You're making a big mistake in questioning the verifiability of my candidacy. You'll regret it yet. I'll elect myself as president and by the first decree, I will cancel sausage, then you'll realize..."

"No, no, don't!"

"Don't what? Don't have sausage?"

"No to you, we don't want you to be president!"

Brunhilda quickly put an end to the dispute.

"Listen, no one is going to lead anyone. We will go together, me, Beast, Cow, Submarine and Eejit."

No-one raised any objection. Even Eejit. "All right, at least with me you won't get lost," he managed to grumble,and at that it was decided. After brief preparations, they set out on their journey.

THEATRICAL PERFORMANCE

The diva and the priestess stood near the mirror confused. They ran their fingers along its invisible surface, tried walking along it to one end and then the other but everywhere – it was the same – an impassable wall that stretched to boundless limits.

"Matilda, what do you know about mirrors?" asked Itfut.

"Just what everybody knows: mirrors reflect everything that stands in front of them," answered Matilda.

"What else?"

"That in a reflection, left becomes right, and right, left."

"What else?"

"Sux! That it's impossible to pass through a mirror! We're stuck here!"

"But we did get here somehow. By the way, what's 'sux'?"

"It's the same as 'woot!' only the opposite, when everything is really bad, and you want to swear."

Immediately after Matilda had spoken, the sky became overcast and a storm began tobrew on the sea.

"Tili, you see, the mirror reacts!" exclaimed Itfut.

"Yes, but what good is that to us?" said Matilda.

"This is what, this is what! We are on the side of images and that's the side of the reflection. The mirror seems to be producing a reflection of our thoughts!"

“I have one thought only. How do we get to the other side?”

“Imagine that we are already there. Let’s hold onto each other. You activate the bow, or rather the feeling in your spine area.”

“Okay, let’s do it. I just hope things don’t get any worse than they are now.”

“Tili, Tili! Don’t give in to negative thoughts. Concentrate on imagining us there on the other side.”

The diva and the priestess embraced so that they would not lose each other if anything happened and then they stood still and looked in the mirror. And then the landscape on the other side began to change. The grass and the palm trees dissolved into the air and the sea waves gradually turned to sand. They broke and threw sand onto the shore until they were smooth and calm. On that side, as on this, there was nothing but endless desert and the city of the glamrocks appearing in the distance. Now the friends could clearly see their reflection in the mirror. The scene on both sides was exactly the same.

“So that’s what we had to prove,” said Matilda. “We are in the reflection. We have not gone anywhere.”

“Yes, we are there, but we are also here still,” said Itfut. “You can’t deceive a mirror.”

“We got what we ordered. But no, I won’t stop at that! Let’s hold hands and walk forwards imagining that we are passing through the mirror.”

“Okay, let’s try it.”

And that is what they did but just as was to be expected, they hit their foreheads up against the wall.

"It's not working," said Itfut.

"Just one more try," said Matilda. "Let's try walking backwards. It worked once before."

But even that did not help. The friends sat down and began to pour sand aimlessly from one hand to another and then lobbing it at the mirror. The sand bounced off and was reflected as in an ordinary mirror.

"Well, Itfut, priestess, priestess, any ideas?" asked Matilda.

"Nothing is quite that simple with this mirror," answered the priestess. "It is the mirror of the world after all. We need to find a different approach. Let's try and remember exactly how we ended up here."

"I was acting in a performance that was being simultaneously filmed and there were mirrors everywhere..."

"That's it! Remember the chain: life, performance, movie. You ended up in the movie by moving along that chain."

"What about you? Do you remember anything?"

"Only very vaguely. Not much at all. But judging by the fact that I'm covered in ritual paint, we must have been carrying out a ritual, which is almost the same thing as your performance."

"So, you were part of a performance too. But you weren't being filmed, were you? Were you holding mirrors?"

"No, they weren't filming and there were no mirrors."

"Then how did you get here?"

"We dedicate our rituals to the God, and they watch us."

"And where do they sit? In an auditorium?"

"They aren't in our world, Tili. They reside in meta-reality and watch from this side of the mirror where we are now."

“Then it all fits. There was a performance, a mirror and your Gods were watching you like a movie.”

“Yes, so now we have to trace the chain back in reverse order: from the movie to the performance and back into life.”

“But how do you imagine that happening? Are we going to put on a performance here or something?”

“No. My intuition tells me that we are required to somehow come back to life right in the movie.”

“So, it would be like the heroes of a film coming to life, leaving the screen and walking down into the auditorium?”

“Something like that, yes.”

“But we are alive already!”

“Well, clearly not entirely. We need to do something.”

And with that they sank into contemplation once again. Meanwhile, the landscape on the other side began to transform to its former guise. The grass, palm trees and sea were just as inviting as before, as if nothing had happened.

“Oh, God, the screen saver on this mirror is just playing with us.” said Matilda. “It’s like a travel agency that says, ‘come to us, run to us, crawl to us and we’ll send you to paradise!’”

“Tili, I’ve had an idea.” said Itfut. “I don’t know who promises to send you to paradise but let’s try looking at what’s happening now in our normal reality. The mirror might show us.”

“Futichka, yes, let’s! We have nothing to lose.”

“Let’s start with you.”

“Okay.”

“Same as before, focus your attention on the scene you want to see and don’t forget about the bow.”

“I want to see what’s going on at our theatre.”

Matilda concentrated, mumbled something and in that moment a clear image flashed up on the mirror, as on a screen…

On a stage flooded with spotlights, couples were moving about slowly and imposingly dressed in Renaissance fashion. The women were dressed in luxurious, white gowns with large full skirts. The men were also in white, dressed in silk tabards and tight-fitting hose. They donned wigs, the women's high and light, the men's dark and styled in curls. All the dancers' faces were hidden behind gold-painted masks. The stage was filled with the sounds of harpsichord music. The couples appeared to be dancing a minuet. They came together and moved apart again. The men made graceful bows and the women elegant curtsies holding their fans open.

The dance movements were simple and reserved with one small detail: for some reason, none of the dancers turned their back to the audience.

Evidently, the play was not only being acted out on stage but also being filmed because there were video cameras everywhere. Standing close to the stage, the director was managing the action giving instructions to actors, camera operators and lighting assistants. The scene was so realistic and close up that Matilda instinctively began knocking on the mirror and shouting.

"Victo-or! I am here, I'm here!"

The diva's ghost-like reflection moved about on the other side copying her movements but, clearly, no one could see or hear her. Realizing that she was only present on the other side as a momentary reflection, she began to move so that she could get closer to Victor. She tried with the help of her double to grab hold of him and give him a shake, but it didn't work. There, she was nobody, an invisible, intangible ghost.

"Tili!" Itfut said placing a hand on the diva's shoulder. "Don't upset yourself, we should have known that this would happen."

"No, I can't bear it. I'll go mad! You can't imagine what I'm going through!" Matilda pressed up against Itfut on the verge of tears. Itfut stroked her shock of hair and soothed her friend as best she could.

The stage was decorated in the style of a ballroom with opulent chairs arranged along the walls. The sides were equipped with open toilets, the ladies to the left and men to the right. There were no booths, but the areas had immodest mirrors, probably intended to ensure equally indiscreet visibility.

Meanwhile, the central figure appeared on the stage, a diva, who stood out from the other actors with her blue hair and gorgeous dress of dark-green velvet with a large pink bow at the waist. Her face had no mask but was covered in blue stage paint instead and deliberately vulgar eye make-up. The diva strutted about proudly, making broad movements with her hands as if raking apart the crowd, which respectfully parted into two ranks making bows and curtsies.

Witnessing the spectacle, Matilda could no longer hold back the tears.

"Well, they didn't mourn for long, did they!" she said, the pain audible in her voice. Tears were already streaming down her cheeks. "And they found a replacement quickly enough! And where did they find the same bow as mine?"

"Tili, Tili, stop it," Itfut said trying to calm her down. "You know very well, they wouldn't find another like you if they searched the whole world over! That's a miserable parody of you!"

"Futi, don't bother. I can see it all very well for myself. You can see perfectly well how amazing it all looks and what would they want me there for with my rubbish jump-suit and pitiful twist!"

"Tili, Tili, don't talk about yourself like that. I know what you're worth," said Itfut pulling Tili to her chest. "You are beautiful and irreplaceable! No-one could replace you. And that's me telling you, priestess Itfut! And I've seen all sorts, believe me."

Matilda stopped her sobbing but buried herself in the priestess's chest. She had no desire to watch what was happening in the mirror anymore. Itfut hugged her and began rocking her gently from side to side.

"Tili, that's enough now, calm down. We'll think of something. We will get back home, I promise you."

Matilda was quiet and did not say a word.

"Look, something new is happening there."

Suddenly, for no apparent reason, the harpsichord was replaced by club music and the actors started dancing techno only their movements were just as unhurried as before in a paradoxical combination of imposing ballroom and club-style abandon. The rows of dancers came together facing each other but not coming into contact.

The men and women exchanged masks then turned their backs to the audience and made for their own changing rooms. The women's dresses were open-backed, and the men's coat tails folded so wide that all their charms were bared except for the thongs that both genders were wearing. Moreover, the male treasure of one individual protruded unnaturally beneath his tight-fitting leotard.

Itfut could not help but notice it.

"Ooh, Tili, what men you have!"

"Do not be fooled," replied Matilda who had cheered up a little, "it is the protective covers they are wearing. You can get them in any sports shop."

Meanwhile, representatives of both sexes went to their corresponding dimly lit toilets while the music began to play rhythm and blues. The diva was the only figure remaining on the stage. She was dancing in the usual rhythm not forgetting to show off her charms, including her naked back, in a dress that was either meant to be revealing or was simply completely open-backed.

Matilda could not help herself.

"Hey, beautiful, cover yourself up with the bow! You have nothing worth looking at!"

"Ha, ha, ha, Tili, she can't hear you!" said Itfut in good humor.

"She'll dance for me yet, you'll see! So, this mirror responds to mental statements? We'll see."

Matilda was now watching the action wide-eyed. What happened next was not for the eyes of the virtuous at least if one wished to preserve that same virtue.

In the half light of the men's room, figures were moving together to the rhythm of the music. The bodies were intertwining and writhing; the dancers swapped partners bending down and straightening up again in a frenzied dance. Some ripped off their tops although weren't completely naked. There were clearly certain boundaries to the play despite it all. There was no need for the dancers to strip as the viewer's excited imagination could easily fill in all the details that were invisible to the eye.

The men's orgy was accompanied by stifled moans. However, in the female half, truly eerie screams could be heard that chilled the heart. Spirits were evidently raging unfettered by boundaries or constraint. Wanting to be seen to observe at least some notion of the limits of decorum, the performance organizers had prudently used dim lighting. In the half light, however, much was still visible due to the dancers' white clothing. Although recently displaying a more languid demeanor, the ladies were now wildly excited tearing at each other, trying to reach under dresses and décolleté and generally doing all sorts of things that are difficult to describe.

It was impossible to tell whether this was a staged act or something that was happening for real. Although, what is the difference? "All the world's a stage," as the classic goes, and life is just a stone's throw away from the stage. Matilda watched it all calmly as if waiting for something. Itfut did not seem to know how to react and made muffled sounds like 'hmm' covering her mouth in shock.

Finally, a gong sounded, and the orgy suddenly came to a halt. Slow blues music began to play, and representatives of both sexes began slowly leaving the 'battlefield' and returning to the stage. They all looked fairly disgruntled. One had lost a wig, someone else's clothes were torn, and someone else appeared half-naked. Only the masks on their faces remained untouched.

The couples lined up opposite each other and began to draw closer. Coming into contact (men with women now), they pulled their arms back to the sides and began to rub their bodies and make swinging, advancing movements looking at each other from behind their masks.

Itfut could not contain herself and asked, "So, this is what your performances are like?"

"No, not all of them are like this, not always. Don't assume that. It's just chance that we're watching this one. But sometimes they do show this kind of peculiar art."

"Is it all for real or is it a play?"

"It's a play. But you won't see this kind of thing in any theatre. Sometimes it's staged outside in nature."

"Why don't they take off their masks?"

"Because in moments like these, people don't necessarily feel comfortable looking another in the eye. You might see hell."

"Right, I know what you're referring to."

"What do you mean, Futi?"

"Another time."

"Come on, it's all basically marginal underground. There's very little art here."

"Well, I quite liked it," giggled Itfut. "I love expressiveness."

"Watch what happens next," said Matilda as if preparing herself for something.

Meanwhile, the blue-green diva continued her parade around the swinging couples, who were rubbing up against each other moving to the rhythm of an open blues composition. But suddenly, she stumbled for no apparent reason and turned awkwardly on one heel. There was the sound of something tearing and the bow fell off her dress. Leaning backwards, the diva got her heels caught up in her ribbons and came crashing clumsily to the floor with her legs tilted upwards. The glamor and pathos of the scene dissolved instantly. The other actors froze in confusion while the director was filled with rage.

Matilda gave a little jump, clapped and laughed harder than she probably ever had. With mock seriousness but barely containing her laughter, Itfut turned to Matilda and said, “Oh, Tili-Tili! That’s no way to behave. You should be ashamed of yourself!”

“I’m not ashamed, not one bit!” shouted Matilda, looking pleased with herself. “I told you that beauty would dance for me yet! My bow is with me! My bow is for me!” she rapped, continuing to spin and jump about.

“Okay, okay, Tili, that’s enough! Look, your Victor has gone completely wild.”

The director was rushing around the stage waving his arms about and shouting, “Get lost, fools! Go, all of you!”

The troupe ran from the stage in all different directions and then Victor sat down on the edge of the stage, clasped his head in his hands and groaned.

“Where are you, my Tili, my darling!”

On hearing these words, Matilda went from laughing to crying and sobbing again.

"What am I going to do with you, my joy, my sorrow!" said Itfut. "You see, you are remembered and missed."

The theatre scene gradually faded, and the mirror resumed its usual maritime backdrop. The friends sat down in the sand and gave each other a hug, each busy with their own thoughts.

SECOND NAME

"What is it Tili, you seem a little down?" said Itfut.

"Not a little, a lot," replied Matilda. It's strange and terrible. My world is so close I could reach out my hand and touch it, and yet I can't. Now, everything there is happening but not to me, and totally without me"

"Don't be sad. Didn't I promise you that we would go home?"

"Futi, Futichka, I want to believe you, I really do, but what can you possibly do if you can't remember how to engage with this kind of reality?"

"Don't forget, I'm a priestess, and priestesses don't lose their gifts irrevocably, just like that. And there is something you have."

"My bow?"

"The bow simply helped you feel something you've always had. A certain lever or trigger around your spine which you can use to shape reality."

"Yes, but we don't yet fully know what it is. All I could do was give that girl a slap, and even that was on the other side of the mirror. The lever-trigger thing won't let us pass through to the other side."

"You're not the only one who has it," said Itfut. "I don't yet know precisely what it is, but you definitely do have something. You said yourself, that you are special."

"Did I? When?" asked Matilda.

"Surely you haven't forgotten the girl with the milk soup?"

"Ah, that was just childish bravado..."

"No, it was more than that. You are special. It's true. Tell me, what do you see? How do you see reality in this moment?"

"Oh, Futi, I see us as being like fish stuck in an aquarium. Beyond the glass is the open sea but we have no way of getting to it."

"No, this isn't an aquarium. The sea is on that side, but this side is the same at that, remember?"

"What do you mean, the same?"

"I can't explain it. I just know that what is there is equally here in some mirror-like sense. We have to reflect back the opposite."

"You're talking in riddles as usual, Futi."

"I just need to remember something."

"Could you ask, you know, that thing you call Threshold?"

"Let's try. Threshold, where are you?" shouted Itfut. "Are you here?"

In that moment a wind picked up that seemed to blow from all directions.

"I am here and everywhere, here and everywhere." a whisper responded.

"Can you tell us, how to pass through the mirror?" asked the priestess.

"Remember your name, priestess-priestess!" answered Threshold.

"But you said my name yourself! Am I not Itfut?"

"Remember your second name and Knowledge will gradually return to you!"

"Gradually...?" Itfut barely had time to speak than the wind subsided, and the whisper would not respond however much the friends tried to call it back.

"Your adviser does not say much, does he," Matilda commented.

"No, there's no point in expecting an explanation from him," said Itfut. "But still, there is always something behind his words, something important."

"What does he mean by your 'second' name? Does that trigger anything for you?"

"No, I have no idea. All I know is that when I first heard it, the name Itfut felt as if it was mine and not mine at the same time."

"There we go. Nothing but riddles again."

"We'll have to get ourselves out of this mess somehow. But if Threshold has promised something, it means there's hope."

"Futi, this is the perfect time to look at your reality. Perhaps things will become clearer if we do," suggested Matilda.

"Yes, you're right. We should."

"Then let's start, quick, quick!"

The priestess concentrated and turned her gaze in the direction of the mirror. Her eyes looked as if they were unfocused on anything in particular while demonic features appeared on her face hinting at an extraordinarily strong character hidden behind her fragile appearance. The mirror transformed into a black screen. A few moments later, flashes began appearing across the screen in all the colors of the rainbow and then gradually, a scene emerged of an incredibly beautiful place.

Judging by the general scene, it was a warm summer evening. The sun had already set but the sky was illuminated with a shimmering green and blue light. The central part of the landscape was taken up by a wide alley laid with smooth paving slabs. On either side, narrow paths extending in various directions were covered in carpets of soft, springy moss. The paths like the alley were framed with manicured plantings of flowering shrubs and trees. Everywhere, a soft light glowed from an unknown source making the entire landscape visible, and at the same time, keeping it wrapped in a cozy twilight, especially in the more secluded corners. The magnificent play of light and shadow was accentuated by a fluorescent radiance that emanated from the flowers and their unabashedly wide-open buds. Rather than intrude on the intimacy of the twilight they simply seemed to be trying to show themselves in all their glory.

Along the alleys and maze of paths, people walked in pairs, others in small groups or individually. They are all dressed in clothing of different cuts and shapes yet in the same beige color. Some were silent, others chatted quietly among themselves. On meeting, they would touch each other's cheeks with the tips of their fingers, smile and continue on their way without saying a word. The peaceful quiet of the summer evening was complemented by an orchestra of restless grasshoppers.

"God, it's so beautiful!" Matilda exclaimed. "I've never seen anything so beautiful!"

"Can you hear the grasshoppers and how much effort they're making?" said Itfut. "They're so diligent! And the aroma, can you smell it?"

The mirror it seemed did nothing to hinder the wonderful air filled with the smell of flowers and herbs from crossing over to the other side.

"Futi, do you live in paradise or something? I'm already desperate to go there! How much longer are you going to torture me?"

"Wait, this is just the beginning."

The majority of people in the scene were moving along the alley in the direction of a small square. Above the square towered a classical-style temple decorated with malachite, deep-blue columns and gilded frescoes. The entire building was lit on all sides by a strange source of light. Once enough people had gathered in the square, an old, gray-haired man dressed in a white robe appeared on the temple steps. He stretched his arms out signaling for silence. The entire square became hushed in anticipation.

"That's my Teacher," whispered Itfut, as if afraid she would be overheard.

"You see, you're already remembering. We're getting warmer," Matilda whispered back.

The old man brought his palms together, then pulled them apart and a translucent, golden ball appeared between his palms. Then he stretched his arms forward and extended them out to the sides, and the ball took off above the square increasing in size and showered down in golden rain. The people in the square caught the golden drops with enthralled shouts carefully placing them in the palm of their hands. Then each one blew at their golden drop as if it were a spark and soon all their hands are filled with golden glowing balls. On the Teacher's command, they all raised their hands and the balls soared upwards before dissolving into a radiance that unfolded across the sky.

"What are those balls, Itfut?" asked Matilda.

"Love energy," replied Itfut.

"And where is all this light coming from? Is there some kind of hidden illumination system?"

"No, it's the Gods watching us. We send them our love and they illuminate our ritual."

"What's the ritual?"

"You'll see it now. It's how people find their partner, their other half."

The people who were gathered in the square made way moving towards the edges, leaving just two dozen men and women of different ages at the center. This group arranged themselves in a circle and then closed it by pressing their palms up against the palm of the person standing next to them. Music was also playing but instead of a melody, it was more like a series of trills and chords similar to the sounds of a harp and an organ. The people began to turn smoothly and freely to the beat of the sounds, with each turn taking a step around the circle, so that the whole round dance was transformed into a graceful waltz.

As they turned, they all gradually began to acquire different colored auras: red, white, blue, yellow, green, purple, orange and other shades. Then it became clear that some of the individuals in the circle shared the same color aura. Noticing each other, these pairs left the circle dance taking each other by the hand and climbing up the temple steps. The others continued turning until only those remained whose aura colors did not match. The music faded, the dancers became still, and then they turned to face the center touching each other with the tips of their fingers at which point their auras faded. Totally unembarrassed, they turned around and parted with a smile moving off in different directions.

"That was amazing, Futi. I understand it all!" exclaimed Matilda.

"It is beautiful, isn't it?" said Itfut.

"Awesome! Only what about the ones who didn't find their other half?"

"They'll find them, maybe next time or the time after that. But they'll definitely find them."

"Does it ever happen that more than two people's colors match?"

"It is possible, but you rarely come across it."

"And how do they sort it out between themselves if there are three of them for example?"

"Don't worry. They work it out. There's still no guarantee that the chosen pairs will be together. What do you think it takes for that to happen?"

"Love?"

"Exactly. Compatibility doesn't guarantee the birth of love. Often couples find each other without the need for ritual. The ritual just helps them make an appropriate choice."

"Have you ever taken part in a ritual like that?"

"No, I was prepared for the special status of High Priestess. If I was there now, it would be in the position of Teacher."

"Futi, are you saying that you're doomed to solitude?"

"Not quite. I've had a number of relationships but I still haven't found my chosen one."

"Haven't found anyone worthy of you?"

"It's not that they weren't worthy... You know, many might well want to be close to me, but they are wary of my status. Or, perhaps, to them, I appear inaccessible."

"Are you inaccessible?"

"Ha, ha, ha, Tili, I'm an ordinary, approachable person!" said the priestess who laughed and then gave Matilda a hug. "But I am also extraordinary and unapproachable. That's just how I am!"

"You'll understand me then! I do understand by the way. It's just a pity that we have a deficit of courageous guys, who could truly appreciate who you really are."

"And who am I really?"

"You're amazing, you're wonderful, you're entrancing! You are love itself!"

"Well, not exactly," said Itfut. "You see my face paint?"

"Yes, what does it symbolize?" asked Matilda.

"There are two sides to love. I imagine you know that yourself."

"What are they?"

"You're about to find out."

Meanwhile, the chosen pairs descended the temple steps and went for a walk holding hands. The rest of the crowd wandered off in various directions along the labyrinthine paths.

"Is that it? The presentation is finished?" asked Matilda.

"No, soon the entity parade will begin," replied Itfut.

"What's that?"

"You'll see Tili, you'll see."

ENTITY PARADE

And so, the mass celebration of all these kind, friendly-looking people continued. Only now, something unusual began to spin and turn in the evening air. Suddenly, everywhere multi-colored translucent balls began to appear from all directions. They happily circled in the air and flew about among those walking the paths. People smiled and held out their palms for the balls to sit on like birds. Having sat for a short while, the balls assumed a more saturated color and then easily flew off and away in search of other raised palms.

"What is that? What are they doing?" asked Matilda.

"They are entities from the subtle world," answered Itfut, "they are actively interested in our life. They like to attach themselves to us out of curiosity and to feed a little."

"What do you mean, 'feed a little'? You make them sound like vampires…"

"Don't worry, they're harmless. The majority of them at any rate. People are happy to share their energy with them, the energy of love."

"Are there ones people should be wary of?"

"Yes, they are all different. The beautiful, transparent ones are the entities of love, gratitude, compassion, nobility, generosityand kindness.They carry the same qualities we have."

"Futi, are you saying that how we are is down to these entities?"

"No, it's not that simple. The main point is that at birth a person's soul is like a blank sheet of paper. If an entity likes a person, they might settle near them and then the soul can acquire certain qualities."

"You say incredible things!" said Matilda. "In my world people believe that a person becomes the way they are because of their relatives, society, the environment and circumstances..."

"That's true, too, but all the things you mention contribute only indirectly to whether one or other entity will settle near an individual. A person becomes like the entities that are present in them."

"It's still hard to believe!"

"Yes, people tend to believe only in what they can see with their own eyes whereas entities are invisible, intangible. We are seeing them with our bare eyes now because the Gods are giving us the opportunity and also because the atmosphere of our ritual is saturated with the energy of kindness and love. Mostly good, kind entities are attracted to energy of that kind."

"But can dark entities come in too?"

"Yes, but they're usually attracted to a malevolent atmosphere. Look, look!A muddy looking ball has settled on someone!"

The friends saw a brown colored ball with muddy green spots land on a girl's palm.

"That is an envy entity," said Itfut. "Perhaps the girl was unlucky this evening."

"Oh, but what if the entity possesses her?" exclaimed Matilda.

Something else happened instead, however. The girl did not chase the entity away or accept it. She just smiled thoughtfully and gently blew on the ball sending it a ray of golden energy from her other palm. The ball swayed and swayed and then flew away.

"Wow!" said Matilda in surprise. "Is everyone that spiritually advanced?"

"No, of course not. We are all different, too," said Itfut. "We get infected with all sorts of negative entities. And I'm no saint, either."

"I still can't believe how it can be that an entity settles in a person and is changed as a result...or that a person changes because the entity has settled near them... Is falling in love down to entities, too?"

"Exactly. Being in love is a manifestation of the entity of love. It will enter a person if they are ready to accept it but there has to be a potential object of that person's love nearby, too."

"Futi, you're killing me! You really blow my mind with this stuff. How do you know all this?"

"Is it so hard to believe? Judge for yourself. You must have come across people who were living and perfectly normal, healthy life, and then suddenly for no obvious reason became immersed in some warped obsession. They can't sleep, they suffer with imaginings, write poetry, commit all kinds of foolish acts, and can't think about anything except the object of their passion. They have an entity. That's the issue. They may be a pleasant individual in many ways, someone who usually lifts the spirits and warms the soul, but they can also be capable of tormenting a person if the object of their love expresses indifference."

"Yes, when you put it like that..." Matilda agreed. "And when two people fall in love, does that mean that entities have settled in them both?"

"Yes, if you're lucky of course. Love at first sight is proof of that. Again, ask yourself, why would two people meet and suddenly feel something that defies all rational explanation. Almost any feeling can be explained: something hurts, something pains, annoys or pleases you, and so on. The most important thing is that you understand what it is and why you're feeling it. But can anyone explain what love is or why it appears so suddenly?"

"No, Futi, you have me completely flummoxed."

"Right, and the reason why it is so inexplicable and indescribable is because of entities, which the average person has no clue about, mostly because they have never seen one. They don't even know that they exist."

Itfut's eyes suddenly lit up.

"Oh, Tili, look what's happening over there!"

The friends watched two golden balls land simultaneously on the palms of one of the newly-formed couples.

"Now it'll all kick off!" exclaimed Itfut.

The balls shook filled with an even richer gold color and without pausing for a moment floated right into the chest cells of the two lucky individuals. They gave each other a strange look and for some reason dropped hands but then half a step later they stood closer to each other and set off with an easy step wherever their feet took them. They walked side by side sometimes bumping into each other, sometimes standing apart.

"Lucky couple!" said Matilda. "It's a good thing there aren't any balls flying about on this side. An entity of envy would definitely have got its claws into me."

"Don't you have a chosen one?" asked Itfut. "That Victor... are you and he..."

"I don't know. There's definitely something between us but it's confusing."

"Don't worry. Entities don't always come straight away and very rarely do they come to two people at the same time. You have to be patient. It takes attention and care. In order for a miracle to happen, you have to nurture it, work at it, not with the mind and not with the body but with the soul. That pair was incredibly lucky."

"It makes me uncomfortable to think now of how people worked with their bodies in our theatre. If we compare our two worlds, we have outright depravity and you are all innocence itself."

"It's not quite like that. Do you think that innocence is the ideal?"

"Well, all our so-called highly spiritual personalities call us to innocence, to the sublime and the spiritual at the same time as judging the so-called low and carnal. And how are we to argue with them? They have the upper hand because they are the righteous."

"Your righteous ones aren't necessarily right. And what you had in the theater was not so much a falling into sin as a revealing of one side of life, even call it love if you like. I told you, I liked it."

"But why?" asked Matilda surprised.

"Because there are two sides to love: Tenderness and Strength."

"Okay. Tenderness I can understand but how does Strength show itself?"

"Strength manifests as just that, Strength. It manifests in expression and even to some extent in aggression."

"In aggression towards the person you love?"

"It's a different kind of aggression. It's difficult to explain, like being in love."

"You mean sex?"

"Yes, there is duality to love, like so much in this world, and it is made up of two entities: Tenderness and Strength. They have to exist in harmony, in unity. Without Tenderness, Strength is violence. Without Strength, Tenderness is simply sugary sweet. Even a medicine is only effective when it contains a moderate dose of poison."

"Futi, how do you know all this stuff?"

"I couldn't say exactly but I suspect that in the course of talking to you, I am remembering the things I was taught and had forgotten."

"So, you say that love has two types of entity. Which type settled in that pair?"

"Tenderness is a golden color. Strength is more purple. So far, they have only tender feelings for one another, but that's just for now."

"Aaaa! So, there you are, Futi! That's why your coloring is purple!"

"I am neither one nor the other. I can be different things. Evidently, back then, I wanted Strength to prevail and that's why I was made up like this."

"And so, in reality, sometimes these same entities of Strength settle in a pair in love?" asked Matilda. "And then they'll have a stormy night of passion?"

"Yes, if they let it in," answered Itfut.

"In what sense?"

"Remember, you said that the reason your actors don't remove their masks is because not everyone is able to look another in the eye at such moments because they might glimpse hell?"

"Yes, there is that."

"So, what do you think? Why is that? Why does this unusual instinct arise in a normal, balanced person like some infernal fire that lights up their eyes making them seem like a different person altogether? It is impossible to explain the condition and cause of being in love. Defining sex is just as impossible."

"Yes, I'm beginning to understand it though. Sex happens because the entity of Strength has entered them."

"It enters if a person allows it to and accepts it, but if a person is frightened by the thought of changing and can't accept themselves in that form then Tenderness remains without Strength and then there is no sex and eventually Tenderness itself is lost."

"An interesting philosophy," remarked Matilda. "It sounds logical to me."

"It's not a philosophy," said Itfut, "it's just how things are."

"So, you have to let yourself go and allow Strength in?"

"Exactly, there can be no love without Tenderness but without Strength love will eventually fade, too. The creator made love a dual reality for very good reason. Almost everything in life is dual in nature. A world in which there is only evil is doomed. Such a world simply could not exist. Don't you think? And a world in which there is only good is equally doomed."

"It's true. Ideal worlds obviously don't exist."

"And because they don't exist, there must be a balance between good and evil, between Tenderness and Strength, or righteousness and sin as you call it. So, there is nothing wrong with your theatre except that it lacks Tenderness. You should add a little more Tenderness."

"Yes, I understand. Still, if I had to choose between my world and yours, you can guess which I would choose?"

"Your own?"

"No. Mine may be familiar to me but yours suits my soul."

"You see, we have solved our dilemma of either being in our own different worlds or staying together."

"Yes, that's great but there's another dilemma. We have a saying, 'the grass it always greener on the other side.' As soon as you get to where the grass appears greener, the picture unfolds, and everything turns out different from how you expected."

"Yes, I know, I know. We'll see how things go but first, we have to get out of here."

In the meantime, the square and the pathways had almost emptied as the people set off home. Only now did Maltilda notice that aside from the trees and shrubs, the length of the alley was lined with sculptures.

"What are those statues?" she asked.

"That's the pantheon of our Gods."

"How many are there?"

"There is one Supreme Creator, but he has helpers."

"It would be nice to take a closer look... Oh!" Matilda suddenly became very excited. "Look, in the same dress as yours, who is that?"

"That's me, I suppose," said Itfut with a note of sadness in her voice.

"You mean, they've already buried you? That didn't take them long, the bastards!"

"What else were they to do? I disappeared; I don't know how long ago. And all these tricks with time... Maybe years have passed."

"Hang on, there's an inscription beneath your statue. It looks like it reads...Tufti!"

Itfut froze becoming as still as her statue. She stood motionless without uttering a word. Frightened, Matilda started tugging at her.

"Futi, come back! What's wrong? Oh, my God! It's your name only spelt backwards!"

"I knew it... No, I sensed something..." said the priestess barely audibly and stammering as if lost. "They called me Tufti but for some reason, here, I became Itfut."

"Hooray! We've found your second name!" Matilda was totally delighted while the priestess still could not quite get used to it.

"Well, it's nothing to be surprised about! We're on the other side of reality and here, just as it should be, everything is the other way around."

"Yes, but not everything. Your name is the same here as it was before."

"Yes, that's odd. Then, what should my other name be here? Ilit?" As this thought came to her, Matilda went completely wild. She started whirling about, jumping and shouting.

"I'm Ilit! I'm Ilit! And you're Tufti! And I'm Ilit! Almost like Lilith, Adam's first wife! Woot-la!"

Itfut tried to calm Matilda down, but Matilda was not having any of it. She ran behind the priestess and called to her, "Tufti! Tu-u-uf-ti-i-i! What an exotic name you have! Soft like a feather bed! I'm going to call you Tufti! No, sometimes I'm going to call you what I did before, my Futichka, Futi!"

"Okay, Okay, Tili-Ilit, Ilit-Tili! Calm down!"

"Tu-u-uf-ti-i-i!"

Matilda was not letting up. "Okay, Okay, that's it. I'm calm now. Tufti!"

"Well there we go, we've found my second name and even yours, too." said Itfut. "But I'm still so astounded, I can't think straight."

"It'll soon pass. Threshold said that Knowledge would gradually come back to you."

"Let's hope so. Maybe your second name will come in handy... Oh, look, the mirror is returning to its screen saver."

The image of the miraculous world of priestess Itfut gradually dissolved and the mirror was again filled with the image of slow splashing waves and palms whose wide leaves swayed in the wind. And just as before, the friends remained beyond the reach of our reality. Still beyond the reach...

EXPEDITION LID

And so, the company we have already met, or rather 'Expedition Lid' as we shall refer to them went in search of the edge of the lid which had covered the world for reasons not yet understood. As Queen Brunhilda had adequately reasoned, in order to find out what kind of lid it was, they had to at least locate the edge of it.

The procession was led by Eejit Green who carried his club on his shoulder. Brunhilda walked second because she had condescendingly agreed to the suggestion that Eejit could serve as her bodyguard. The warrior-like queen did not really require the service but, knowing Eejit, she decided not to engage in an altercation with him, which could take up a lot of time. Next came Orange Cow with her wings folded so that they would not get in the way. Behind her went Yellow Submarine in her orange boots. Finally, Shaggy Beast brought up the rear and was very unhappy not to be next to the queen, but Brunhilda looked at him sternly and ordered him to obey, as well as to guard the expedition from the rear, which was a mission of extreme importance.

Suddenly, Eejit stopped and turned back to face the others almost hitting the queen in the face with his club. The others stopped too, confused.

"Your Majesty," Eejit said, addressing Brunhilda. "Allow me to make an assumption, or rather to pose a question, which has lit my clear mind with insight."

"What's the matter?" asked the queen. "What's lit you up?"

"The point lies in the following, or in other words, in this."

"In what, then?"

"Our path lies along winding tracks, ravines and valleys."

"Be brief!"

"So, our path which is full of danger and leads who knows where, undoubtedly, evokes a feeling of consternation in my chest and a question of blatant moral concern."

"Briefer!"

"In short, where are we going? In which direction is the edge of the ominous lid to be found?"

"Your Majesty," said Cow joining the conversation, "the honorable one wishes to know exactly where the path to the edge of the lid might lie."

The lid stretched across the entire sky and so its edges could not in fact be seen.

"So, what does the honorable Eejit suggest?" asked Brunhilda.

"In a complex issue such as this, one that is convoluted not in mind but in feelings that arise from the depths of the soul, pure and sacred, it belies us to measure our path and direction," said Eejit.

"It's not our path that is convoluted and not the mind either," said the queen, "but your manner of speaking with its fanciful constructions and ostentatious rhapsodies".

"Eejit, so you mean, you have, feelings too?" said Submarine who just wanted to ask a simple question.

"I shall swallow the sardonic, sarcastic poison of your irony meekly, like a tear. However, my feelings tell me that the edge of the lid lies in a special, sacred direction incomprehensible to the mind and accessible by insight only."

"And what are your wonderful feelings and noble insight telling you?" asked the queen.

Eejit adopted a deeply thoughtful look and pointed in the opposite direction.

"That way. I am certain of it and simultaneously exceedingly convinced."

"Oh, and why is that?" squealed Submarine.

"Only the self-opinionated can be exceedingly certain," said Brunhilda. "On what grounds?"

"I have a special gift to know things that others cannot," Eejit answered proudly.

"Don't listen to him." Cow said intervening, "he just wants to massage his ego."

"Right, well firstly, we're not going that way for the simple reason that it leads to a swamp," said the queen. "Secondly, the lid, if it is a lid, must have an edge along all its sides, so the direction does not matter. Another thing is that we should be aiming for the edge that is nearest, but we do not know where that is. Therefore, we will go in the direction that is simplest and easiest which is this straight road that we set out on initially. Any objections?"

"No. No objections. That's right!" shouted Cow and Submarine.

"Well, if you insist on your monarchical, so to speak, autocracy, Your Majesty, then I am forced to humbly submit," said Eejit.

"I will not allow anyone to contradict my queen," said Shaggy Beast entering the conversation for the first time. "Even someone who has a club as authority, or authority as a club."

"Thank you, Beast," said Brunhilda.

"But my authority is undeniable! Or what's the word, unde ...." Eejit was halfway through objecting when he was interrupted.

"Enough! No arguing! Let's go."

Without further delay, the expedition set off along their chosen path. They walked and walked and finally arrived. In front of them stretched an amazing azure sea with grass and palm trees on the shore. The gray lid ended just above the coast and immediately beyond it was the blue sky and floating clouds, just as it should be.

"Tremendous! This is where I can swim!" shouted Submarine.

"Hooray-hooray! We've reached the edge! Here's where I can fly!" screeched Cow.

"I had the honor of strolling along the coast the other day but there were no palm trees there, only snags," Eejit said.

"Yes, it's like it's a different sea, not ours," said Brunhilda.

"What difference does it make? Let's go now! Let's swim!"

The entire company rushed enthusiastically towards the open embrace of a dream. Beast rushed ahead of the others as his paws meant he could run faster than anyone. So, he was the first to throw all four paws up against the invisible wall that rose unexpectedly before him. The others, unable to believe their eyes or Beast's unsuccessful experiment, repeated the same. They bumped into it, fell and were convinced that the wall did really exist.

Having got back up on their feet again, they began walking back and forth feeling their way along the barrier in complete bewilderment. Being completely transparent, the wall also turned out to be solid and impenetrable like glass and, in addition, it had a reflective quality, although not quite that of a mirror. To everyone's surprise the strange mirror, rather than reflecting the surrounding objects and landscape, reflected the blurry silhouettes of our heroines, who from this side looked like ghosts. This confused everyone even more.

"What madness is this?!" exclaimed Eejit, who had lost all his eloquence.

"Well, we got out from under the lid only to stumble into a mirror," Submarine added in disappointment.

The queen was silent and pensive, Beast snorted in displeasure, and Cow kept fumbling along the mirror surface first with horns and then with hooves but all in vain. They had reached a dead-end.

"Well, I dare to expose this profanation with my profaner," said Eejit. Swinging his club, he pounded against the glass with all his foolish might, but the mirror did not even vibrate, let alone crack. It was as indestructible as a rock although at the same time, there was something intangible about it.

"What's needed here is not power, but something else," Brunhilda said.

"No, harder and with something more solid," said Eejit throwing Submarine a sidelong glance.

"Don't you even think about it!" No sooner had Submarine shouted than Eejit grabbed her and thrust her up against the glass like a ram. The result, nonetheless, was the same.

"Oh, you bastard!" shouted Submarine, "Beast, save me!"

Shaggy Beast jumped at Eejit who immediately released his victim, taking a few cautious steps back.

"You know what, Eejit," said the queen. "One more trick like that from you and you will be driven from this team in shame."

"All right, all right!" said Green trying to justify himself. "What are you all so cross about? She's made of iron, nothing will happen to her!"

"Let's give your head a try then. It's probably even harder." shouted Submarine.

"You wanted to swim. I was trying for your sake. Okay, so it did not work out, what can you do? You're wearing boots not flippers, anyway. How do you intend to swim in boots?"

"That's none of your business! I don't need flippers. I hate you, scumbag!"

"Okay, don't be angry, I'm sorry," said Eejit, softening his voice to a tone more conciliatory. However paradoxical, although he really was a scumbag, Eejit Green was kind at heart.

"Your Majesty," said Cow addressing Brunhilda, "we need to do something. Maybe I should climb up there, as far as the lid goes and take a look around?"

"Good idea, my dear, and then come back and tell us what's there and in which direction we should go," said the queen.

Orange Cow straightened her wings and took off drawing spiral circles. Her wings were surprisingly small but in some incomprehensible way she managed to fly with great ease. The others stood with their heads tilted backward watching the whole piloting process in great anticipation. After circling a little under the lid itself, Cow began her descent and soon, to everyone's satisfaction, landed back down again successfully.

"Well?" asked the queen.

"Over there," said Cow pointing in the direction with her horns, "some kind of city. I did not notice anything else unusual. Maybe we should head over there?"

"Yes, let's do that" said the queen.

Everyone else nodded their heads in agreement and even Eejit did not object. Having decided, they set off once again.

LOVESICK

They walked and walked until finally they arrived. In the city, the buildings of all manner of institution were squashed up right next to each other. There were no shopping centers, entertainment parades or even residential buildings to be seen, just institutions and each building had a sign marked with a long and incomprehensible abbreviation from which it followed that the full names of these institutions were even longer and even more incomprehensible.

The densely arranged and diverse accumulation of organizations, which were undoubtedly working exclusively for the benefit of society, indicated that this was a city a great significance and that its servants were people of note. Rarely did one meet a passer-by on the street but everywhere there were cars shooting about, their owners in a rush to carry out some extremely urgent business. Each driver was holding a cell phone managing to control the car and carry out no less urgent negotiations at the same time. From all this, one might conclude that the city's inhabitants were not going to work but were instead extraordinarily busy with state affairs, which is, of course, a very different thing.

Our company roamed the streets in search of an institution that might be able to assist them with their ongoing problem: the notorious lid that was hanging over the city.

The inhabitants were no doubt concerned with the same issue and their vigorous activity throughout the city was all for the sake of some lofty purpose. Being the most educated and competent among them, Eejit was entrusted with the task of reading the signs on the front of the buildings.

"What do we have here," he muttered, tilting his head back to see. "Borsch Borsching. Hum, a weighty institution. We should pop in."

"Hell with you and your borsch!" shouted Submarine. "We're looking for something connected to lids!"

"So, what's the problem? Borsch is directly connected to lids! You cook it in a saucepan which is covered with a lid."

"Move on, move on," the queen ordered.

"Here's another one. Very curious. 'Frill Frilling'" read Eejit. "Shall we go in?"

"Are you kidding me?!" Submarine interjected indignantly.

"Okay, maybe their niche is a little specialized. Oh, look here! 'Aftertaste Correction'. Interesting, what aftertaste might that be, I wonder? Maybe a liddy kind of aftertaste?"

"Eejit, don't talk nonsense," said Brunhilda. "We did not come here to mess around."

"Ah, just what we need, 'Alcohol-free Toilet'.

"...!!!"

"Okay, okay, I'll shut up. Read for yourself if you're all so clever."

"None of this is what we want," said Cow. "We'd be better off searching for institutions with abbreviations. They usually deal with serious matters, matters of superior seriousness."

"Exactly, if there's nowhere else to go, then you have to go somewhere else," answered Eejit in his own characteristic manner. “We need somewhere that is in principle to and categorically from.”

“Shut up, will you?” Submarine interrupted. “Look, over there. That looks like a serious institution. They’ve got ‘INSTHEALPROTHAPFUN’ writ in large letters. Sounds most convincing. At least it has the root ‘heal’ in it so it probably relates to public health. They have to care for our health, don’t they? And the lid’s harming it, right?”

“Okay, let’s go inside,” the queen said.

A duty doctor met them at the entrance.

“Are you sick?” he asked.

“No, we’ve come about the lid,” Brunhilda replied.

“What lid?”

“The one hanging over the city and blocking out the sky.”

“Right. And...?”

“Well, the lid does not let the sunlight through!”

“Ultraviolet radiation, my dears, has an extremely negative affect on the normal cycle of disease. A disease must be allowed to develop in the way that it is supposed to develop.”

“Very reasonable arguments,” Eejit said, enjoying having come across a like-minded person. “Allow me to shake your hand.”

“But wait,” said the queen, “the lid is suffocating us and that directly harms our health, too!”

“No, we have strictly, scientifically proven that the lid is totally harmless,” the doctor declared.

“Could you tell me, please,” said Cow, addressing the doctor most politely of them all, “how is the name of your esteemed establishment to be deciphered?”

“Institution for Health Protection and Happy Funerals”, the doctor replied condescendingly.

"So, you do in fact deal with issues regarding health?"

"We do, only not so much issues as protection."

"So, this is a security organization?"

"Precisely."

"So how do you provide for the security of the population's health?"

"We don't protect the health of the population, we protect the population from its health."

"So, do you treat diseases?"

"Naturally. Treatment of disease is our main profile and ultimate goal."

"Sorry," said Cow, "but shouldn't the ultimate goal be recovery?"

"Not quite. Recovery is an intermediate stage, since it is inevitably followed by the onset of another disease. For this reason, all our attention is focused exclusively on diseases. It's the process of treatment that is ultimately essential."

"So, healing doesn't interest you?"

"Firstly, we already have diseases that are incurable. And secondly, if everyone recovers, who will we treat? You have exhausted the list of possible questions, so dear people, if you have a disease of some kind, welcome, but if you haven't..."

"It's quite clear there is nothing for us here. Let's scram." Brunhilda whispered in Cow's ear.

"Please, just one last question!" said Cow, refusing to be pacified. "What do you mainly treat? What is the main disease?"

"Love, damn it! A very dangerous thing."

"Can we take a look at the treatment process as it is so important!"

The doctor hesitated for a moment but the cunning Eejit joined the conversation.

"My dear colleague, I was so inspired by your philosophy that I cannot help but express my admiration!"

"Okay, there's a doctor coming, look. She's the person you need to talk to."

"Are you sick?" the doctor asked welcoming them with the standard question.

"No, we are trainees," said Eejit answering for them all. "We are interested in methods for treating love."

"Oh! Are you now? Commendable I'm sure."

"Allow me to enquire what success you have achieved in this constructive and important field?"

"The field is very poorly equipped from a technical point of view. We are barely coping. Moreover, the disease is painfully contagious."

"And are there any medicines available for the treatment of this extremely harmful disease?"

"Our doctor-researchers are very close to inventing a universal remedy called 'Antilovsis' but it is still being developed."

"And how do the other methods work?"

"The fundamental principle is to make it clear to the patient that he is very, very sick. Sometimes, the disease cures of its own accord."

"Oh, that's wonderful! So, there are some positive results?"

"Yes, but they aren't significant. We treat them, the scumbags, but they're parasites. They don't want to get better."

"But recovery is not that important. The main thing is the treatment process itself!"

"True-true! What a promising young man! You are quite correct in your understanding."

"Can we not take a quick look at the process itself?" asked Cow, joining in. "We value your rich experience very highly."

"Yes, you may," the flattered female doctor agreed. "We are just about to begin a session of intensive therapy. Let's go to the lab."

The whole company followed the female doctor and Cow asked more questions along the way.

"Tell me, do people come to you for healing themselves?"

"Sometimes, they come alone or in pairs but that is in cases where one of the two is sick. When both are sick, they don't want to be treated at all and then they have to be brought in by force."

"Why so cruel?"

"How else would you have us deal with antisocial elements? If you don't fight them, what will become of society?"

"And what methods do you use to treat them?"

"For couples we conduct a course of therapy that is love-killing. If someone comes in by themselves with a diagnosis of unrequited love, we send them straight to the intensive care unit. But you are lucky. At the moment we have a couple. He loves her, she does not love him, so they turned to us for help, voluntarily. We are very encouraging of this kind of self-awareness in our citizens, so we are going to carry out a light session with them that won't be too painful."

They approached the operating room, which was equipped externally with glass and internally with a mirror which made it possible to observe the entire process, unnoticed.

"See how convenient it is," said the female doctor turning to the delegation. "I will lead the operation from here, and you can watch."

The interior arrangement of the operating room was a little unusual. The main thing missing was the operating table with its standard accessories and tools. At the center, there was a sturdy-looking chair with belts attached to it, and positioned beside the chair, a small table and a glass case resembling a drugs cabinet. A young man and women were sitting on chairs along the wall and on both sides of stood two strong physicians as well as a nurse who was busy with syringes and vials.

"So, guys, start by sitting the patient in the chair," the female doctor ordered through a microphone.

Without ceremony, the brothers grabbed the guy by the elbows and dragged him to the chair. Not expecting to be treated in this manner, he began to resist but they quickly dealt with him, fastening his arms and legs tightly to the armrests and legs of the chair.

"What are you going to do to me?" shouted the young man.

"It's okay, calm down, this won't hurt," came the sound of the female doctor's voice from behind the glass.

"Darling!" his girlfriend called out. "Don't worry, we only want what's best for you! They'll cure you and you'll be normal again."

"Untie me now!" the young man shouted again. "I withdraw my consent to the operation!"

"Sorry but you don't have that right," the doctor answered him. "Calm down, everything will be fine." And then turning to the brothers, she added, "Seal his mouth with

tape! Or no, take an adhesive bandage from the first-aid kit. No expense spared for such a handsome, young man."

Our company looked on with undisguised horror and surprise.

"Why are you sealing his mouth?" asked Cow.

"If they start talking to each other, this will turn into a standard quarrel, and since they might reconcile later, all the treatment will have gone down the drain. Only the healthy patient should be allowed to speak."

"Nurse, give her the serum!" commanded the doctor.

"What's that, then?" asked Brunhilda.

"The serum is a highly effective tool. It completely eliminates the capacity for diplomacy in such matters."

"What's diplomacy got to do with it?"

"Don't be naive, dears. People aren't naturally inclined to tell the whole truth just like that. And then, she'll start to feel sorry for him, start trying to persuade him, and heaven forbid, even fall in love. We have had cases like that before, so we've learned the hard way."

"Don't forget to inject a good dose of caffeine," added the doctor.

"What is that for?"

"Makes her more talkative. It is best she gets it all out straight away, as soon as possible, says exactly what she thinks of him, and not like normal, hedging around it going sideways here and sideways there. Otherwise, the session could go on forever."

The girl had objected, they say, insisting that she would speak the whole truth anyway, that there was no point in it all and that she had nothing to hide, wishing only the best for her poor partner. It was, however, rigorously instilled in her that this part of the procedure was mandatory and impossible to avoid. In the end of course, she concurred. The nurse quickly did her job, sat the girl on a chair opposite the young man and stepped aside.

The unfortunate lad sat tied to the chair, staring at his beloved with his mouth sealed. She sat calmly opposite him for a while but then suddenly became much more energetic, jumped up from the chair and began to pace back and forth, gazing round at the tethered guy, who continued to follow her with his eyes. Then she began her monologue.

"Honey, don't look at me like that! You know we only want what's best for you! And it's not just me but all of us! It's for your own good! You are just sick, very, very sick! They say it's treatable and will soon pass! Of course, I am flattered by your feelings, but you must understand, you aren't worth loving, not even a little bit! Yes, I know, you've done so much for me and I'm grateful, I really am! I will shower you with gratitude! But that's not enough for you, is it? Yes, you're a good person and a loyal friend but I could not for a moment think of you as a lover! Stop looking at me like that! I'll say it again.You're not worth loving, not even a little bit! I'm saying this not to hurt you. I just want you to recover more quickly! I know, I often hurt you, but I am always quick to apologize. You know that. What more do you need? I promise, I will always, always hurt you and immediately apologize afterwards! Isn't that how things are meant to be? I swear I will shower you with generous apology and gratitude! I would never begrudge you that! And now I want to say something nice, I mean, I do really like you! But love you? I don't feel anything close!

And I just can't understand how my superficial flirting could have given you hope or groundsto...?"

The young man's eyes were filled with tears, but the girl was so wound up she showed no sign of backing off. Even the male and female nurses were casting glances at each other thinking it was time for her to stop.

"Listen, stop this now!" shouted the queen. "Can you really not see what a complete piss-take this is?"

"Don't get all worked up, dear. This is a treatment session. You asked to observe. It should be stopped although not because you demand it but because this patient is a serious case. The painless procedure is having no effect."

"You call this painless?" asked the queen, clearly indignant. "So, what do you call painful?"

"Right, untie him," the doctor commanded, oblivious. "Take him to intensive care, quickly!"

"Good lord, what do you intend to do to him?!"

"Nothing special. First, a course of electric shock therapy until he starts to settle down, then outpatient treatment with drugs, which will calm him down completely."

"You're planning on turning him into a vegetable?!"

"What on earth do you mean? We only use officially certified antidepressants and sedatives here. It is all very humane and for the good of the patient and society as a whole," said the doctor fixing the queen with a stare.

"My dear, it is quite clear that you are the one in need of treatment!"

"Your Majesty, I beg you, pretend nothing has happened, otherwise they might decide to calm us down, too," Cow whispered in the queen's ear. "Look, Beast has curled up into a ball. He's in love too, with you, and is afraid they might lock him away in here too."

"All right, you've convinced me. It probably would be for the best," the queen said keeping her voice calm.

"It's for the best, of course, it is. Of that have no doubt."

"So, what do you do if the patient turns out to be completely untreatable?"

"Oh, in that case, we have a special 'Happy Funeral' department."

"And what does that department do?" asked Brunhilda unable to hold herself back.

"Similarly, humane procedures. A completely painless injection is given, and the patient finally finds their happiness."

"So, what you're saying is, you kill them?"

"Why, of course! Judge for yourself. If a person is unable to find happiness in this life, who are we to torment them? Our motto is, 'have mercy!' We treat everyone who comes to us with the upmost humanity. And those who are stubborn and refuse to accept our help end up poisoning themselves, drowning, or they hang themselves ... Well, it's hardly very aesthetically pleasing, is it? Jumping from the skyscrapers and dirtying the asphalt? It's a complete disgrace. Now do you understand how humane the goal we are pursuing really is, and how important the mission is that we are carrying out?"

"Yes, yes, you may consider me finally fully enlightened," said the queen. "I agree, totally and completely."

"Well, there you have it! Now, if you do get sick, please, don't hesitate!"

"Absolutely!"

In the meantime, the young man had been released from the chair and forced into a straitjacket. The girl still was not letting up and wished him all the absolute best.

She, too, had to be taken by the arms and led into the 'relaxation room'.

"Come on everyone! It is time for us to get out of here," Eejit whispered, giving everyone the sign. "I am exceedingly grateful to you for such an instructive demonstration and lecture."

"Do come again. Always at your service!" said the doctor, clearly very pleased with herself, and led the entire delegation to the exit.

Once free, the company sighed amiably with relief and immediately hastened to get away from the institution under the guise of 'INSTHEALPROTHAPFUN'. Even once they had gained a reasonable distance, they carried on wandering for a long time, silent with their heads held low.

"Poisonous supervisor...," said Eejit finally. Even he was affected.

"I pity the guy," said Submarine.

"And they injected the girl with serum unnecessarily. She would have managed fine without it," added Cow.

"Okay, let's try approaching other institutions," said Brunhilda. "Only this time, we should be more careful."

Only Beast remained silent, lost in his own thoughts. With tacit consent, the team set out further on their search.

SHAGGY BEAST

Shaggy Beast had not uttered a word since the company left the mysterious spot where the lid ended and the other side of reality began, which they could not enter.

Beast saw something in the mirror there that astounded him so much that he did not know what to think or say, and so for this reason, he did not say anything to anyone. There, in his reflection, he saw something that was not quite himself, or rather, was him but in human form.

Despite the fact that his reflection, like that of everyone else, was vague and ghost-like, Beast could quite definitely make out a young man of pleasant appearance with large sad eyes, brown hair to the shoulders, and a suit of indeterminable era and nationality. He was wearing trousers and something between a coat and a long-sleeved blazer both in black velvet with large gold buttons, as well as a snow-white shirt with a ruffled frill. Strangely incongruous with his elegant suit, his feet were shod in shaggy loafers made of chestnut-colored wool.

Beast was in no doubt that the figure was he, but he could not understand how he could possibly look like that. In what kind of reality would he be capable of assuming that form?

Something similar had happened to Beast before. Beast had the gift of being able to remember his previous incarnations. He had never told anyone about this ability partly because he did not understand what the incarnations actually were: past lives, metamorphoses, or just dreams.

So, this was not the first time Beast had seen himself in a different guise and in a different reality, only never before had he seen himself as a handsome young man. By the will of some providence, as a rule, brutal characters befell him and even then, they were not always human. In this incarnation for example, it was not clear what he was: basically, animal but one of unspecified breed. He was of right mind, totally competent and if you looked in his eyes, you could even tell that he was endowed with extraordinary, spiritual qualities.

The recent 'love-killing' scene had affected him no less than the reflection in the mirror. Beast was lost in reminiscing about one of his recent incarnations, in which he lived his life as a lonely caveman.

More precisely, he did not become a hermit straight away. Before that, he lived among a primitive tribe of hunter-gatherers. The tribe was divided into humans and women. Women were not considered totally adequate or fully entitled. Humans decided it should be that way because they were stronger than women. It was not something they decided from the very outset. The idea came to them gradually as they began having thoughts, which was a rare occurrence.

In the beginning, women were human, too. But then humans turned their attention to the fact that women were more beautiful than they were. They looked and looked, and at some point, it occurred to them to ask, "Why are they so beautiful? And what about us, are we any less beautiful than they are?" And then they said to women, "Take off your new clothes. From now on you will wear old rags."

"Why?" the women objected. "That's unfair. We don't want to!"

"Then we'll beat you," answered humans.

"Okay, we agree. We understand."

But humans beat them anyway just to make sure they properly understood.

Then women began dressing in castoffs. But the rags laid bare their beautiful hands, legs, spine and chest and women aroused desire in humans. They looked and looked at them, and the thought came to their minds, "Why do we want them more than they want us? Are we any worse than they are? Can't we control ourselves? Or are we just depraved?' And then they said to women, "You are lustful. You are lascivious. Cover your wicked bodies. Cover everything up and don't show yourselves. You will only reveal yourselves when we allow you to."

"How come you decide everything and get to allow or disallow?" the women objected.

"Because we are stronger," humans answered.

"Then we won't give ourselves to you."

"If you are obedient, we'll gift you jewelry."

"And if we aren't?"

"We'll beat you."

"Okay, we agree, we understand," women said.

But people beat them anyway just to make sure they properly understood.

That was how they lived. Humans thought that they were clever, but they tried to decide everything for themselves and their decisions were not always crowned with success. In many ways, women were wiser than humans. Humans looked and looked at women and thought, 'Are we really any less clever or are we more stupid than they are?' And then they said to women, "You're stupid."

"Why do you think that?" asked women.

"Because we're smart."

"We're smart too."

"No, you're not. You're stupid. We're taking away your right to vote."

"But that's not fair!"

"Your opinion doesn't matter anymore."

"But that's unfair! It's wrong!"

"Well then, we'll just have to beat you."

"Okay, we agree, we understand," women said.

But people beat them anyway just to make sure they properly understood.

That was how they lived. There was plenty of work. They hardly had any free time. They all worked on equal terms and received equal reward, humans and women alike. People looked at them and looked and then the thought came to them, 'Why are they on a par with us as if they were no worse than us?' And then humans said to women,

"We are only going to hunt. You will do everything else: build homes, cook food, raise children, dress skins, make crafts, sew clothes and manage the rest of the household."

"Why?" asked women in surprise.

"Because hunting is more interesting, simpler and altogether easier," humans answered. "Because it suits us that way."

"But that's outrageous?! As if you were any better than us!"

"We are better than you."

"And if we refuse? If we won't?"

"Well then we'll just have to beat you."

"Okay, we agree, we understand," women said.

But people beat them anyway just to make sure they properly understood.

That was how they lived. People hunted while the women cooked and did everything else. If the hunt turned out to be unsuccessful and there was not enough food to go around, only humans ate. Women went hungry. Humans thought, 'We're the ones who bring back the bacon, after all. We're more important. That's just as it should be.' And as they ended up having quite a lot of free time, they sat ceremoniously on the humans' council and made important decisions. And so, humans looked at themselves and looked until the thought came to them, 'We are actually very important.' And then they said to women, "We are important humans. We are humans."

"So, who are we then? What kind of beings are we?" asked women.

"You are unimportant and inferior. You aren't humans."

Women did not bother objecting because that they knew that they would only be beaten if they did. But they were beaten anyway.

That was how they lived. Beast looked and looked at all this and said to humans,

"You're wrong. This is not right. You mustn't behave like this."

"You are not like us," humans said in surprise, and then they all began to stare at him.

"No, it's you who aren't like me."

"We're going to drive you out."

"No, I'm going to leave anyway," said Beast and went away to live by himself in a cave.

ABDUCTION OF THE WILD MAID

Beast's cave was nice and cozy. The entrance, a secluded spot in the foothills, was camouflaged by a dense, impassable bush. To access the cave, one had to crawl on all fours through a secret gap known only to Beast himself.

Occasionally, a passing illiterate prehistoric man or wild animal would stop at the edge of the undergrowth and stare at the bushes, dumbly thinking, 'Is there anything there? No. Looks like there might be something interesting there. No. Food of some kind? No. So, what am I doing standing here then? It's not like I'm stupid.' And with that, they would move on.

Beast's cave was like a studio apartment combining the living room, kitchen and bedroom into one spacious room. At the center he had a neatly laid stone hearth. Smoke from the fire rose up to a dome above and then through a crevice leading somewhere up and, evidently, out. It was all very practical. There was warmth, light and no offspring.

Bright resin torches on all four sides provided an additional source of light. Beast lit them sometimes to make things a little cheerier.

The floor was covered with straw, which he changed at least once a fortnight. This was also very practical because all the dirt and rubbish was swept out along with the old straw. The cave was kept clean and tidy. That was Beast's nature. Despite being shaggy, he was also very neat.

The cave even had a bathroom with a fitted shower. In one spot a spring emerged right from the wall bursting forth into a waterfall that poured down into a voluminous stone hollow from which the water flowed deeper into the depths of the cave. The cave itself stretched deep into the bowels of the mountain but Beast did not ever venture further in. The most distant recesses of the cave were dark and cold and of no interest to him.

No less importantly, there was always a bowl on the edge of the stone basin with a mixture of volcanic ash and clay to use as soap. It you wanted, you could take a shower, but if you wanted a bath instead, the water was not too cold and it had a pleasant flavor, perhaps even healing qualities.

Overall, it was a dwelling equipped with all the necessary amenities. The sleeping area was also arranged very comfortably. In the rock wall beside the hearth there was a wide, flat ledge luxuriously lined with thick, soft skins. Other animal skins were lain out across the corners to add a little more comfort. And everywhere, all kinds of horns and antlers hung from the walls as evidence of successful hunting, some branched and bent, others straight. There were necklaces hanging from the wall too made from claws and fangs. The fangs were large and scary, the claws long and sharp.

A special place was reserved for weapons used on animals of all markings. The spears were light and pointed. The axes weighty and made of flint. The bows were large and graceful. The knives made of obsidian, like razors. The arrows were sharp, their tips also of obsidian. The boar spears were impressive and convincing. The handles of all the weapons were solid and reliable so that they would not slip easily from one's grip.

Finally, in a separate corner, simple but useful utensils were neatly laid out: kitchen utensils, tools for dressing hides and sewing and other household items. Beast was an exceptionally capable caveman. There was nothing he did not have or know when it came to cave life. All he lacked was a companion, or rather, a girlfriend. He most definitely had no need of any other kind of companion since he disliked the so-called 'human' intensely.

So, Beast sad and lonely, concluded that he needed a woman. Why? He reasoned as follows: you can look at a woman. You can watch her walking, sitting and lying down. You can watch how she eats, bathes, combs her hair and preens herself. You can watch her messing about with household chores. You can watch her watching you. It would be so interesting to watch a woman. Right now, everything around him was the same. There was nothing worth looking at. He had even tired of watching the fire in the hearth that normally he could watch endlessly. Now if a woman were to appear, you would never get tired of looking at her if, of course, she wanted to look at you too.

You can touch a woman, touch her hair, shoulders and chest, stroke her back, arms and legs, hug her from behind, hold her and not let her go. Or you could face her and hold her pulling her tight. You could touch her and stroke her everywhere. A woman was nice because she had soft skin and all her parts were rounded, chubby and soft. This was how Beast reasoned with himself about having a girlfriend.

He also thought that it would be nice to take care of a woman, to feed her, clothe her and walk with her, to protect her from predatory animals and pesky people. He could bring her game, make her laugh, tug at her, play with her, make her mad and watch her get angry, and then immediately calm her down and console her, entertain her in lots of ways. He would figure out how when the time came.

Beast decided he needed to catch himself a woman. But how? Obviously, he had to steal, heist or kidnap one, whatever it took. He would catch her and drag her into his cave. Naturally, she would squeal and struggle so he would have to hold her tight and drag her to his place. It was all quite clear in his mind.

And so, Beast set out in search of a girlfriend. Search options were very few: either he would look in his former tribe or someone else's. As it was a long way to someone else's, he set off for his own. The tribal camp was located in a valley surrounded by mountains and forest. From time to time, Beast stopped along the way and listened. He had not gone far before he heard voices from somewhere in the distance. He headed in that direction.

A group of women were grazing in a forest glade gathering berries. The gathering was mainly done by young women who did not have small children. 'What luxury!' thought Beast staring at them wide-eyed. 'Fools. They don't guard their luxury. They don't value it.' He hid in the thicket and watched wondering which one to choose. Finally, his gaze fell on the one he liked the best. She was standing just on the edge of the glade.

Beast jumped suddenly into the clearing, grabbed hold of his victim, threw her across his shoulder and set off into the forest at speed. The rest froze in shock and fright, then started shouting, but no one rushed in hot pursuit of the kidnapper. Accustomed to occupying the position of the lower class, women did not know how to stand up for themselves.

Beast ran as far as he could. The woman he was carrying was not large, but she was not skinny either. She was nicely rounded which did not make her light. Of course, she kicked and yelled for the whole forest to hear. In contrast to the idyllic paintings 'Abduction of Proserpine', 'Europe' and 'Psyche', this primitive abduction scene was quite startling consisting of a shaggy savage in an animal skin with his prey, just as wild and also half-naked.

Having reached his lair, Beast lowered the woman to the ground and ordered her to climb into the narrow passage between the bushes that lead to the cave. To add a note of conviction, he gave her a shove from behind. She squealed but climbed through the passage even so. Once inside the cave, the woman began to look around her, still yelling.

Catching his breathe a little, Beast said, "What are you yelling for? I'm not going to eat you." But she did not stop. Then he grabbed her and pulled her tightly to his body. This calmed her down and finally she became quiet. Beast sat her on a soft skin, lit torches and busied himself with the hearth. The wild maid was still afraid, but she observed him with curiosity.

Beast thought he had a woman now and he could see that she was looking at him. How amazing! And he could look at her too, for as long as he liked and even touch her. Although, he had probably touched her enough for now. His first task was to feed her. Beast had plenty of supplies, but he wanted to treat his woman to something fresh and tasty.

Beast did not take long to get ready. He took a spear, bow and arrows and the knife which he always kept on his belt. He did not have to go far either. All his hunting was right here in the forest. He turned to the woman and said, “Sit here and don’t go anywhere. There are predatory animals all around us that scratch and bite. Do you understand?”

“Yes, my lord,” said the maid, her voice sounding human for the first time.

“And why are you so grimy? Go and wash. I have a whole pool here, see? And this is for you.” He handed her a beautiful bone comb for her hair.

She took the comb and with obvious pleasure began twirling it in her hands.

“I will be back soon,” said Beast and then he left the cave.

To feed a woman, you need the meat of fresh game. A new skin wouldn’t be bad either. Now there are two of us, Beast thought, and we’ll need more of everything.

The most suitable candidate for such a matter would be a dumb, horned animal. Beast knew where a dumb animal usually grazed, and headed in that direction, just nearby.

In order to hunt the animal, you had to creep up unseen and then jump out suddenly and spear him in the neck. That was the surest, quickest way. Beast started to creep cautiously into the clearing where the dumb animal was grazing. But unexpectedly, the whole mystery of the hunt was disturbed by a silly bird. For some reason, she became attached to Beast, whether out of curiosity or pure mischief-making, and totally betrayed his presence with her silly cries, “Kli-kli-kli”.

The bird was large, flightless and very silly. She ran around Beast on her long legs pecking at him and crying, “Kli, kli“. It was not clear what she wanted but either way, she had spoiled the hunt. Beast tried to drive the bird away, but she would not leave him alone. Trying to get free of the bird, Beast suddenly found himself in the clearing almost face to face with the animal.

The dumb animal was chewing grass and looking at Beast indifferently. ‘This won’t do,’ he thought. ‘What kind of hunting is this? No danger and totally uninteresting.’ Hunting in virgin forest was not exactly complicated. The forest was full of birds and animals and no-one was afraid of Beast. Annoyed, he had finally had enough and so he hit the bird on its silly head with his spear. The bird fell down dead before she had time to realize what was happening.

The dumb animal was not at all surprised by the scene that was playing out in the clearing and continued chewing its gum with complete indifference.'All right,' thought Beast. 'It's a big bird. There'll be plenty of meat. It's not bad game. And it'll probably taste good, too.'

He performed the game 'funeral' ritual as he usually did in such cases. He said to the bird, "You, silly bird, were a stupid bird, but now your soul will enter a higher being, maybe even a woman, a beautiful woman with smart eyes. And you will be smart and happy, a beautiful bird-woman."

Beast picked up his kill and hastened back to his cave and to his woman. He found her waiting for him already washed and combed sitting on the bed covered with soft skins.

"Hungry?" asked Beast.

"Yes, my lord," said the maid.

"Here, chew on this for now," he said and handed her the fruit of a sweet tree, which he had plucked along the way.

She took it and began to gnaw at the fruit enthusiastically looking at her master, who looked at her with pleasure while he prepared dinner.

Beast quickly plucked the bird and put it on a skewer above the fire. Soon, the delicious smelling dish was ready.

BEAST AND HIS WOMAN

Beast removed the bird from the skewer and began to feed his woman. He cut off the most succulent slices of meat and handed them to her. Beast did not eat. The most important thing was that she was eating and that she was looking at him. He enjoyed it very much and could not stop looking at her.

"Why aren't you asking me why I'm not eating?" Beast asked her.

"Why are you not eating, my lord?" she asked.

"Because I like to watch you eating."

Beast liked watching how woman ate very much because if woman was eating, it meant all was well and that counted for a lot because if a woman was eating, it meant that in that given moment there was food and shelter, and everything was calm and safe.

Having eaten to her heart's content, the wild maid settled down half-reclining on the many soft skins and began to observe what her lord was doing. Beast then fed himself and afterwards decided to make a soft pillow for his woman from the feathers of the bird, so that they would not we wasted and so that his woman would sleep comfortably.

Beast had stretches of carefully crafted leather, which he cut as needed. Then he took a bone needle and thread from thin fibers and sewed the pieces of leather into a pillowcase. Next, he filled the pillowcase with the feathers. There were enough to make a decent pillow, as his prey was a large bird with plenty of feathers and fluff. Then he sewed a pillowcase and he ended up with a good, soft pillow. Beast tried hard for his woman and busied himself with tasks all evening. When he had finished, he straightened out the pillow, gave it a good thump and then handed it to his woman.

"Here, this is for you."

Without saying a word, she took the pillow and quite content pressed it to her stomach.

It was time to go to sleep. Beast extinguished the torches, threw a thick lump of wood onto the fire and lay down on the bed. His woman lay down next to him. He liked that too, very much. He was no longer alone. His woman was lying next to him and looking at him.

"Put the pillow under your head. You'll be more comfortable," he said.But she hugged the pillow pressing it to her chest and lay there looking at him.

'A wild one', he thought, and said out loud, "As you like."

Beast carefully covered his woman with the best, most cozy hide and then covered himself with another, a little flatter. No sooner had he done this than the maid was already falling asleep contented and reassured. He gently stroked her hair and lay looking at her for a long time listening to the sound of her breathing. He smiled to himself and then he too fell asleep.

The next day, Beast decided that he should clothe his woman. She was wearing some old rags that barely covered her body. He gathered his things and said,

"I'm going to hunt a wild, fluffy beast. Don't go anywhere without me. Wait for me here. Keep the fire burning."

"Yes, my lord," said the maid.

"I'll be on my way then."

And so, Beast went in search of a wild, furry beast, from whose skin he could sew clothes for his woman. The wild, furry animal lived in the trees and hunted birds. It was quite a large animal with a beautiful, soft fur but it was also very dangerous. It scratched hard and its bite was painful. Catching it was difficult. You could not kill it with an axe or reach it with a spear. You could only manage to shoot it with a bow and arrow and even that was tricky as it was a very mobile animal.

As usual, Beast did not have to search long, and the hunt soon turned into a fast-moving encounter. Beast again came across another silly bird although naturally, a different one this time. The silly bird was standing under a tree with its head up, its legs apart and its wings crumpled, and it cried, "Kli-kli-kli!" And why was she crying? Because on a branch up above, there was a wild, furry beast. The beast swayed and swayed and then jumped on bird breaking her neck instantly. Beast quickly took aim from his bow and arrow and shot the wild, furry beast right in the head so as not to spoil the skin. In that same moment, another wild, furry beast with clawed paws suddenly appeared out of nowhere and attacked. Beast instantly grabbed his knife and slashed the wild animal's throat, but not before it had managed to scratch hard at Beast with its claws.

'Bloody hell,' thought Beast standing above his trophies. 'The second one was probably trying to protect his woman, and accepted death alongside her. And what a silly bird! It was like she was deliberately seeking death. Maybe she wanted to be reincarnated quicker?'

Beast honored his prey as always, "You, wild animals, were furry animals, and now you will become fair, noble people. You will protect women and bring them game. And you, forest bird, you were a silly, unthinking bird but you will become smart and wise. Be now whoever you want to be."

Beast removed the skins from the animals, threw them over his shoulder, grabbed the bird by its legs and set off with large strides back to his cave, to his woman. He was lucky. Instead of one animal, he had killed two and there was the bird to boot, a tasty one too. The only downside was the deep cuts the wild animal had left on his body. Beast gathered medicinal herbs on his way back with which to treat his wounds.

The maid met him when he returned to the cave and examined the spoils with interest. She paid no attention to Beast's scratches. Neither did she pay much attention when Beast treated his wounds by applying ointment on them made from ground herbs. But still, as before he prepared dinner quickly and managed to deal with his own problems, also. Once again, he fed his woman first and watched her eat.

When the time came to sleep, they lay down together and the maid easily dropped off again snuffling blissfully.

And again, Beast lay there watching her, smiling to himself and he listened to her breathing even softly touching her shoulders and chest very quietly, so as not to wake her up. The woman adorned his life. Nothing else mattered.

The next few days were spent making clothes for the woman. The skins of the furry animals had to be dried and worked very carefully so that they became soft and pleasant to touch. When Beast tried pieces of skin up against the woman for size, which he did quite often, no doubt on purpose, he took the opportunity to hug her and pull her to him. She did not pull away from him, but she did not express any reciprocity either.

However, Beast was content with the fact that there was now a woman in his life who he could hug and pull to him, at least sometimes. Moreover, his life was now filled with pleasant cares and encouraging concerns. There was new meaning to his existence. He had a goal.

Beast worked diligently and dutifully on the clothing for his woman. And finally, the moment came when the masterpiece of couture was ready. The result was a pair of cute knee-high pants and a jacket with sleeves that came to the middle of the forearm. Dressed in the outfit, the wild maid did not look quite so wild. Naturally, she was pleased, or rather, very pleased but she was most pleased with Beast. It was even more pleasant to hug and stroke his woman now that she was wearing a soft, fluffy, fur coat.

Now that his girlfriend was dressed up, Beast took her out for the first time. Once they were out of the cave, he took her by the hand and led her along a winding path halfway up the mountain. There they sat on a high cliff and admired the panorama of the forest valley, nestled among the mountains in the rays of the setting sun.

As they sat watching the sunset, Beast gently put his arm round his woman's shoulders and waist. As before, she did not seem to mind, but she did not respond with any affection. When they went to bed, Beast could not fall asleep for a long time wondering how to get his hot, and at the same time cold, woman to reciprocate. He decided that he should make her a gift of some jewelry.

But how would he get it? Steal some from other women? No, that would not do. He'd make something himself. But first, he had to find some stones, beautiful, semiprecious stones. There were beautiful, semiprecious stones at the very top, at the very crown of the mountain, but they would be very difficult to reach. Nonetheless, Beast was decided, and he set off the very next day.

So, he climbed to the very peak, to the crown of the mountain. The path was not easy and ran across steep slopes, screes and narrow paths on the edge of high cliffs. At one point, Beast almost fell into an abyss and injured his arms and legs which were covered in blood, but he still reached the top and found his semiprecious stones. He chose some of the most beautiful among them, placed them inside his leather bag and made his way back to his cave, to his woman.

As usual, the woman was waiting for him sitting on a soft hide beside the fire. Beast dumped the stones from his bag before her.

"Look, this is all for you," he said. Her eyes lit up. "Do you like them?" he asked her.

"Yes, my lord," said the maid clearly delighted.

'Maybe now her heart will melt,' thought Beast who was tired but set to treating his wounds. The maid sorted through the semiprecious stones examining each one without giving a thought to where they had come from and paying no attention to her lord's misfortune.

So, there you have it. Beast worked hard for several days trying to make the best and most beautiful things for his woman that one could possibly make in such conditions. Finally, the work was finished, and the solemn moment came. Beast adorned his woman's ankles and wrists with bracelets and hung a necklace at her neck.

The maid was more pleased than ever. She walked back and forth in the cave admiring her jewels and showing her lord how beautiful she looked in them. And Beast enjoyed it all, too. However, a long-forgotten sadness and longing took root in his soul again and he felt lonely despite the fact that his woman was with him.

When they went to bed, she did not fall asleep straight away but carried on showing him her ankles and hands admiring her own beauty. And then he asked her, "Do you miss home?"

"No, my lord," said the maid.

"Why do you keep calling me that, you silly thing!" said Beast, unable to contain himself. "I'm not your lord."

He hugged her and pressed his lips to her hair which smelled of the forest. He buried himself in her hair and lay there, pulling his woman close. She, too, lay quietly but after a few moments he heard the same old sniffing.

PUNISHED BY LOVE

Beast did not sleep all night, tossing and turning with all that was on his mind. The next morning, he fed his woman and said, "I can't do this anymore. I'm taking you back to the camp. Pack your things."

"Why, my lord?" asked the maid surprised. "I don't want to go."

"Do you love me?" he asked her.

"Yes, my lord," said the maid.

"You're lying. You love what I have and the things I give you."

"But my lord, I like being with you."

"Of course, you do! You like it here because I take care of you, but I can't live with someone who is indifferent towards me. You're more likely to love someone who beats you. Come on, let's go."

The maid burst into tears. However, Beast had made his decision and was not to be placated. He handed her the pillow and gently pushed her towards the exit.

They walked through the forest in silence. The maid trudged onwards her head drooping and the cushion held to her stomach letting out a sob from time to time. Beast's mood was darker than the clouds. He understood that what he was doing was cruel and that he was behaving badly.

What he was doing was making him feel bad and making her feel very bad, but he could see no other solution. It hurt, a lot but it would hurt even more to be with her and constantly be reminded of her indifference towards him.

Beast led her to a spot from where the tribe's camp was visible and from there, she carried on alone. Beast turned around and walked slowly and entirely without enthusiasm back to his cave where his woman would no longer be. She used to be there, but she was not there anymore. He literally felt physically ill but could not behave otherwise. He did not know how. The only justification he could see was that at least she had not pretended to make it look as if he meant something to her. But she had not even tried.

He was just sorry that humans would take everything from her, the jewelry, the pillow, the jacket and pants. He felt sorry for her, but it was her own fault. But what was he to blame her for? What had she done to him? Failed to pretend that she loved him? And why should she pretend? And why was she obliged to love him? Simply because he had done something for her? Do we really fall in love for a specific reason or for the sake of a thing?

* * *

Awakening from his reminiscing, Shaggy Beast found himself wandering numbly amongst the team of 'Expedition Lid', which continued its search for a solution to the lid problem.

His memory of what happened after breaking up with his girlfriend and how he had lived on alone in his cave was a blur. All he could remember was that he constantly blamed himself for behaving badly, immorally, and that when he wasn't blaming himself, he was justifying himself. As a result, his heart had hardened, and this appeared to be the reason why he had acquired his current bestial appearance. That said, he had not yet lost the ability to love.

And yet he had become the type that it would be hard for anyone else to love. What were his chances with Brunhilda? It was ridiculous. It was as if the Creator were purposely punishing him for behaving so unattractively back then. And no doubt, it was punishing him so that Beast would finally come to understand something. After all, he still did not understand why love is given, how it arises or why one sometimes loves another who is unable to love them back?

Was there anyone in the world who could answer of all these questions? Perhaps, when it came to love, there were no answers to all our how's and why's? Maybe love had to be taken as it was. Maybe you had to love unconditionally without asking any questions? Yet if you couldn't ask questions, might it not be better not to love at all? And still, love does not ask 'can you love?' or 'do you want to love'. It simply hits you like a disease, and then 'it's your own problem' as they say.

Disease? The recent 'love-killing' therapy session sprang up in Beast's mind and he recalled the words which had made the deepest impression on him as if they were meant for him personally: 'you aren't worth loving, not even a little bit'.

And so, still torturing himself with depressing thoughts, Beast drudged along silently in the company of our friends.

His reverie was interrupted by the sudden noise of a siren, which sounded like an ambulance. In that moment, the vehicle turned the corner, hung with flashing beacons, like a Christmas tree. Having caught up with the little company, it braked sharply and stopped.

"Oh look, it's that same crazy doctor!" exclaimed Yellow Submarine.

The female doctor climbed out of the ambulance and addressed them, arms akimbo.

"Ah, my old friends, interns! Where are you headed? I have been having doubts about... I think one of you might be sick after all. I had my suspicions at the time but somehow overlooked it," she said, staring at Beast. As she spoke, two strapping male nurses appeared from behind her.

"You are deeply mistaken, dear colleague," answered Eejit, speaking for them all, well-practiced in giving the run-around. "We are all perfectly healthy and very far from suffering the disease that comes under your profile."

"But this one, the shaggy one, is he healthy in your opinion? Just how much of a state can a person get themselves into! He's clearly a case of acute relapse!"

"Yes, indeed, our comrade just went a little over the top yesterday. What he needs now is a sobering-up station, not your very respectable shock therapy."

Beast gave Eejit an angry, side-long glance but he was prudent enough not to say anything. They were all in danger of getting into major trouble and the doctor was not letting up.

"You can't fool me. I can smell the sick a mile away."

Eejit made an attempt to change the topic of conversation.

"And where are you rushing from and to, may I ask?"

"We've picked up a very dangerous patient. Fortunately, conscious citizens reported it in time. Imagine, we found the patient loitering in the street all disheveled and reading poetry in what can only be described as a state of total inadequacy. A patient like this might infect another at any time."

"Ah, yes, imagine!" said Eejit piling on the charm. "It is so good that you are always on guard for public health. Would it be possible to let us have a quick look at the patient as an appropriation of your valuable experience? After all, we are young trainees, and obliged to take our example from you!"

"Well, all right then, in that capacity, yes, I suppose so, look."

The doctor opened the ambulance door. Inside sat a young but crestfallen woman. She was reading the same poems over and over, rocking her body and looking into nowhere.

'I have stopped smiling,
The icy wind freezes my lips,
One hope less,
One song more morose.
And this song, I unwittingly give
to mockery and defiance
Because it is beyond all bearing –
The pain of a loving soul's silence.'*

---

* A. Akhmatova

“You see what the disease can lead to!” The doctor said, admonishing her ‘trainees’. “The poetry is also sick, but at least it speaks the truth. The less silly hopes, the healthier songs there will be, and we shall all live in a happier, healthier society. And so, your lips don’t freeze you must dress warmly and use lip balm. And anything that is unbearably painful, we will fix and instantly put right.”

From then onwards, events developed so rapidly that the doctor and the nurses, were completely dumbfounded, and barely had time to think let alone move. The whole team froze in amazement, too. Right before their eyes, Beast’s appearance suddenly transformed, just like in the movies. It’s one thing to see it in the movies, but in reality, it looked far from real. In a matter of moments, the shaggy monster was transformed into an attractive, young man with brown hair to his shoulders, dressed in a black velvet suit with gold buttons and a snow-white shirt.

Of all those present, only Beast failed to notice his transformation. What he saw behind the ambulance door made his heart freeze. It was his woman! No, it could hardly be her, that very same woman, for how many millennia had passed since then? And yet he could remember himself in those times and he was here, too, albeit in a different form. Was it really possible that it could be she? And could it really be that she too had been punished, and had in some incomprehensible way found herself here with the same problem?

There was no time to stand there thinking, trying to work it out. Beast, or rather his new ‘release’, grabbed the woman, threw her over his shoulder, and just like the last time, ran away with her for as long as his strength would allow ...

STOPPING THE DREAM

If it ever happens that the reader dozes off with this book in his hands and then wakes up suddenly remembering that while he was sleeping he dreamed of the measured rustle of waves falling onto a sandy shore where a light breeze swayed palm trees , where the hot airs tremored in a haze, where wakefulness imperceptibly flew into half-forgottenness and reality into a dream, then maybe that reader will be lucky enough to see a certain boundary, beyond which another world begins, a world that is immeasurably enormous in comparison to that tiny island of material reality, which we think of as the infinite universe.

And if this is the case, then, perhaps, the same reader will also be lucky enough to spot two individuals on the same side of the mirror, both of eccentric appearance, trying in vain to pass through to this side of the mirror. One individual has her face painted in ritual crimson face paint, her hair in a black bob and is wearing a long dark-velvet dress with a diamond collar. The second individual has blue theater makeup on her face, turquoise-colored hair and a green jumpsuit with a large pink bow attached to waist level at the back. The careful observer will in fact genuinely see diva Matilda and priestess Itfut in the mirror mirage because everything that is happening in the here and now is happening there, simultaneously, for no temporal distance exists between that word and this.

We left the diva and the priestess beside the mirror after their unsuccessful attempts to break out of meta-reality, in which they found themselves by the will of providence. The friends had not yet fully come back to their senses after the shock of having acquired a second name, when they noticed disturbing changes once again taking place in their environment.

The light of day which came from who knows where because the sun was absent from the sky, was replaced with twilight. But it was not like the normal twilight, when it gets dark and day gradually turns into night. Dusk poured into the atmosphere in streaks and stains, like ink dripped into water. The dark stains were absorbed quickly by the illuminated space, as if darkness were a material substance.

"Futi, what's going on?" exclaimed Matilda. "I'm afraid."

"Aren't you tired of being afraid?" answered Itfut. "I'm getting used to it."

"True to your usual style, I see! You talk about fear as if it were a class or occupation!"

"But it is. You're currently occupied with being afraid."

"Well, aren't you?"

"No, I'm scared."

"Isn't that the same thing?"

"No, when I am afraid, I'm in a panic, whereas when I am scared, I am on the verge of putting myself back."

"Putting yourself back where?"

"The question is not where but into what. I put myself back together into one mass ready to face the danger head on."

"You'd be better off putting me back together!" squealed Matilda, trying to drive the smoke-like darkness away from her body. "And no, I'm not tired of being afra-a-id!"

"Tili-Tili, look how interesting it is!" As Itfut ran her hand through the dark stain a luminous trail stretched beyond her hand. Then she fully entered the swirling darkness and began turning in circles. Her entire figure was instantly lit up with a bright aura.

"Futi, I'm not remotely interested in your tricks! You won't be able to reassure me. This time something terrible is going to happen!"

"Okay, okay! You did say that whatever happens here, it's always terrible. But we are still alive and well, aren't we?"

"Futi, I am amazed you can be so calm."

In a matter of seconds, the clouds of semi-gloom had filled the entire space. Only on the side of the mirror that belonged to physical reality did the seascape shine resembling a cheery screen in a dark cinema hall.

"You see," said Itfut, "whether you want to or not, you've got to calm down. You can't carry on worrying about something that has already happened and is continuing to unfold."

"Yes, I can! Yes, I can!" said Matilda, unrelentingly.

"All right Tili, that's enough. Just imagine that night has come."

"But what are we going to do now?"

"Let's go back to the megalith."

"I'm afraid to go there. It's dark and sca-a-ry!"

"But inside, it'll be light and there'll be food, if you hadn't forgotten."

“Really?” said Matilda in surprise as if she were receiving this for the first time. “Food? I could really do with something to eat right now.”

“Let’s go then, one step at a time. We can see everything around us, and it’s not scary at all, not at all scary.”

Itfut took hold of Matilda’s hand and led her along like a child. After that Matilda calmed down considerably and obediently followed the priestess. Even though it was dark, they could still make out the space around them. The contours of nearby buildings blackened, and among them the megalith tower stood out in an even fuller black silhouette. The friends’ figures were shrouded in luminous auras, which gave the eerie night walk a shade of fantasy romance.

“That’s what you are, Tufti,” said Matilda. “A brave priestess. If it was not for you, I would just lie down and die.”

“Tili, don’t call me by my second name for the sake of it. You can use it but only in special circumstances. And I will do the same with yours.”

“Why? What for?”

“I get the impression that here our second names have a kind of magical meaning. When I heard mine for the first time, a flurry of memories and knowledge flashed through my mind but then it all disappeared just as suddenly and my memory was all a fog again. And now, when you called me by my second name, I remembered what I know about the world of dreams.

“And what’s that?”

“You remember me telling you before that meta-reality, where we are now, and the space of dreams are the same thing? Our attention zooms off into this space when we're dreaming, only now, we're here not only in our focus of attention but in our bodies too."

"Okay, and so?"

"A dream only spins when it has an observer. When there is no observer everything in this world is static, like a still image. All events and eras are frozen into one endless landscape. There is no flow of time. But as soon as the dreamer's awareness enters the space, the image comes to life. Attention sets time in motion, or rather in meta-reality time only manifests as a flow when attention flies into this space and watches."

"Woot-la! Like in a movie, right? It's shot on a film roll and there it stays - still, but when we watch, it starts to move."

"Yes, only I don't understand. Why have all these gray mannequins stopped moving? They are the characters in a dream and the dream should be turning since we are here as observers."

"Yes, but not everything has stopped here. There is always something happening, even the glamrocks and the water are moving, as you saw for yourself. It's just all slowed down."

"But why isn't our time in sync with their time?"

"God knows. When I woke up, I was fine, but they were standing there like statues."

"They froze when I appeared, I think. When I first found myself here, I got the sense that time stood still."

"What were you doing in reality, just before that moment? Do you remember?"

"No."

"Try, Tufti, try to remember!"

"Tufti-Tufti, priestess-priestess, what were you doing?" said Itfut talking to herself. "Hang on, Ilit, what were you doing with the mirrors in the theatre? Hum, it feels really odd using your second name... It's like I'm talking to your double."

"To my reflection, you mean? We installed mirrors on the floor and the walls so that the viewer would not be able to tell what was real and what was imaginary. Something like that."

"You can't joke with mirrors. Reality itself is mirror-like. She does not like it when we play with her models. She can play jokes too, but her jokes aren't that funny, as you found out."

"Yes, you're probably right. I also know that reality does not like it when you stare at her intently."

"How's that?"

"There's a concept in quantum mechanics. It's called the uncertainty principle."

"Tili, wherever did you learn ink-horn terms like that? I would not have had you down as someone who was into quantum mechanics."

"Yup! But I'm not Tili now, I'm Ilit! I had a boyfriend once, a physics student, and he told me all sorts of things. I did not understand it all back then, but I did remember some of it."

"Go on then, spill the beans."

"So, the principle of uncertainty consists in the fact that if you stare at reality, it slips away from you."

"How do you mean, 'slips away'?"

"It does not want to show itself, its true essence. For example, if you try to work out what a ray of light consists of to the tiniest detail, you can't. It pretends to be a continuous stream but then it turns out that it travels in portions, in quanta. And the more carefully you consider what light is, the more incomprehensible it becomes.

"Tili, that's amazing! And I've remembered too!" Itfut let go of her friend's hand and began to twirl, like she did whenever she was thrilled about something and a trail of glowing vortex instantly extended out behind her dress.

"I remember, I remember!"

"Futi, you're scaring me again! Give me your hand! Can you speak calmly?"

"Okay, okay. Before I ended up here, I was busy staring very closely at reality."

"In what sense?"

"There is this magical practice. When you are in that borderline state between sleep and waking, the true nature of reality can be revealed to you."

"And something revealed itself to you?"

"Yes, I saw reality moving, only not in a continuous stream but in portions, like what you were saying about light."

"Really? Come to think of it, a movie is also made up of individual frames."

"And how do you watch a movie, scene by scene?"

"No, the film roll turns very quickly and the frames merge into continuous motion, even flickering imperceptibly as they turn."

"So, your movie is a model of reality. It all fits. Reality likes to be discrete. That's what I saw!"

"Interesting. So, you made reality angry because you took her by surprise during a costume change and for that she dropped you here?"

"Yes. Reality does not want to reveal the secrets to how her movie is shot. But I still don't understand why the dream froze."

"Ah, well, it's probably that same principle of uncertainty. Reality tries to slip away when you look at her or she might completely freeze, like a beetle does when you pick it up."

"So that's it! Tili, you're really not the bimbo you sometimes seem."

"Bimbo-ninny yourself!"

"If we return to my world, we'll make you a priestess."

"Humbly grateful, I'm sure. But I don't want to be a priestess, I want to be an ordinary girl."

"Impossible. You're too unusual. All right, you'll be a diva then. We also have something like your theater."

"Really? I'd like that but let's continue. What is it you were saying about observers?"

"Our attention is the observer," said Itfut. "Here in the dream space, our attention sets the movie running and watches it as if it were a dream. In reality, on the other side of the mirror, it's the opposite, the movie runs of its own accord and our attention lives within it."

"Like a character in a movie?" asked Matilda.

"Yes, we are characters both there and here."

"Then what's the real difference between here and there?"

Itfut thought for a moment.

"You know, I don't think there is a fundamental difference. I haven't figured it all out yet. Reality slips away as you put it when you try and figure her out. You could roughly say that on that side everything is physical and material whereas here it's all virtual."

"And yet, we're in our bodies here, aren't we?"

"All I can say for certain is that we are in our own mannequins. The difference between the material and the immaterial is also approximate. After all, in a dream, all objects we touch feel solid if, of course, one's attention is positioned within the mannequin. I have not met my mannequin yet. I got here by walking through a wall."

"What about me? Is my real body here or did it stay there on the other side?"

"Judging by the fact that your Victor lamented, 'where are you, my Tili, my darling', your body was not found. As for me, I don't know. We only saw my statue. If my body had remained there, they would have buried it."

"Futi, does that mean you won't be able to get back there?"

"No! I will return, I will! Reality can arrange anything it wants to. You just have to come to an agreement with her and come to an agreement we will, of that you may have no doubt!"

OBSERVERS AND CHARACTERS

"Wow," gasped Matilda, finding herself inside the megalith finally. "Right horror! Horror, right!"

"Now we're home," said Itfut.

After the eerie walk through the darkness, which as it turned out, might have been viscous, the friends returned to the place where they began their stay in meta-reality.

"Futi! If this is our home, then things aren't looking great."

"All right! All right! At least it's light in here, and see? The table and chairs are still here, and they'll feed us again I'm sure."

They approached the black cylinder and sat down at the table to rest.

"Now it's your turn." said Matilda. "You will feed me, and I will treat you."

"What do you mean, 'treat me'" asked Itfut.

"You'll see. Go on, try and give the cylinder your menu. I want to try your home dishes."

"What if it does not work?"

"Tufti, the brave priestess! You surprise me. How can you be so bold in an emergency and now, when there is nothing to fear, so indecisive?"

"And you, Ilit the wise diva, do you not understand that this is how it is meant to be? In emergencies, normal people fall asleep, whereas those who see reality do the opposite and wake up. You are a seer too, Tili."

"It has nothing to do with dreaming! I just start to lose it when I feel I'm in danger."

"Exactly! You're beside yourself, which means, you're not properly in yourself. Panic is a kind of trance too. When you aren't properly in yourself, you have no self-control."

"True, that's true. When I lose it, I am controlled by fear or anxiety, anger or resentment."

"Almost but actually the emotions only immerse you in the dream. It's the movie you get immersed in that really controls you."

"I'm being controlled by a movie? That's an interesting thought, a rather strange thought..."

"There's nothing strange about it. Don't you remember? We were talking about the observers and the characters just now. Once in the dream space, attention runs the movie and watches it like a viewer. In reality, it's the opposite: the movie runs by itself and attention lives inside it like a fictional character."

"Yes, you did say that. We're characters, both there and here. It's hard to believe though."

"You're still finding it hard to believe even after everything you've experienced?"

"I just can't get my head round the idea of being a character in a movie."

"Then be an observer instead! To stop being one of the characters, you have to wake up. Your emotions should arouse you, not lull you into sleep. It's a kind of habit only it works the other way around."

"You have this habit it turns out then, Futi? I'd like to have that habit too."

"You can acquire it, too, if you try."

"And what would trying look like?" asked Matilda.

"In my country, people who see, learn to develop this reverse habit," replied Itfut. "The moment something scares you, alarms you, pisses you off, then instantly, instead of indulging in your passions like in a dream you wake up and begin to act with conscious awareness. Unlike an emotional trance, a state of awareness enables you to act decisively, correctly and clearly."

"But that way, you could end up turning into a marble statue, without emotion, without passion..."

"Who says you have to suppress your emotions? Express your stormy passions to your heart's content. Be fearful, angry and full of hate but be aware of it."

"Wonderful! But how does that work? How can I be afraid, angry or full of hate with awareness? Deliberately you mean?"

"No, not deliberately but with awareness. Don't get the two confused. To be in a state of awareness means to be in full charge of your senses and able to be completely responsible for what you are doing. You can do what you want. The most important thing is to observe yourself while you are being afraid, angry, and full of hate. Own your attention. Track where it is focused and to whom it belongs, to you or to the movie in which you are immersed. When you can control where you direct your attention, you have self-control."

"Futi, you talk about things that are simple and obvious but with you they become totally unobvious! Are you starting to remember your Knowledge?"

"Yes, some things are gradually becoming clearer in my mind as Threshold promised."

"This state of awareness you're talking about. How do you acquire it?"

"Very simply. You just have to engage your Witness."

"What's that exactly?"

"It's paying attention to attention itself, like a kind of superstructure. The witness can track what your attention is focused on, where it is: inside yourself, in your thoughts, or outside, in your everyday reality. In ordinary people, the Witness is almost always sleeping, so they pay no attention to what their attention is immersed in. In those who see, it's the opposite, the moment something happens, the slightest waft in their space and their Witness is instantly awakened and drags their attention out of the immersion zone and up into the awareness center: I see myself and I see reality."

"So that's how it works!" exclaimed Matilda. "I think I understand now! I really can see where my attention lies. And I can see reality and myself within reality both at the same time. Wow! I can observe myself!"

"That's right," said Itfut. "When you observe yourself, your Witness is activated. It stops sleeping, and you are aware of your actions. It's not difficult to activate your Witness, just like that, whenever you want to. What is difficult is to include it in a 'situation'. A situation absorbs your attention. You forget and fall into a dream, a trance."

"Yes, wow! That's true! So how do you learn to activate it in time?"

"Set yourself the goal of doing that. Literally set yourself the goal. Say to yourself, 'I will wake up every time something happens or when something is getting me down or when something goes wrong in my external reality.'

"Okay, from now on, as soon as anything happens, I'll wake up straight away. What next?"

"You see yourself and you see reality. You are fully aware of your actions. You can be afraid, enraged, fuming...anything, as long as you are being consciously aware, observing yourself and reality."

"And what's the benefit?"

"I'll tell you what the benefit is. It returns you to yourself. In this state of awareness, you can cope with any problems that come your way and act impeccably in any situation."

"Wonderful! That's it. I'm going to do it. I want to be like that! How long will I have to practice?"

"Until the habit of falling asleep becomes the opposite, the habit of waking up. You have to push yourself at first. It's like cleaning your teeth. At first, you're too lazy to, then you make yourself do it a couple dozen times and then it becomes a habit and the procedure runs of its own accord no longer feeling like it's a chore."

"Great! And it's all so simple! A helpful habit. It's even better than learning to develop willpower or some other skill. You don't have to feel like your squeezing something out of yourself. It's easy to do because it's a habit. Brilliant!"

"Yes, yes, yes, that's exactly it, that's it exactly!"

"We even have a saying that goes, 'Good habits are better than good manners'. And there's another that goes, 'a smart person can be called a fool on account of a bad habit'.

"Pithy sayings. I'll remember them."

"Futichka, let's eat now," said Matilda and then got up and went over to the cylinder. "We've been chatting so much. Although with you any little chat can turn into a philosophical discussion."

"I don't like to philosophize," replied Itfut, also rising from her chair. "I prefer things to be empirical."

"All right then, so feed me! As you say, quickly-quickly!"

"Tili-Tili, you're testing me! I really am afraid that it might not work."

"Then be afraid and observe yourself. Teee-hee! "Don't worry, Futi. It can't not work. You're a priestess after all!"

"But I don't have a bow like you."

"Give over! You know the bow has nothing to do with it. It's some kind of trigger-lever thing. What did you call it?"

"I have forgotten what it's really called and how to use it. Tell me again what you do with your bow."

"I don't actually do anything with the bow as such. It just reminds me of something, a kind of sensation in my spine area."

"What kind of sensation and where do you feel it exactly?"

"It's somewhere behind my shoulder blades, perhaps a little lower about half a forearm's width out from the spine and it gives me a kind of heavy feeling. I can't really explain it any better than that. You know, try this. Imagine something pushing from the middle of your chest through your body towards the back, through your spine and then coming out the other side. It does not matter what it is, it's just to give you an idea of the feeling. Then hold on to that sensation in your back and imagine what you want."

"Okay, I'll give it a try."

Barely had Itfut spoken these words than the cylinder started buzzing and ledge-like segments emerged from it, each carrying a different dish.

"Tufti-Tufti!" cried Matilda. "Priestess-priestess, wow! And there you were complaining, 'I'm afraid! I can't!' How come you managed it so quickly?"

"It was just spontaneous, like a random thought. While you were describing what to do, I was imagining and feeling it, and then I imagined a table covered in delicious dishes as if we were getting it ready for a celebration."

"Wow! What a delicious range of dishes! It all looks really swanky!"

"Quite, quite! Try some."

Matilda picked up two plates and sat down at the table.

"Well, there you have it! It not only looks tasty, it is tasty. What's this one?"

"Seaweed, specially prepared."

"Who would have thought it. And what's this? A crustacean of some kind?"

"Yes, our diet is mainly based on plants and seafood."

"Yum, Futi, this is way too delicious. I can't compete with this."

THE TRIGGER-JIGGER

They both tried a little of all the dishes in turn until they were full.

"Well, thank you for feeding me," said Matilda. "We're living the good life! If they let us go to the sea as well, we could really live life."

"First you say, 'we're living', and then 'we could really live'. It's funny. Give it time. We're only just beginning to test our capabilities. There'll be more to come."

"Yes, and our capabilities are fabulous!"

"Tili, thank you for helping me activate my trigger-jigger. I'll remember the feeling from now on and be able to use it."

"My dear Futichka, Futi!" Matilda said moving closer to the priestess and giving her a hug. "You have done so much more for me and still are doing! I would have been completely finished without you."

"I wouldn't have lasted long here without you either. It's so amazing that we met and that we complement each other so well!"

"Itfut, you said something before about 'random thoughts'. Can you remind me, what do you mean exactly by a 'random thought'?"

"You can't control reality by using will power, by giving orders, making requests or even through prayer. Reality is controlled by a random thought, the kind that arises fleetingly, unobtrusively," said Itfut.

"Does that kind of thought arise all by itself, then?"

"Sometimes, spontaneously, yes, but you can create one deliberately, too. If you want something desperately, passionately, then you have to turn that desire into a random thought."

"And yet I can activate the cylinder without creating a random thought."

"That's in the megalith. Here everything is easier to achieve. Reality is much more complicated. It turns out. The same goes for meta-reality, too."

"But when I was being 'led to the slaughter', I wished desperately, vehemently, that everything would be alright with me, and then it was."

"You used your trigger-lever. Of course, desperate desire can work as well but random thoughts combined with the trigger-lever work more powerfully."

"I still don't understand exactly what you mean by a random thought," said Matilda.

"I don't fully remember myself yet. All I know is that reality does not like being given orders and is indifferent to our pleas. A random thought is not a desire, a command or a request. It's more like an allowing, a permitting. Reality is like a child. She likes being allowed to do whatever she wants."

"So, I have to tell her that I permit her to manifest what I want?"

"Not what you want but what reality wants. You have to make her want the same thing as you."

"And how do you do that?"

"I can't explain it. Intuitively, I feel that a random thought arises somewhere from behind you, which is why, I suppose we think of random thoughts as originating somewhere at the back of the mind."

"The trigger-lever is at the back, too! Well, not right on the back... a bit behind it. Maybe it's something located in the subtle energy body?"

"You know about subtle bodies, Tili?" asked Itfut in surprise.

"Well, yes. I heard something somewhere about the aura and all that. Only 'all that' is still very little studied."

"It's better studied in our world but sadly, I still don't remember much."

"Don't worry Futi, Knowledge will gradually return to you. Threshold promised. You've already revealed so much to me that I had never even thought about before."

"All right, all right, all will be revealed in due course. Have you forgotten that you promised to give me a treat? I kept my side of the agreement. Now it's your turn."

"No, I haven't forgotten. I haven't forgotten," Matilda replied, teasing Itfut imitating her manner of speaking. "Now, now, one treat coming up." Out of habit, Matilda straightened her bow and said a kind of spell to herself at which point segments began instantly emerging from the cylinder displaying beautiful turquoise saucers with a blue rim. On the saucers lay something with an alluring aroma.

"There you have it, all-powerful priestess Tufti, oriental sweets on a dish with a blue rim.

"Why with a blue rim particularly?"

"That's what we say when all whims and desires are fulfilled and there is nothing left to wish for, but you start being capricious: 'But I want it with a blue rim!'"

"Oh, how delicious! What is this?"

"This one is halva, this is Turkish delight and that is sherbet fudge. That's enough for now though otherwise we'll pop. Next time, I'll think up something else as well."

"With sweets like these we need tea," said Itfut. "I'll treat you to a drink that is popular with us." This time, the priestess confidently approached the cylinder, leaned forward slightly lowering her head, and then in one movement, raised her arms to shoulder level bent them at the elbows and raised them higher in a gesture of supplication.

Segments holding two neat cups and a tall jug with a long neck immediately emerged from the cylinder.

"Futi, what did you just do?" asked Matilda.

"I don't know. I just did it automatically," answered Itfut. "I must have used that gesture many times before and I think I can guess what it's for."

"And what is it for? What?"

"It instantly activates the trigger-jigger."

"Interesting, let me try."

Matilda stood up and made the gesture she had seen Futi do moments before.

"Yes, I can sense something but why is nothing happening?"

"You probably weren't thinking of anything. When you activate the trigger, you have to set your focus, pick your random thought so that you can manifest your idea."

"True. I didn't set a focus."

"And there's no need to. You have to be careful with your random thoughts and the trigger."

"Evidently. Come on then, let's try your drink," said Matilda reaching out to take one of the little teacups. "Oh, look at those sweet 'kalyambochki'!"

"What-what, those what?"

"Kalyambochki –'little cups'."

"The drink has a powerful effect, so it's served in small cups so that you have to sip it."

"What's the effect?"

"You're about to find out." Itfut poured the drink into the two cups and then they began the ceremony. Matilda chuckled every now and then sipping from her cup.

"It reminds me of something although I don't know what," she said.

"It's herb-based tea," replied Itfut.

"Hum, another cup?"

"Okay," Itfut refilled their cups.

After the second cup, Matilda's eyes began to shine, and she was visibly more animated.

"Futi, What is it, uh?"

"I told you, it's a herb-based tea."

"Herb-based you say? Safe herbs?"

"Ha, ha, ha! Tili, there's nothing to worry about. It won't bring on a trance state or anything. It isn't addictive either."

"Herby herbs, harmless little herbs. Another quirky cupful?"

"Tili, take it easy. The drink is energy-giving but too much of it can be harmful."

"Exactly! I need to be invigorated! Relieve my stress. Pour me some more!"

Itfut poured some more for Matilda and herself.

"You're not about to do something weird, are you?"

"I don't know yet, we'll see."

"Tili-Tili!"

"Yup! Now it's my turn to frighten you! Another quirky cupful?"

"That's enough, no more, otherwise you'll get out of hand. You're far too expressive a diva. Don't forget where we are."

"Okay, okay, I was just joking!" said Matilda. "Great little drinkthough. I've refreshed my spirits. And now, as can you imagine, I feel totally ready to do something about this bloody-minded reality. It's not just her who's going to muck about with us!"

"Reality isn't something to be played with, as you well know."

"Yes, but Futi, I've been thinking, what's to stop us launching a dream of our own with the help of our triggers?"

"What will happen if we do? What will come of it?"

"Weren't you surprised that the mannequins froze? You said yourself that the dream should be playing out because we are here observing it."

"Maybe it would be better if it wasn't playing. That way things can't get any worse."

"But we could also end up spending our entire lives here in limbo with nothing happening! Life should be about keeping things moving, not lackadaisical tea-drinking."

"Hey hey! Tili, I like you when you're in this mood."

"Only first I want to get something straight in my mind. You said that when we are in the dream space, our awareness is focused on watching the dream which makes us a viewer, whereas in the waking reality space, we are actually living it, which makes us like characters, right?"

"Right."

"So, what's the difference between a viewer and a character?"

"A viewer only watches, whereas a character participates in what's unfolding."

"But you can take part in a dream as well as watch one?"

"Clever, Matilda! In a dream, our awareness can be present both as a viewer and as a participant. Sometimes, we just watch our dreams as if we were flying through a movie. Other times, we take part in them as if we were living inside the dream."

"So, what's the difference then between a viewer and an observer?"

"A viewer simply watches passively, whereas an observer watches and participates at the same time."

"So, what's the difference between an observer and a character?"

"Aren't you meticulous! An observer is a conscious participant. If, in a dream you are a sleeping participant, then you're a non-conscious character. It's the same thing when you are asleep in waking reality. You're still a dependent character and the movie controls you. But if you wake up either in a dream or in waking life, it doesn't matter which, you become an observer, an independent, conscious individual."

"So, what's the difference then between waking reality and a dream? Because you've said that we are in the dream space now, like in a movie. And now you're say-

ing that reality is like a movie, too, only one that's controlling us."

"That, Tili, is a very complex question. If we ever find the answer, reality might destroy us. She does not like to reveal her secrets and that is her biggest secret yet. Does that scare you?"

"No, I'm not scared, I'm not scared! The only thing that really scares me is the thought of being stuck here forever."

"Okay, so I mentioned one possible answer already. When no-one is watching it, the dream space is static and at rest like a still landscape image, but as soon as the dreamer's attention penetrates the dream space, the frames starts moving again and time is set in motion, at which point, the dream becomes like a movie. In waking reality it's the opposite. The movie plays of its own accord and the dreamer is living within it."

"So, you think we're dreaming in physical reality, too?"

"Of course. We talked about that already. Most normal people are in the habit of sleeping in waking reality, which is why they are just characters, whereas those who see reality have the opposite habit which is what makes them observers."

"So, who are we being now?"

"Most probably observers because we have woken up and understand where we are."

"Right. That means, in reality the movie is playing of its own accord and we are living inside it. In meta-reality, it's the opposite. We get the movie playing and we're here not only in our awareness but in our physical bodies too, living it! So why shouldn't we set our own dream playing, or is the fact that we're living here the reason why we can't?"

"I don't know, Tili."

"Well let's try to set something in motion with our trigger-levers then."

"And how do you see us doing that?"

"Let's go find a couple of glamrocks and get them going again."

"Right now?"

"I don't have the patience to hang around here any longer-r-r-r! No patience left at a-all!"

"Okay, let's go. Whatever happened to your fear? Is it the drink that's had this effect on you?"

"What difference does it make? Let's get a move on, Futi, before the effect wears off. Shall we take the jug with us?"

"No, Tili, better just to get moving quick, quick, there and back."

LAUNCHING THE DREAM

The moment the diva and the priestess left the megalith, they were engulfed in an almost intangible darkness. It was a peculiar feeling for darkness usually assumes an emptiness, the absence of light. In night-time meta-reality however, the element of light was still present, the only difference being that it did not illuminate objects so much as color them in various shades of black. Even the air was as if literally painted black and the buildings were blacker still. Only the figures of the two friends shone, and the details of their silhouettes were particularly bright.

A blue luminosity surrounded Matilda's face and hair, while her platform shoes and bow shone pink. Itfut's face burned crimson and her diamond-studded collar sparkled in all the colors of the rainbow. The diva's dark-green jumpsuit and the priestess's dark-blue dress glowed in deep, rich tones. The priestess's hair seemed even blacker than usual while the hands of both were a dazzling white.

The overall picture was evocative of two gleaming figures, who had come to life inside a watercolor painting. The friends were noticeably 'animated' after partaking of the reviving drink. Matilda trotted along in her platforms, and Itfut took bold strides making expansive movements with her arms.

The drink had clearly given them courage since the walk they were taking was hardly a pleasant diversion. The eerie dream space had transformed into an even scarier realm of shadows. Whether their desperate outing displayed more courage or recklessness on their part, it is hard to say. Perhaps they were just more comfortable in this worldnow and were no longer intimidated by anything much.

"Futi, are you afraid?" asked Matilda. "Me, no."

"Me neither," replied Itfut. "My fear has faded and shrunk."

"Like an old dress?"

"Kind of like that. When things can't get any scarier, nothing afterwards is quite as scary."

"You always have a pithy phrase for every situation! I'm proud of you, proud of having a friend like you."

"I'm proud of you too, Tili."

"I'm prouder than you are!"

"No! I'm more proud."

"No, I am!"

The friends laughed. Giggling and jostling each other as they went, they failed to notice how far they had walked from the safety of the megalith. Caught in a dark maze of streets, they fell silent and began moving more cautiously, looking from side to side. The scene was far from idyllic and the clicking of their heels in the deathly silence sounded strange and unnatural.

Turning a corner, they came to an abrupt halt. The silence was now truly sepulchral. In the middle of the street, two mannequins stood as if they had frozen right in the middle of a discussion. Their eyes burned ominously in the darkness. For all their bragging, the diva and the priestess stood stock-still from fright, numbed by the spectacle before them and the hypnotic, all-encompassing stillness.

Finally, the friends recovered from their astonishment and walked around the mannequins studying the statues more closely.

"All my insides have gone cold," said Matilda.

"I've got shivers going up and down my spine," said Itfut.

"Who's going to try first?"

"You go first. You've seen them alive."

"Oh, mamma-mia, I wouldn't say that they were alive in the full sense of the world. They aren't even the living dead, as much as mannequins that have come to life."

"That's what they are — mannequins in a dream, pure characters without souls or consciousness. When the dream is playing, they act in accordance with the plot, not with their own will," said Itfut

"You're saying that they follow the dream script like the heroes in a movie?"

"What's a script?" asked Itfut.

"It's the same thing as a plot, only as well as outlining the characters' roles it states who should say and do what when." Matilda replied.

"Yes, in that sense, then, the movie script controls the characters."

"But we can also influence the characters in the dream, right? I managed to at any rate."

"We can but only if we are of a higher level of consciousness than they are. Without conscious awareness, we might as well be a character letting the movie control us."

"Both in reality and in dreaming?"

"Totally, Matilda, dear, only it would be more accurate to say that we could influence the plot the characters were following rather than the characters themselves."

"Really? So, it turns out, I did not influence the glam-rocks, I influenced the script instead? It felt to me like it was the opposite, as if I had subjected them to my own will."

"It only appeared that way. In fact, the dreamer just sets the dream plot, be it intentionally or unintentionally."

"Right! And in waking reality it's exactly the same! For example, if you are scared of something, it's like it just has to happen."

"Yes, that's when it's happening unintentionally."

"So, when is it happening intentionally?"

"When you deliberately set the course of the plot."

"I see. And that's possible in dreaming and in waking reality too?"

"Totally, Matilda, dear."

"Futi, you never fail to surprise me. Okay, so I get it when it comes to dreaming. But in reality? I mean, how can I set the course of events then? They just run their own course, don't they?"

"Tili, you never fail to surprise me either. You've already pulled off one trick with reality."

"With meta-reality, you mean? Everything is simpler here. We're in the dream space."

"No, I mean with reality. Have you forgotten how you overturned your understudy?"

"Oh! Yes, I know, but still, I did it from here, from this side of the mirror."

"And what's the difference?"

Matilda seemed baffled by this question. She stared at the priestess lost for words.

"What's the difference?" she said, repeating the question. "But you said yourself that everything is much more complicated in reality than it is here."

"More complicated does not mean impossible."

"So, we're back to the same old question: what's the difference between dreaming and reality? You're saying there's no difference?"

"We're best off leaving that question alone for now. The less we know, the longer we'll live."

"And why are you so certain that we affect the plot and not the characters themselves?"

"I don't know. I'm just certain of it, that's all. I can't explain why. You forced your understudy to fall over! You imagined her falling, true?"

"Yes."

"Well, that's the plot."

Matilda stopped and looked again at the priestess open-mouthed.

"Okay, Futi, so what do we have to imagine to set the glamrocks moving again?"

"Activate your trigger and just imagine that they have come to life and are moving around."

No sooner had Itfut finished her sentence, than the mannequins who had been frozen in front of them suddenly jerked into action speaking in raised voices and gesticulating wildly.

"Give up smoking, wretch! Go pump some muscle instead!"

"What did you say? Douchebag!"

"Shut the fuck up, and listen, dick-head!"

"Piss off, douchebag!"

"Stop right there! Or I'll knife half the patch!"

"What patch are you from, douchebag?"

The skirmish was accompanied by characteristic hand and finger gestures.

"Show some respect, dickhead!"

"You aren't us; we aren't you! Piss off, scumbag!"

"What's your problem? Stop getting rat-assed and take up sport."

"Fuck off! I'm busy right now! Some other time! Come back tomorrow, dude."

"You're an animal! When are you gonna show some love for the homeland? Get yourself some muscle..."

Mid-sentence the glamrocks suddenly froze again. The diva and the priestess looked on in amazement, first at the mannequins and then at each other.

"Tili, did you do that?" asked Itfut. "Was that your dream?"

"I don't know how that happened. Some random thought just flashed through the back of my mind."

"But what on earth was that?"

"Two guys met on home turf and had a serious chat. Ha, ha!"

"I couldn't understand a word of it!"

"It's irrelevant, forget it! It was just that when I started imagining these two lads, they reminded me of someone back home. But why have they stopped again? Go on, now it's your turn to try."

"Okay."

Itfut made her magic gesture. Leaning slightly forward, she dropped her chin and then in a single movement raised her hands to shoulder height, bent them at the elbows and straightened them upwards, this time accompanied by an unusual invocation:

"OO-OO-OO-LA!"

The glamrocks jerked into action 'getting all wound up' again, made a few movements and then, just as abruptly were still again.

"Ooo-la-la Futi! What was that invocation?" asked Matilda in surprise.

"I don't know. It must be something I was used to doing before."

"They've stopped again. Why?"

"Launching a dream clearly isn't as easy as we thought."

"Yes, this is going to take something different. Something different is required."

"Something, something that we don't know."

"It's like, 'What do you want, Nadya girl?' 'I don't want anything. I need chocolate!"

"What? Tili, I don't understand what you're talking about."

"I'm just kind of talking to reality, asking, 'what is it that you want?'"

"Yes, quite, what does she want generally and from US specifically?"

"Come on, Futi, let's go back."

"Okay, okay," replied Itfut in her characteristic manner. "Let's go, let's go."

And so, the friends began making their way back the way they came. They walked in silence, tired now lacking their earlier enthusiasm. Their first and very long day in meta-reality had ended without result. They were left with many more questions than answers. Having entered the megalith, the diva and the priestess sat down at the table and drank 'another quirky cupful' of herbal tea to lift their spirits.

"What are we going to do, Futi?" asked Matilda.

"Positively sleep!" replied Itfut.

"Perfect. Everything will look different in the morning, as they say. And what are we positively going to sleep on?"

"What do people sleep on in your world?"

"Now, now, I'll show you. I'm hoping the megalith will work this time."

Matilda conjured up her magic with the bow and a comfy bed rose from the floor carefully made up with clean linen, a pillow, a blanket and a pair of pajamas as her mother always did for her darling Tili.

"How wonderful! What's all this?" exclaimed Itfut.

"It's a patchwork quilt," Matilda said, showing Itfut and telling her about it. "It's sewn from multi-colored pieces of fabric with a cotton fleece lining. I love these quilts. And this is a feather pillow. And these are my soft pajamas. I always sleep in them."

"Oh, Tili, you're so cute! I want one!"

"Who would have doubted it? Coming right up."

The diva conjured up a similar set for the priestess who sat on the edge of her bed and started touching it and exploring the details.

"Do you like it?" asked Matilda.

"Very much," answered Itfut.

“What do you sleep on then?”

“I’ll show you another time.”

They began to yawn in a friendly manner and then performing exactly the same actions in synchronicity as if they were twins, they took off their tired clothes, put on their pajamas and got into bed.

“How did that whole story with the milk soup end?” asked Itfut, about to doze off.

“They didn’t make me eat it. And I grew up beautiful and strong,” said Matilda already half asleep.

THE LITTLE RED QUEEN

Priestess Itfut stood tied to a pole in the square beside the megalith. The glamrocks were circling the pole, monotonously mumbling their usual mantra.

'Mamma mia, here I go again
My my, how can I resist you?
Mamma mia, does it show again?
My my, just how much I've missed you Mana-mia, here I go again,'

They paused from time to time turning to the center of the circle and shrieking loudly.

"Little Red Queen! We will eat her! Eat her!"

Then they resumed their stomping and muttering.

'Yes, I've been brokenhearted
Blue since the day we parted
Why, why did I ever let you go?
Mamma mia, now I really know
My my, I could never let you go.'

The outward appearance of the awakened mannequins had not changed. They wore the same grey hooded robes and had the same grey, wax hands. Despite their emotional cries, their faces were totally without expression. The priestess held herself as proudly as a staunch Indian chief at a torture post. She paid no attention to the savages silently fixing her gaze on a spot in the distance above their heads. Their victim's coolness was beginning to irritate the glamrocks. They stopped stomping and mumbling, turned to face her and stuck out their tongues, letting out a howl and wildly shaking their heads. This action clearly failed to have the desired effect on the prisoner, quite the opposite in fact as an ironic smile spread across Itfut's face.

"Little Red Queen!" they continued, either to threaten their victim or agitate their own displeasure. "Eat her! Eat her!"

Then the savages thought up a new ritual. Each in turn ran up to the captive, removed their hood and rubbed their bald head on her belly, before turning to face the others, shouting 'Little Red Queen!' And then just as quickly, they pulled their hood back up and jumped away from the post and back into line. The others joined inamiably.

"Eat her! Eat her!"

Evidently, they lacked sufficient imagination to think of a wider variety of words and actions. But they did not need it. Judging by their triumphant cries, this treatment alone was considered an expression of unequalled insolence and audacity towards the 'queen'.

After they had all taken part in the ritual, the bravest of all the glamrocks decided to do something extraordinary. This glamrock ran behind the victim's back, made a horrible grimace, stuck out his tongue and licked the diamond collar on Itfut's dress. The crowd responded with a howl of approval. But the daredevil did not stop there; stepping forward, he pronounced the essential question.

"How will we eat her? How?"

As usual, the crowd's replies showered forth in two different versions.

"We'll fry her!" shouted one group.

"No! Boil her!" repeated the other.

The savages easily pronounced the letter 'r' now, so the squabble continued at least without any phonetic problems. It was like a bargaining in which the one who yells the loudest wins. The first group won.

"Fry her!" they shouted, now amicably unanimous.

Out of nowhere, a handful of glamrocks dragged up a huge griddle the height of a human in diameter. The others set to various tasks, some starting the fire, others dancing around the victim with their tongues sticking out and their eyes bulging. The entire bacchanalia was accompanied by two standard yelps of, 'Little Red Queen!' and 'We'll eat her! Eat her! Eat her!'

"Matilda!" The sound of Itfut's voice was finally heard. "Matilda-a-a!" Itfut called out to her friend loudly but calmly as if she were doing nothing more than inviting her sleeping friend to join her for breakfast.

No doubt waking now on account of the noise, Matilda ran barefoot out of the megalith still in her pajamas.

"A-a-ah!" cried Matilda. "What are you doing, you disgusting freaks? Free her, now! Futi!" Matilda ran to the post and tried to untie the straps, but they were fastened too tightly.

"Ah, you freaks! Free her this instant!"

Taken aback, the glamrocks stopped what they were doing and started shouting in excitement.

"Mana-tida! Mana-tida! Our Mana!!"

"What do you have to do?" asked Matilda, realizing that she had to gain control of the savages somehow.

"Read gibberish!" they answered in chorus.

"What mustn't you do?"

"We mustn't do what isn't allowed!"

"More specifically. What mustn't you do?"

"We mustn't eat each other!"

"And what are you planning to do?"

"Eat her! Eat her!"

"But you've been told that you mustn't eat each other!'

"Yes! We mustn't eat our own. She's not one of us!" This was the glamrocks' sure-fire argument and they continued tossing firewood into the fire with the same enthusiasm as before.

"But I am your mana!" objected Matilda. "I forbid you! This is my friend and you will untie her right now and let her go!"

"We can't!" answered the glamrocks. "We must eat her!"

"They can't, Tili," said Itfut calmly. "They follow their scenario instinctively like an unconditioned reflex."

"We'll see about that! Hey! Do you hear me? You're not allowed to eat her!"

"Yes, we are, we are!"

"If you do, there'll be an almighty crash!"

"No there won't. There won't."

"There will, there will! She is mana too! We are both manas."

The glamrocks looked slightly confused. They talked amongst themselves and, then, one of them, the daredevil who had dared lick the priestess's collar, stepped forward.

"Let her prove she's mana!"

Matilda threw Itfut a worried look.

"Don't worry, Tili, just make them untie me."

"Listen, you turkeys, untie her!" ordered Matilda. "Then you'll see that she's mana too!" Then she turned to Futi and whispered, "Futi, what are you planning to do?"

"Hack the script," replied Itfut.

"How?"

Their conversation was interrupted by two glamrocks who started unbinding the straps, while the others surrounded them in a tight circle. The daredevil stood at the center. As soon as they had freed the priestess, he started singing out of habit.

"Little Red Quee..." But before he could finish the line, Itfut leaped towards him, grabbed him just below the knees and pulled him sharply towards her. The glamrock fell over backwards. Giving him no time to recover, the priestess fell down on top of him, clasped his head between her palms and shoved her lips up against his in a long kiss.

Then she stood up and started turning circles and laughing.

The daredevil lay on the ground stunned while the others including Matilda stood completely still staring at Futi open-mouthed. Itfut stopped suddenly, stretched out an arm and began to circle them, running her palm across each as she went. Then turning around, she asked the same question three times.

"Do you realize that I am dreaming, and I am seeing you in my dream?"

"Do you realize that I am dreaming, and I am seeing you in my dream?"

"Do you realize that I am dreaming, and I am seeing you in my dream?"

The glamrocks were dumbfounded and did not seem to understand the question, but that was not what worried them. "She kissed! She kissed him! Is she mana? Is she also mana?" They exclaimed in great surprise.

"Who are you?" the daredevil asked her, still not quite recovered from his shock.

"This is the great and omnipotent priestess Itfut!" Matilda solemnly proclaimed, reverently raising her hands to the priestess.

"Mana-fata! Mana-fata!" the glamrocks repeated concerned. "The great Itfut."

"Yes," Itfut responded. "Yes, and now, so that you really get it, I'm going to eat you all!"

The glamrocks took the news literally and were seriously worried.

"No! No!" They cried out.

"Yes! Yes!" said Itfut teasing them.

"It's not allowed! It's not allowed! Aboo!"

"Yes, is it, it is!" said Matilda living into her role. "I'm going to eat you too. We are both mana and together we will eat you all. Aba!"

Failing to come up with a counter argument, the savages huddled together trembling with fear. The script was hacked, and the roles were reversed. The friends stood beside each other with their hands on their hips and cast an appraising eye over their victims. The fire was already burning well, and the griddle lay close by.

"Disgraceful glamrocks!" shouted Matilda in a threatening voice.

"Yes, pathetic and worthless!" shouted the diva angrily.

"What are they good for?"

"Meat!"

"Let's eat them!"

"We'll eat them!"

The mana began moving towards the glamrocks with a threatening stance. The glamrocks howled and edged backwards timidly.

"Mana-fata, I'm as hungry as a wolf! Yes, a wolf!"

"Mana-tida, I could eat a horse! A whole horse!"

"The brains are mine, all mine! All the brains for me! They're so deliciously fatty!"

"The eyes are mine! They're so crunchy! I love the way they pop!"

"Useless glamrocks!"

"Let's eat them! Yes, eat them!"

The bloodthirsty mana were so living in their new role that even the diva's home pajamas and the priestess's elegant dress did not prompt them to doubt the seriousness of the women's intentions.

"And how will we eat them? How?" asked Matilda.

"Let's fry them!" responded Itfut.

"No, let's eat them alive!"

"No! We'll fry them!"

"No, alive! We'll eat them alive!"

They turned to face one another starting a serious argy bargy which almost turned into a fight.

Finally coming to an agreement (fry them) the manas ran towards the griddle, took hold of it on both sides and decisively set it up above the flames. Having shaken their arms out, they rolled up their sleeves and stared right at the glamrocks with a predatory look. The glamrocks scattered in all directions shrieking. The manas set after them with treacherous screams.

"Catch them!"

"Hold them!"

"Crush them!"

"Throttle them!"

The glamrocks rushed around the square as if already doomed. The thought never entered their heads that they could just run away along the city streets. Who knows how long the chaotic running around, like a game of tag, might have gone on for if the manas had not finally succeeded in catching one of them, the very same daredevil, whom priestess Itfut kissed. They knocked him to the ground and dragged him towards the fire. The sorry glamrock was rendered helpless by fear and could do nothing except release a heart-rending scream. The rest huddled together again and fearfully observed events as they unfolded. Having dragged their victim towards the fire, the manas grabbed him by the hands and feet and began swinging him from side to side with the intention of throwing him onto the griddle, all the while saying, "We'll eat him! Eat him! Fry him! Eat him!"

The entire scene was accompanied by the howls of the savages filled with horror and a sense of impending tragedy. Despite the fact that the glamrock was quite heavy, the friends found the strength to sway him from side to side. Eventually, understanding the plan without needing to speak a word to each other, the two friends flung the glamrock away to the side and onto the ground. The glamrocks, including the defeated prisoner, froze with anticipation. Having caught their breath for a second, the diva and the priestess looked over at the glamrocks, then at each other and suddenly broke into chuckles, rocking from side to side with uncontrollable laughter.

HACKING THE SCRIPT

The diva and the priestess ceased their merriment and stared at the glamrocks frowning.

"The good-for-nothing glamrocks must be punished for wanting to eat the great Mana-fata!" said Matilda.

"And for wanting to eat the great Mana-tida!" said Itfut. "For this they should be severely punished!"

"And we, the great manas, will now go and hold council and decide what that severe punishment should be!"

"Yes! And you, good-for-nothing glamrocks will wait here for us in fear and trembling!"

The friends simultaneously turned and strode towards the megalith. The savages watched them leave with looks of devotion, filled with reverence and awe. They had already survived the worst reprisal which gave them hope that their awaited punishment would not be too terrible.

Once inside the megalith, the diva pulled the priestess to her and gave her a tight hug.

"My dear Futichka, Futi! You can't imagine how scared I was when I woke up and found you gone! What happened?"

"Tili, I didn't want to wake you. I just looked out onto the street and those gray beasts attacked me so suddenly I even had time to get scared."

"Didn't have time, you mean?"

"No, I mean what I say. I had time to get scared. The quicker and more suddenly that danger befalls you, the more thoroughly and positively you are sacred. You don't have time to come to your senses."

"In what way, come to your senses?"

"In the sense of waking up. When something goes wrong, you have to be able to see reality and yourself within it. It's the reverse habit to sleeping in waking reality. Remember?"

"Oh, yes, it was when we were talking about movie characters and those who see reality."

"I got scared. My Witness was not activated, and I conceded."

"Conceded? With what?" asked Matilda in surprise.

"With the script!" laughed Itfut. "That I was the 'Little Red Queen' and they were going to eat me."

"It's not as if you had a choice?"

"There is always a choice, whether to concede or not. If you concede, the movie has you under its control and you are transformed into a movie character. What's more, if your Witness is sleeping, you always concede, whatever's happening."

"I don't get it. How can I concede to being eaten?"

"You might resist, and you might not like it but that's different. To concede means to accept that something is possible, as something that is likely to happen. When all sorts of unlikely things happen in a dream, it appears genuinely real to you, but we've also got used to the idea that in waking reality, only things that are likely to happen can occur."

"So, what does it mean not to concede?"

"That's when you understand that what you're seeing is a dream. Then you wake up in the dream and can change the script."

"And if it isn't a dream? We're not sleeping now, right?"

"It makes no difference. A dream is real, and reality is a dream. You can change the script in both."

"And if I can't not concede? If what is happening is more than likely to occur? They could quite easily have eaten you alive and me, too."

"And yet, when something like that happened to you, you found the strength to pull yourself together and ask, 'is this my reality? And you said, 'no, this isn't my reality. Everything will be all right with me, whatever happens'."

"I used my trigger-lever then. But you did something different, didn't you?"

"Yes, I hacked the script."

"How do you do that? Explain."

"If your movie has already rolled to the scene of an inevitable scenario, it might be too late to use the trigger-lever. With me, this is what happened: I was scared, I conceded and by the time I came to my senses, it was too late, and I was already tied up and sentenced. In a situation like that, you have to do something extraordinary that does not fit with the logic of events as they are unfolding. When the script is broken, as long as you don't let the opportunity to take the initiative pass you by, you can rewrite the script to your own benefit. But what can I teach you? Your trick with the dead head was a brilliant example of hacking the script."

"I just acted intuitively," said Matilda. "I don't even know why I did it but at least now I understand the principle.

Futi, tell me, what was it like kissing the glamrock? Was it creepy?"

"I just imagined I was kissing a mannequin," replied Itfut, "which is what he is after all."

"Not exactly! And why did they come back to life? Did the dream start spinning all by itself?"

"It looks like the dream needed to be restarted."

"Like a reboot?"

"Yes. Remember, it stopped when I appeared here. I entered your dream as a new observer."

"And it crashed!"

"Yes. And to restart it, all we had to do was fall asleep together and then wake up again."

"Why didn't we think of that before?"

"I know! I know!"

They organized breakfast for themselves in the normal way by using the black cylinder, which remained one of the most mysterious and incomprehensible objects of all they had seen in this world so far. Now the friends had to work out what they were going to do next. The priestess's bed was already neatly made. The diva also made her bed and put on her extravagant outfit: the dark-green jumpsuit and pink platform shoes. Helping Matilda with her equally extravagant pink bow, Itfut giggled and said, "Tili, darling! Tili-Tili, da-a-arling!"

"Tufti, stop it, you're teasing me! You're bringing back sad memories."

"Okay, okay!"

"Will we really never return home to our reality?"

"We will, Tili, we will. Either to your reality or to mine, or maybe even each of us to our own."

"No. I want us to be together!"

“So, we’ll be together then. Everything will be as we want it to be.”

“The only thing I’m cross with you about is for leaving me here alone. How could you?”

“Tili, you were sleeping and anyway, I only intended to take a peep outside for a second. Anyway, everything turned out for the best in the end.”

“But it could have turned out differently! It could have turned out for the worst! Promise that you’ll never abandon me, otherwise I won’t survive!”

“I promise. I won’t make it without you either.” They sat down at the table to think through their plan of action.

“What are we going to do, Futi?” said Matilda asking her favorite question.

“We need to somehow get on top of the glamrocks,” said Itfut, “get them into a stable condition.”

“But we’ve already done that. To them we’re like goddesses.”

“Maybe but not entirely. They could go out of control at any moment. What’s the point of ‘Mana-ti-i-i-da! You’re our ma-a-a-na!’? They’d wolf me down given half the chance and your command would be no law for them then.”

“Yes, who knows what they might get into their heads. What do you suggest?”

“We’ll make up a system of punishments for them,” said Itfut.

“That won’t work.” said Matilda. “They’re movie characters. They’re led by the script.”

“A system of intimidation then.”

“Fear won’t stop them either. That’s all been tried and tested since biblical times.”

"Since what times?"

"La-la, it doesn't matter. Any other ideas?"

"We could establish a rigid hierarchy. We are the great manas, we are the most important, then appoint one senior overseer among them and two or three assistants or leaders."

"They'll start weaving backstage intrigue and the whole hierarchy will constantly be falling apart."

"Then let's establish equality. How do they resolve disputes? By fighting and arguing. We'll teach them how to make decisions by majority vote."

"Ah! Democracy? We've already tried that."

"You've tried what?"

"Futi, trying to introduce something alien into an individual society is a thankless task. Society has to organize itself in whatever is most natural to it ."

"Tili, where did you acquire such wise insight into how society works?"

"The society in which I live was constantly trying to rebuild itself but was never rebuilt. Anyway, I have no desire to reshape glamrock society. I just want to get out of here as soon as possible."

"Yeah, me too. So, what would you suggest whilst we are here?"

"We need to keep them busy."

"But with what? With what?"

"With themselves. That's the best option."

"And how are we going to do that?"

"They are deprived of any sense of self-identification. They live like a brainless herd. They don't even have names. We need to give them names and instill in them the idea that they too can be manas if they want to be, that they can create their own reality. And then they can deal with their own lives and society."

"Right! That's a pretty major task. Have you forgotten that their life is our dream, and that it continues to unfold only because we are here observing it? Without us here, reality will freeze again."

"Are you sure that meta-reality does not come to life or move without an observer? Who can confirm that this is true? If there's no observer, then there's no-one to confirm it. To say nothing of the fact that we still don't understand how reality differs from a dream."

"I give in. When it comes to that, I can't be totally certain of anything."

"You see! You said yourself that dream mannequins were mannequins because they had no soul or self-awareness. As far as the soul goes, I can't say but if we try to instill in them the idea that 'you are you' maybe they will wake up and will be able to launch meta-reality by themselves."

"Matilda, that's brilliant!" exclaimed Itfut. "Sometimes, you really astound me! Only, why should we wake them up?"

"Well, at the very least so that they could spend time concentrating on their own lives and leave us alone. But also, if we can get them to the reasonable state of a slightest degree, we can ask them what this place is and how to get out of here."

"I doubt they'll be able to answer, but I agree, let's give it a try. Any ideas on how we can bring this about?"

"You'll see. I do have some experience of entertaining the masses. Let's go and take a look at what they're doing right now."

"Yes, let's go, let's go. Only first, let's wake up and prepare ourselves. This is a serious matter."

"Okay, but don't worry. The worst is already behind us."

"Don't forget, self-control means controlling where your attention goes. Don't fall asleep and if anything goes wrong, don't concede. Don't get immersed in anyone else's movie!"

"I know that now, Futi! Okay, so we've woken up, let's move!"

The friends got up from the table and left the megalith.

I AM ME

When the diva and the priestess went outside, they were met with the following scene: the bonfire and the griddle had been removed. Obviously, for the sake of prudence. Now they were all lying quietly on the ground in a row, as if waiting for something.

"Right!" said Matilda putting her hands on her hips.

"Right!" said Itfut doing the same.

They walked along the row of bodies taking in the spectacle with a look of irony and surprise.

"What are you all lying down for?" asked Matilda.

"Why are you lying down, dear ones?" asked Itfut.

The glamrocks lay still, following their mistresses with a silent gaze. Eventually, one of them sat up and speaking bluntly, said,

"Mana-fata, give us a kiss!"

"Give us a kiss!" the others repeated. "Mana-fata! Mana-fata!"

"Ha, ha, ha! Yes, right away!" said Itfut in a cheery voice.

"So that's what you want!" said Matilda disappointed.

The glamrocks weren't giving up. They got up and crawled towards the priestess on all fours. Those in the front rows tried to grab hold of her dress.

"Mana-fata! Give us a kiss! Mana-fata!"

Itfut dodged their grip and took a step backwards.

"You're bad!" she said laughing.
"Mana-fata!
"You are not worthy!"

But this reproach did not bother the glamrocks; they stood up and thronged behind the priestess droning their continual chant.

"Mana-fata! Give us a kiss!"

Itfut ran away from them laughing.

"Ha-ha-ha, no, you can go without!"

In this manner, the strange procession circled the megalith. Matilda stood watching the action with indignation.

"Well, would you just look! What a cheek! They're not the least bit afraid of us anymore!"

"Stop!" Ifut paused to catch her breath and turned to her friend with a cunning look. "Perhaps Mana-tida will kiss you?"

"What?!"said the diva, stunned. "Futi!"

The glamrocks quickly shifted their attention to the second mana.

"Mana-tida! Kiss!"

Now it was Matilda's turn to run away from the glamrocks. Itfut laughed and clapped her hands watching the procession making the same circle again.

"Stop that right now!" Matilda shouted. "Leave me alone!"

"Mana-tida!" The glamrocks persisted.

Finally, once Matilda had tired of the game, she turned to face her persecutors and threw her arms out to the sides, saying, "Right, stop this, all of you!"

"Useless glamrocks!"said Itfut joining her.

The glamrocks froze in expectation. The diva and the priestess stood before them with their hands on their hips.

"Have you forgotten about the terrible punishment?" asked Matilda.

"Why did you clear away the fire?" asked Matilda.

"Now we're going to have to eat you again!"

"Yes, yes, yes, we will, we will!"

"They won't! They won't!" the glamrocks mumbled confidently.

"No? Why? Why not?" asked Matilda in surprise.

"Manas are kind," replied the glamrocks.

"That's not true," Itfut contradicted them. "Come on. Tell us where the griddle is. What have you done with it?"

"Since you are behaving so badly, we are going to have to eat you all." said Matilda.

"Yup, no other option," Itfut confirmed.

"No! No!" shouted the glamrocks.

"Then behave yourselves," said Matilda. "What must you do?"

"Read gibberish!"

"Well, now we're going to learn a new kind of gibberish."

"Mana-tida-jenka! Mana-tida-jenka!" the glamrocks shouted livening up. "We are being invited to dance!"

"No, letkajenkha was for entertainment. This new gibberish is educational. That's bigger, that's better! Listen up."

The diva assumed a theatrical pose, raised her arms and began to recite the following lines:

"May there always be sunshine!"

Before she could continue, a shining solar disk appeared in the sky above them. The sky in meta-reality, as we mentioned before, had light but no sun. And now to everyone's amazement, including the diva and the priestess, everything was as it should be.

"Tili, you're full of surprises." Itfut whispered. "Was that your bow again?"

"Futi, I'm just as surprised as you are!" Matilda whispered back.

"We have to be careful here with the trigger-lever and our expectations."

"I remember. Or rather, I forgot. It was purely accidental."

"Okay, okay, maybe it's for the best. But be careful."

The glamrocks greeted the miracle with enthusiastic exclamations.

"Aba! Aba!" And then in one voice, "Mana-tida! Mana the great!"

"Stop that! Stand up!" Matilda commanded. "Actually no,sit down. Sit down everyone."

The diva and the priestess sat down on a large boulder and the glamrocks arranged themselves in a semicircle on the ground around it.

"We are both great manas." said Matilda. "And you must obey us."

"Yes! Yes! We will obey!"

"But you can be manas too."

"How can that be? How can that be?" The glamrocks repeated in surprise.

"We, the great manas will teach you."

"Yes, you will become manas and be able to kiss each other," said Itfut.

"Can we really? Can we really?"

"Yes, yes" said Matilda. "Didn't I teach you to read the letter?"

"Yes, yes! We read the letter!"

"Then listen to the new gibberish." This time, sitting and without waving her hands about, Matilda spoke the following.

"May there always be sunshine!
May there always be blue skies,
May there always be mama,
May I always be me."*

"May there always be mana! May there always be mana!" the glamrocks repeated.

"Not mana, 'mama'," Matilda corrected them. "Now repeat the gibberish from the beginning to the end."

The glamrocks tried diligently to reproduce the words. They managed it in chorus but out of tune.

"May there always be sunshine!
May there always be blue skies,
May there always be mana,
May there always be Me."

"Idiots! You do have a mama, right? It should be, 'May I always be me', not 'May there always be me.' Try it again."

The glamrocks stubbornly repeated the rhyme in their own style.

---

* L. Oshanin

"Okay, let it be mana if you like it so much," said Matilda. "But you have to say, 'May I always be me.' That's the most important bit."

The glamrocks were confused. They conferred a little between themselves after which one of them came forward and asked, "Who is 'Me'? Where is he? Can manas show us?"

"Right," said Matilda. "Come here. Tell me, who are you?"

"We are glamrocks," the one who had come forward said. "We read gibberish. And we read the letter! Aba!"

"**They** are glamrocks," said Matilda pointing to the others. "And altogether, you are glamrocks. But who are you?"

"We are glamrocks..." The mannequin repeated just as puzzled as the others.

"Tili, they don't understand. They don't have their own 'Self'," said Itfut. "And they don't have a mama either. They're mannequins, models of human beings."

"Okay. Watch how I ask her." Matilda turned to face the priestess. "Who are you?"

"I'm Mana-fata." replied Itfut.

"Now you ask me."

"Who are you?" asked Itfut.

"I'm Mana-tida. You understand?" said Matilda addressing the glamrocks now.

"Yes! Yes!" answered the glamrocks in unison. "You are manas!"

"Now I'm going to ask you." Matilda turned to face the mannequin who had stood forward again. "Who are you?"

"We are glamrocks!" he answered.

"This is hopeless, Tili." said Itfut.

"No. I'm not giving up just like that!" Matilda thought for a minute. "Let's take them to the mirror. Let them look at themselves. We can ask them what they know about it at the same time."

"Yes, of course, let's. I'm curious."

"Listen!" said Matilda addressing the glamrocks. "We are going to the mirror now. Have you ever been there before? Do you know what it is?"

"We don't know any mirror," answered the glamrocks. "What is it?"

"The mirror. There's sea and palm trees. Over there!" Matilda pointed in the direction of the spot where she and Itfut had tried to penetrate the invisible wall.

"The edge of the world! The edge of the world!" the savages cried in alarm. "Not allowed to go there! Not allowed! Aboo!"

"You can with us, though." Matilda reassured them. "We are the great manas. We will take you there."

The glamrocks shifted indecisively from one foot to another. It wasn't easy for them to overcome their 'aboo'.

"You want to become manas, don't you?" Itfut asked.

"Yes, yes, we do!"

"Then you must come."

"You must, you must!" Matilda emphasized in her authoritative manner. "You'll become manas, and you'll be full. No, you won't simply be full, you'll be wonderful! That's bigger, that's better. Aba!"

"Aba!" the glamrocks shouted, inspired.

The agreement was reached, and the entire procession set off in the direction of the meta-object which we, in the absence of any other definition, had called a mirror. Along the way, the diva and the priestess took the opportunity to confer.

"Tili, any ideas? What do you plan to do?" asked Itfut.

"We'll stand them in front of the mirror, let them look at themselves," answered Matilda.

"That might not work, though. Seeing yourself in a mirror isn't the same thing as discovering a sense of inner 'Self'."

"What do you mean?"

"We talked about it before, the movie characters and the observers, remember?"

"Ah! Yes, the glamrocks are pure characters."

"Exactly, they don't have their own 'Self'. Or the opposite may be true: they don't have their own 'Self' which is why they are characters."

"What is the Self, though? I mean, I can say that I am me, I am myself, but what is that 'Self' exactly?"

"It's simply your awareness, your attention."

"I don't get it."

"The glamrocks don't have their own 'Self' because their attention is totally immersed in the movie, they're a part of. As characters, they lack conscious awareness. In a way, we become this kind of character when we dream. It's as if we are in a fog or a delirium, unaware of the 'Self' because we are fully immersed in the dream. And yet the moment we remember 'Self', that is, the moment we take control of where we are placing our attention, we wake up in the dream, or we wake from sleep."

"Tufti-Tufti! Priestess-priestess!" exclaimed Matilda. "Looks like your memory is completely restored?"

“Shush, Ilit, not quite, not yet but there are times when I remember the things my Teacher taught me.”

“You’re talking about simple things in the most extraordinary manner again! I never thought of it all like that before. So, that means that I am my attention? That’s it?”

“That’s it. Well, what else did you think you were?”

“Well, there is a certain higher essence that lies behind every ordinary human being.”

“The soul, yes, naturally. Only your average human being not only does not feel or listen to their soul, they aren’t fully conscious in an intelligent way, either. What’s the point of incarnating as a higher being and yet remaining unconscious of who you really are?”

“What do you mean, unconscious of who you really are?” said Matilda in surprise. “Here I am! I am me!”

“But you are you only when you ask yourself that question. You become yourself only in the moment that you turn your attention to yourself, when you pull it back from the external movie or from your inner thoughts. Only then can you truly say that you are you. The rest of the time, you are a movie character lacking conscious awareness and being controlled by the movie. You aren’t aware of your own being and you can’t be your own authority because you have no authority over where you place your attention.”

“Both in sleeping and in waking?”

“Yes, it makes no difference.”

“Sux! Exactly! Futi, we’ve discussed this theme many times now, but I still can’t get my head round it.”

“I know, it’s kind of simple and complicated at the same time.”

“Right. I’ll try and unscramble it.

When I'm asleep and not aware that I'm sleeping, I am a movie character led by the dream. I have no control over my attention. It's totally immersed in the dream.

When I suddenly understand that I am sleeping, I wake up inside the dream and can potentially live lucidly within the dream, observing and even influencing the course of the dream's events. I am in control of where my attention goes. As soon as I lose that control, I forget again that I am sleeping. I forget myself and I lose myself.

And when I forget myself in waking life, I transform into a movie character, too. My attention is not my own. It's immersed in the movie and the movie is controlling me.

So, that means that my 'I' is my attention? When my attention is my own, I am me, but when my attention is immersed in something, in a sense, I don't exist. Only the movie I'm immersed in exists.

Futi! Now I get it! When I'm asleep, it is like there's no me. It is like I'm lost in a state of forgetting! And waking life is the same. I often act unconsciously, on automaton, as if it weren't really me but a movie character. So, it turns out, I'm living like a character in a movie most of the time? That really sucks! It sucks, I mean really!"

"That's right, Tili." said Itfut. "You are your attention. And you are either a conscious observer or a movie character depending on where you focus your attention, within yourself or not within yourself."

"Unbelievable! I get it, finally!"

“Yes, we are at least capable of waking up and being consciously aware from time to time. But there’s no way the glamrocks can say, ‘I am me’ because their attention is firmly entrenched in the dream, or the movie.”

“Oh, God! And how are we going to explain all this to our savages?”

“Ha, ha, ha! There’s zero chance of explaining it to them. Even you didn’t understand it straight away. And you’re smart, Matilda; but they are mannequins. You see the difference.”

“So where does that leave us? Defeated?”

“We’ll see. The task is to somehow jolt their attention out of the dream.”

Meanwhile, the procession had finally arrived at its destination.

REALITY KALEIDOSCOPE

The diva, the priestess and the glamrocks approached the mirror, or more precisely, the invisible wall that separated waking reality from this imaginary reality. The only hint of the wall's presence was the abrupt shift from rocky wasteland to grassy cover. In the mirror, on the other side, the standard screen was playing as before: ocean waves rolling onto a sandy beach and palm trees with their leaves swaying in the wind. At least here, on the side of meta-reality, there was sunshine radiating from the sun Matilda had 'created'. So, two suns hung symmetrically in the blue expanse, a sun in that sky and a sun in this one.

Seeing the picture that opened up before them, the glamrocks became extremely agitated.

"Big much! Big much!" they shouted in surprise. "Big much! Big much!"

They had evidently never seen the seascape before.

"Yes, big water. Much water." Matilda agreed. "This is the sea. So, is this the first time you see it? You said, you'd been here before?"

"We have, we have," the glamrocks replied. "But it wasn't like this, it wasn't like this!"

"What was it like then?"

"A wall! The edge of the world! A wall in the sky!"

"That's weird," said Matilda.

"Yes, it's strangely-strange," said Itfut. "It sounds like they saw a wall here that ran in all directions and up through the entire sky."

"It's still running through the entire expanse, it's just that it's transparent." Matilda approached the mirror and touched its invisible surface.

"It's gone. There's no wall!" said the glamrocks confidently. "Let's go over there!"

"No, wait! Stop!" Matilda shouted at them. "Look in the mirror! Can you see your reflection?"

"Tili, look! They have no reflection!" exclaimed Itfut.

It was true. The reflections of the diva and the priestess, although hazy, were still visible, whereas the glamrocks had no reflection whatsoever.

"Maybe the characters here aren't supposed to be reflected?" Matilda said, thinking aloud.

"Maybe," said Itfut. "If they're pure prototypes, then they have no physical self in reality, on the other side."

The glamrocks were impatient to run towards the sea. All trace of the former 'aboo' in relation to the 'edge of the world' had vanished.

"We want to go over there!" they said. "Let's go over there!"

"We all want to go to the sea," said Matilda, "but you can't get through, silly!"

"Let them try." Itfut suggested.

The savages were no longer paying any attention to their manas. Attracted by the stunning scenery, they rushed forward as if the wall simply did not exist. The diva and the priestess prepared themselves to see the lugs thudding their foreheads up against the wall but something else altogether unexpected happened instead.

One after the other, the glamrocks walked into the wall and disappeared without trace. There was no sign of them on the other side either. A moment later, they began exiting the wall walking backwards as if they were a mirror reflection. Only their appearance had changed entirely. They had transformed into men and women dressed in Renaissance period costumes. The women were wearing luxurious dresses with full skirts, and the men were in hose and silk doublets. They were all wearing wigs, the women's high and fair, the mens' dark and styled in curls. Their faces were hidden behind gold-plated masks decorated in enamel designs. The scene resembled the theatrical performance which the two friends had already seen in the mirror of reality, only now the performance was transferred to this side of the mirror and the diva and the priestess were bang in the middle of the action.

Somewhere harpsichord music was playing. The natural light of day was replaced by dim lighting, and the rocky ground had transformed into the surface of a wooden stage. The couples lined up in rows facing each other and began to dance a minuet. The men made graceful bows, and the women bobbed in elegant curtsies holding their fans open. The couples moved away from each other and then came back together again. Next, palm to palm, they turned in a slow rhythm. Everything was just the same as it was in Matilda's theatre, the only difference being that the costumes were classical and dignified, there was no film crew and the diva-understudy were absent. In the meantime, the image in the mirror remained unchanged: the sea continued to drive its phlegmatic waves into the shore.

The diva and the priestess watched the scene in silence glancing at each other in amazement. Finally, Itfut managed to whisper,

"Tili, is this another one of your tricks? Your dream?"

"This is nothing at all to do with me," whispered Matilda in response. "It's happening by itself."

"Then I have absolutely no idea what's going on."

"Me neither."

A moment later, the rhythm of the music began to quicken, and the dancers arranged themselves in a circle moving faster and faster. Their bodies gradually melted and dissolved into thin air as if they had been placed in some gigantic turning bowl. The whole scene twisted into a whirlwind that gave out a growing rumble... and suddenly it subsided transforming into clubs of green-tinted fog. In the midst of the metamorphosis, the diva and the priestess remained motionless, dispassionate observers.

Soon, the fog dissipated and revealed a new scene in which there was a cave lit dimly by the flames of a fire and primitive beings dressed in animal skins sitting and eating together. The beings finished their meal and set about simple tasks, sewing from animal skins and making tools. One was drawing horned animals on the wall. The images suddenly came to life, began to move, and broke into a run. The dome and walls of the cave unfurled into an open landscape.

Everywhere, the steppe stretched from horizon to horizon, and here and there wild herds grazed. In the grasses, not far away, humans lurked with spears. The hunters jumped out, hurled their spears, and the herd broke into a gallop. Several wounded animals fell, were skinned, the meat cut from the carcasses. The humans carried the meat into the cave, fried it on the fire, and went about their other domestic tasks while the artist painted a hunting scene on the cave wall. This image came to life and the cave unfurled once again into an image of the open steppe.

This time, flocks of sheep were being herded by shepherds dressed in coarse woolen clothing, who wandered about driving the animals ahead of them. Nearby there stood primitive looking dwellings built from poles and skins. Inside, the women were busy with the children, some making crafts, others cooking. A shaman danced around the fire beating a drum. An old man was drawing symbols on a piece of animal skin and these symbols came to life, began to move, and the piece of hide expanded unfolding into a vast meadow.

The people working in the field dressed in linen garments were reaping wheat with sickles and gathering the stems into sheaves. The harvest was being loaded into wagons pulled by oxen and then driven to a water mill and made into bread. The space shifted and changed until an ancient temple with pillars and marble statues appeared; slaves were carrying amphorae, loading them onto ships moored in a harbor. A philosopher was marking geometric shapes in the sand. His figures rose, grew and expanded into a medieval city.

Then narrow streets, stone walls and tile roofs came into view. A potter was sitting at a wheel, sculpting a ceramic vessel. A blacksmith was working with a hammer and anvil. Traders were selling their wares in the market square. A group of mounted knights dressed in armor and carrying spears and flags rode into a castle. The gates were raised, and inside there was a courtyard in which ladies in luxurious gowns were sitting in a coach. In a cell inside the castle, an alchemist surrounded by glass tubes and flasks was scribbling something down in a book. The pages rustled and surged upwards opening up a new picture of reality.

A worker was standing at a loom. There were many looms in the workshop, all making a great noise. Chimneys rose above the factory buildings belching out smoke. A locomotive came hurtling along the tracks pulling wagons behind it and arrived at a station. Ladies and gentlemen alighted the carriages. Dockers in a port were climbing up a ladder carrying sacks and crates. Ships were being built in the docks. A steamboat smoked coming out of the harbor. A scholar stood beside a blackboard on which he was writing something in chalk. The board was peppered with mind-bending formulas. The scribblings were becoming all the more complex, and then started to bend and fly off the board. The scene began to twist transforming into a star-studded cosmos before immediately returning to Earth.

The metropolis burned with the lights of high-rise buildings; the roads were crowded with a continuous stream of cars, and passers-by walked through the streets buried in luminous screens. There were apartment buildings and offices in which people sat in front of other screens. There was an assembly conveyor in a factory workshop. Workers in white coats were standing at a control panel and everywhere there were flashing bulbs and moving machinery parts. A scientist sitting at a computer screen was manipulating complex diagrams and 3D projections. The projections extended outside the building and enveloped the entire scene.

The metropolis then transformed into an accumulation of huge black cubes and cylinders connected by tunnel walkways. Inside the cylinders, capsules containing human embryos hung in concentric circles. The cubes were filled with identical cells, in which adults sat completely still, not looking up from their screens, all in metallic uniform-like overalls. The lamps, cars and machinery were all gone. Everywhere, instead there were glowing panels and monitors. Very occasionally, someone stood up and touched a panel at which a shelf segment would emerge holding a cup. The individual quickly drank its contents and sat back down at the screen. Everywhere silence reigned. The only sound came from a quiet electric buzzer.

Suddenly, the buzzer stopped, and the lights went out. The people panicked and rushed from panel to panel with no idea how it all worked or how to get anything started again. Completely fazed, they walked outside onto the street and wandered wherever their eyes took them without communicating with one another. The streets gradually emptied, the glass in the cubes and cylinders burst and shattered. The buildings fell into disrepair, collapsed and disappeared under a blanket of sand. Then, everything became overgrown with grass and trees and in a cave, primitive people were sitting at the fire, and again, the prehistoric artist was standing at the wall busy painting a hunting scene.

* * *

The diva and the priestess woke up in the square near the megalith. The crowd of the glamrocks were there too, looking at one another and all around in complete disbelief. Their appearance had returned to its former image. They were mannequins once again with the same old gray robes and wax faces.

"Futi! What was that? I'm in complete shock!"

"Judging by what we saw, we were being shown the history of civilization," laughed Itfut.

"Our civilization?!"

"I don't know which. Maybe yours, yes. Did it look like it could be yours?"

"Just about! Sux! Is that really the fate that awaits us?"

"No-one can ever know. The future isn't static. There are infinite potential versions of the future."

"What do you mean 'not static'?"

"Just that. The future does not exist per se. It is changing in every given moment, with every slide of reality depending on what is happening in this moment. It would be more accurate to say that the version of the potential future was changing. If it is changing all the time, how can anyone say that it actually exists?"

"So, what was it that we were being shown just now?" asked Matilda.

"Either a potential outcome or something that has already happened in a past civilization," answered Itfut. "There have been lots of different civilizations on the Earth and there will probably be many more to come."

"Oh, Futi, this is so like us! I mean really, super-similar! I'm scared!"

"Tili, have you forgotten where you are? You'd have to return home first before you could really be afraid."

"Was it anything like your civilization?"

"No, we don't invent mechanisms and screens. Ours is a different path."

"Yes, I can see that. I want to visit your world. I'm scared of returning home, now. I used to think we would annihilate ourselves in a war, but it turns out that's far from the worst thing that could happen."

"Tili, it's not a fact that things will unfold as we've just been shown. No-one knows exactly what the real future will look like."

"Even the mirror?"

"Even the mirror, even the mirror! And as I said, the images we saw could have been images from a different past."

"Futi, we don't even know where we are from. Are you from the future and I from the past or is it the other way around? Or wait, if as you say, there is no future, are you from the past, or am I? Now I'm totally confused."

"Tili, you're overthinking it. Neither the future nor the past exists as fact. All that exists is the present, the current slide. You and I arrived here from different film rolls that happened to coincide in the current slide. You only think that such and such happened in a concrete past because your memory is attached to a certain film roll. It's the same for me. But in actual fact, our film rolls, that is, our past and the versions of our possible futures exist simultaneously and with equal potentiality."

"So, you're saying that there are infinite potential versions of the past, too?"

"Of course. If there are many potential futures, then this is all the more so of the past."

“What do you mean by ’all the more so’?”

“Because the future emerges from the past. The range of the future is defined by the range of the past.”

“But if I can remember that such and such a thing happened, then it must have been real, right? You and I met here for example. That can’t not have taken place? Surely it can’t be that what we remember as having happened did not actually take place?”

“Well, no and yes,” sighed Itfut.

“Futi!” exclaimed Matilda impatiently. “Explain!”

“No-o-o! All I can say for certain is that the past and the future are virtual. Only the present, the now, is actually physically happening.”

“But that now has already happened and disappeared into the past. And it happened? Which must mean it was real.”

“Yes and no.”

“Futi! You’re driving me crazy! I’m driving myself crazy!”

“Tili, Tili, calm down. Just because you don’t understand something isn’t any reason to start going crazy. I can’t fully comprehend the nature of the past, the present and the future either. In truth, nobody can. The most important question is in fact this: what is the current frame? What is the present that is taking place? What is it made of? What is it really?”

“I’ve never thought about it like that before. It just exists, that’s all. I can see it and feel it, which means it exists. And existed.”

“You can see and feel everything in a dream, too, but tell me this: did the events of your dream really take place?”

Matilda was still for a moment, open-mouthed in surprise as what she had heard.

"But hang on, I have never brought any material proof of events back from a dream with me but in waking reality, if I break a cup, the broken pieces are all lying there for me to see."

"Tili, Tili! Where right now is the material proof of your past that actually physically took place?"

Matilda's jaw dropped in confusion again.

"Futi, you're making me lose my thread. There's my bow, my clothes, and there's me!"

"But you're physically present in a dream, too, and in your consciousness, you feel your clothes and even your body. So did your dream actually take place or not?"

"Well, yes and no..."

"See what I mean! Exactly, Tili, exactly!"

"But I still don't get it. You've completely confused me. I don't understand how you can say that the past existed and at the same time, that it didn't."

"All your memories of the past depend on your memory's bond with your own current film roll and the same goes for all the other people who are characters in it. Any proof of what happened in the past is only materialized in the current slide because it was previously present on a film roll in a virtual sense; but it's no fact that this evidence was actually materialized in the past in physical form since every film roll has an infinite range of potentials."

"But my memories relate to one version of the past, not an infinite number of them!"

"Your current slide can only be present in any given moment on one film roll. You remember a past that is connected to the film roll you are playing now; but what you remember, or what you think you remember is just one potential version of the past. Be that as it may, the material evidence of the past is such that everything tends to converge anyway."

"Yes, but it doesn't always converge, does it Futi!" exclaimed Matilda. "I once read about a paranormal phenomenon, in which people from the past appeared in our time and no one could understand how it had happened. The visitors could not explain how they had arrived here, and they even had belongings with them from their own historical period. The whole thing was documented but even then, few believed it. There was nothing they could do to help them, and their story was soon forgotten."

"And those people could remember their past, like it really happened even though it wasn't part of your film roll's past?"

"Yes!"

"Well, there you are, you see! Sometimes the rolls get mixed up and intersect. Just as ours did."

"Thank God that we met otherwise we'd have been lost here and all alone! You're right, not only can we say categorically yes or no about the past, but we can't be sure what is virtual and what is real now."

"Yes," said Itfut. "Once again, it all comes down to the question of where the difference lies between physical reality and a dream."

"And when we find the answer, we'll be able to get out of here?"

"I don't know. Maybe we'll be able to before that. But see, over there, looks like the glamrocks want to ask us something."

GLAMROCK INITIATION

The glamrocks were disturbed by the metamorphoses they had experienced since attempting to pass through the mirror. Huddling close together, they raised and drop their hands in confusion, looking at each other and then at their manas.

"Ok, come here," said Matilda to the glamrocks. "What do you want?"

"We wanted something, we wanted something..." They repeated as if not fully conscious of what they were saying.

"What exactly?"

"Something, something..." The glamrocks shifted from one foot to the other, not knowing how to express the thing they did not themselves know.

"Do you have a question?" said Itfut, helping them along.

"Yes, yes! We want to ask a question! We want to ask a question!"

"Well, ask it then."

The glamrocks exchanged looks and then as if in one voice, they said, "Who are we?"

"At last," said Matilda,"A glimpse of awareness."

But Itfut shook her head. "It's the wrong question."

"How should we ask it? How?" they said in surprise. Matilda was equally as intrigued.

"Ask it right! You have to ask it in the right way!" said Itfut.

"How? What's the right way?"

"You want to be manas, don't you?"

"Yes! Yes!"

"Then think, what's the right way to ask the question!"

"What question should we ask? What is the right way to ask it?"

"Futi, they probably aren't capable of thinking," said Matilda. "They've already achieved a lot more than they're supposed to be capable of."

"We already have!" the glamrocks confirmed. "Let the manas tell us who we are."

"Okay," said Itfut. "You're glamrocks. Happy now?"

"No! No!" the glamrocks replied.

"Why not?"

"We don't know. We're glamrocks but we don't know who we are."

"You're getting closer, getting warmer. Ask the right question!"

The mannequins conferred amongst themselves for a moment.

"Futi, I don't think I fully understand what you mean either."

"Tili, the whole point is just to make them ask questions. We wanted to jolt them out of the dream, right? Questions create the jolt."

"After what has just happened to them, they've already been jolted out of their usual mold."

"No, for now they're just confused."

“So, what is the right question?”

“You’ve already asked it. Only now, they’ve got to ask it themselves.”

“Oh, I get it!”

Meanwhile, the glamrocks appeared to have found a solution. They shouted joyfully and in unison.

“We know the right question! We know it!”

“Come on then, let’s hear it,” said Itfut.

“What are we like? There!”

“Ha, ha, ha!” Itfut laughed.

“That’s what you are like! That’s what!” Matilda teased them making the sign of little horns above her head with her fingers.

“You’re joyful, that’s what you’re like but it’s still not the right question,” said Itfut.

The glamrocks were dismayed, as far as one can say such a thing of mannequins but having conferred among themselves again, they began shouting out questions at random.

“Where are we?”

“Where are we going?”

“When are we?”

“Hey, hey! You won’t guess it like that!” said Itfut waving her hands at them to stop.

“No, you’ll never guess like that,” said Matilda. “Do you remember what I asked you not long ago?”

“The glamrocks thought for a minute and then said, “Whose are we?”

“Closer, but still not it,” said Itfut.

“So, whose are you then?” asked Matilda.

"Yes, whose are you?" Itfut repeated the question.

"Do we belong to you?" they answered with uncertainty.

"Futi, we're not going to get anywhere like this," said Matilda. "They'll never get there by themselves."

"Okay," said Itfut, and then whispered something in Matilda's ear. "Yes, you belong to us. And that being the case, we're going to ask you one by one."

The glamrocks were concerned but the diva and the priestess walked up to them and pulled one out of the crowd. The chosen glamrock squealed.

"The manas are going to eat me! The manas are going to eat me!"

"Stop squealing. We're not going to eat you!" Matilda shouted.

"Answer me. Who are you?" Itfut began the interrogation.

"We're glamrocks!" the glamrock said.

"Yes, all together, you are glamrocks. So, if you're glamrocks, why are you asking us who you are?"

"We don't know."

"If you don't know, then you aren't glamrocks."

"So, who are we?" asked the glamrock in fear.

"Who are we? Who?" asked the others in alarm.

"Ask the question properly."

The glamrock tried to break free and run away but Matilda held him firm.

"Ask me who I am," continued Itfut.

"Who are you?"

"I am Mana-fata. Who are you?"

"We are glamrocks," the mannequin answered looking back at the others.

"Do you remember what happened to you?" said Itfut turning to address them all. "When the action happened, what were you like? Do you remember?"

"We were different! Different!" they answered interrupting each other.

"What were you like?"

The mannequin who had been singled out tried to break free again but Itfut was not letting up.

"Whose are you? Are you lost?"

"I was lost," the glamrock answered instantly dumbfounded by what he had said.

"Ask the right question!" Itfut took the glamrock by the shoulders and gave him a good shake.

"Who am I?" asked the glamrock, as if struck by lightning.

"That's the right question!" Itfut solemnly announced. "But who are you asking?"

"Let the manas say," the mannequin replied. "Do the manas know?'

"Ask yourself! Yourself!" said Itfut giving the glamrock another shake.

"Who am I?"

"Who are you?" cried the diva and the priestess.

"I..." the glamrock was clearly flabbergasted. "I'm Tatana!" he said finally, or rather she said, since as soon as these words were spoken, something extraordinary happened. The glamrock's wax mask shattered and fell off exposing a woman's face, attractive and full of life. The same thing happened to her hands. The gray-hooded robe transformed smoothly into a black and white cowl. The glamrock had transformed into a Carmelite nun before the very eyes of all those present.

"Okay," said Itfut, the first to recover from amazement. "I've never seen anything like this before.'

"I have!" started Matilda. "Tatana, you say? You'll be Mana-tana. Now you're a mana, too!"

"I'm a mana?" The newly transformed figure was still struggling to come to her senses and just looked about her stunned. "I'm a mana, too?"

"Yes, yes, Mana-tana," said Itfut, who then turned to the other glamrocks, who were staring wide-eyed at the miraculous transformation with their mouths open. "Next!"

The mannequins were so amazed by what they had seen that not one took a single step. The diva and the priestess took the next glamrock by the hand and led the individual to one side.

"Who are you?" Matilda asked.

"We're glamrocks..." the glamrock was about to start repeating but Itfut interrupted him right away.

"You're not glamrocks anymore! You see?" she said and pointed at the Carmelite. "If you want to be a mana, you've got to ask the right question!"

"Who am I?" he mumbled hesitantly.

"Who are you asking?" Matilda leapt in. "Ask yourself! Who are you?"

"I'm Tatasha!" he said, and the same miraculous transformation was instantly repeated. Where previously the glamrock stood there now was a second Carmelite nun dressed in the same type of clothing but with a different face.

"Mana-tasha!" proclaimed Itfut, placing both hands on the shoulders of her newly made nun.

"Next!" cried Matilda. "Next! Come on, be bold!"

One by one, all the glamrocks passed the identity initiation asking the question and answering it independently. They all gave female names and all the individuals turned out to be exclusively of the female sex and for some reason true novitiates. Adalina became Mana-lina, Azabela became Mana-bela, Betarissa — Mana-rissa, Valatina — Mana-tina, Vassalisa — Mana-lisa, and so on, until a goodly monastic order was gathered.

"Ooh-la-la, Futi!" exclaimed Matilda admiring the transformed holy servants as they shifted from one foot to the other not quite knowing where to put themselves. "What are we going to do with them?"

"Leave them to sort themselves out now," said Itfut. "That's what you wanted, isn't it? Anyway, what's this image they all have?"

"They're nuns. There are people like those in my world."

"They're whats?"

"Novitiates, who have dedicated their lives to serving God, like your priestesses."

"Priestesses? You mean they're priestesses, too?"

"Well, not quite. How can I put it... it's more like they're humble and modest — virgins."

"How strange that glamrocks have turned into virgins."

"Right. Let's just be thankful they aren't bandits or thieves otherwise we might have difficulties with them."

"Next we need to check how consciously aware they are."

"Hey, you, come here," said Itfut calling one of the nuns to her. "Who are you?"

"I'm Mana-lisa," she replied.

"Right. That's better. And now tell me this, what are you?"

"We're glamrocks..."

"No, concentrate! You are Mana-lisa. But what are you? Can you answer? Do you know ***what*** you are? You are what you do! So, what are you doing?"

"We read gibberish."

"Futi, they have not fully woken up as individuals yet," said Matilda. "Maybe we should ask them all together first? Who are you?" she said addressing the others.

"We are Carmelites," they said timidly. And then more confidently,

"Carmelites! We're Carmelites!"

"There, you see! Well done!" said Matilda encouragingly. "And what do you have to do?"

"Read gibberish!"

"No! Concentrate, concentrate!" shouted Itfut. "You are Carmelites. You are manas. What do manas do?"

"Ask questions?"

"No! They do whatever they want, what they really want."

"How's that? What do you mean?" asked the nuns in surprise.

"Mana-lisa," said Itfut turning to her acquaintance, "tell me, when you do something, do you do it of your own accord or because someone is directing you?"

"We are Carmelites..." the nun said hesitating, not understanding what Itfut wanted from her.

"You are you all together. But you, Mana-lisa, are you just you, or are you not just you? Whose are you?"

"I belong to myself!" Understanding was beginning to dawn on the nun, who became more animated as a result. "I am myself!"

"And before that, when you were a glamrock, were you yourself?"

"No, I didn't belong to myself, I wasn't myself! But now, I belong to me and I'm myself!"

"Right, fabulous," said Itfut, summing up. "So, before you didn't belong to yourself but now you have woken up and you are you."

"Yes, I am me!" shouted the nun joyfully.

"And now what are you? What do you do?"

"I'm a mana and I do what I want! Whatever I want, that's what I do!"

"No, stop!" Matilda decided to intervene. "If we carry on like this, they might end up going too far! Do you remember what aboo is?"

"Yes, we remember. It's when we mustn't do what is forbidden."

"What are you allowed to do?"

"We can do whatever is allowed."

"But more specifically... what is allowed and what is prohibited?" asked Matilda continuing to push.

"We mustn't eat each other!" answered the nuns.

"What about the others?"

"That's okay, that's okay! We just mustn't eat our own. The others aren't our own."

"Just what I thought!" said Matilda, throwing up her hands in despair. "That's how far they've come."

“They still aren’t quite fully aware of themselves as individuals,” said Itfut. “When you get them by themselves, they are like individuals, but when they are all together, they default to the collective dream, in a kind of collective insanity.”

“Hum, Futi, collective insanity is not just a characteristic of the glamrocks ! As far as I can tell, most people are just the same!”

“So, what are we going to do, Tili?”

“You’re asking me? As if I know! Except, maybe I do know. We need to show them something, yes, there’s something we should show them!”

Matilda whispered something in Itfut’s ear and then turned to the nuns and said,

“Wait here. We’ll be back very soon!”

ASKING QUESTIONS INSIDE THE DREAM

The diva and the priestess entered the megalith leaving the newly initiated sisters waiting outside.

"Futi!" exclaimed Matilda once they were alone. "Now I understand!"

"Understand what, Tili-Tili?"

"Everything! I understand the true value of asking questions and the significance of the questions you were asking. When I'm not asking questions, it is like I'm in a stupor or a daydream and you know why?"

"Why, why, Tili-Tili?"

"Because I'm just passively accepting whatever's happening even if it's inconvenient to me or I don't like it. It does not even occur to me to stop and ask what's really happening to me and my environment. I just let the current take me or at best, helplessly flounder about in its waters."

"Exactly, Tili. Passively accepting whatever is happening means taking it all for granted. And taking something for granted means accepting it as a possibility, as something which is likely to occur. And when you accept things, you inevitably plunge right into the dream. Do you remember we were talking about 'conceding and not conceding'? Once you're in the dream, you're powerless. Anything can happen to you, however absurd, because you have conceded and are taking circumstances for granted."

"Exactly, Futi! I don't ask questions when I'm dreaming. I have no sense of my own will. It's as if I'm no longer myself, no longer in charge of my own life and am just being led by the dream. And it is the same in waking life just to a lesser degree."

"Not much less, though," said Itfut.

"I was going to say," Matilda continued, "that it's practically the same. It's not a matter of whether I like what is happening or not, and even whether it suits me or not. The point is that once I accept the possibility that a set of circumstances could feasibly represent my reality, those circumstances can in fact happen to me, whether I want them to or not."

"Precisely. When you concede to circumstances the film takes control and you're transformed into the equivalent of a character in a movie."

"But what I've finally recognized is ***when*** I am conceding. It's the moment I stop asking questions! It turns out that to wake up you have to start asking questions: 'where am I?' 'What's going on with me?' 'Is this my reality?' And most importantly, 'am I being my own person right now or am I being led by others?' Am I acting independently or am I being directed by the movie?"

"You've got it now, Tili."

"Now for our thoughts. I get the question 'who are you?' but I liked the other question the most, 'who do you belong to?' It's the kind of stupid question a stupid adult asks when they find a lost child."

"It is pretty stupid." Itfut laughed.

"It really is, I mean, an adult asks a child, 'who do you belong to?' and how's the poor kid supposed to respond? 'I belong to my mummy and daddy' or, 'I'm a national treasure'?"

"What, what? What's a national treasure?"

"It's what people on television craftily call things that don't belong to us."

"I don't understand, I don't understand!" said Itfut puzzled.

"It doesn't matter. It would take too long to explain. So," continued Matilda, "when a child realizes they are lost, they panic, and panic is the deepest kind of dream you can have. When you're panicking, you aren't capable of doing anything except rush about crying and screaming."

"Have you ever been lost?"

"Yes, once. I burst into tears and threw the kind of strop only a proper little madam can. And then someone came up to me and asked, 'whose kid are you? Who do you belong to?'"

"And how did you respond?"

"I did not say anything, naturally. I just carried on crying and screaming. But I remember thinking, 'what kind of ridiculous question is that?' To me it was obvious that I did not belong to anyone! I was my own self. I did not give it any more thought at the time. It's only now I realize the true meaning of the question."

"Which is...?"

"You already know the answer. People who ask kids that question have no idea what they are really asking but when you put the question to the glamrock and the nun, you knew exactly what you were asking! It is all about whether you can act independently with conscious awareness or whether you are controlled by the movie. In other words, can you own yourself and be your own self or not?"

"Quite, and the answer to the question is, 'I don't belong to anyone. I am my own person', if of course a person has woken up."

"I knew the right answer back then, but it did not help me wake up from the dream because I did not understand its full significance," said Matilda. "It's all about who's running the show in your life, you or some external script."

"More specifically, where are you focusing your attention, on yourself or on the movie?" added Itfut. "And the reason you did not wake up back then is because you did not question what was happening."

"Right! I just carried on crying and screaming, when all I had to do was stop and ask myself, 'has anything really so terrible happened? My mother and I have lost sight of one another temporarily, but would my mummy ever abandon me? No! she'll find me very soon. In the meantime, I'll just wander up and down a bit and calmly observe what's happening because that's what I've decided!' That's what it means to wake up!"

"You're describing an event that took place in childhood, but the same thing applies in adult life, too, both in dreaming and in waking."

"Exactly, Futi! It's amazing! Really cool."

"What? What's 'cool'?"

"It's like 'great', 'awesome'! How amazing to be able to understand all this stuff! I had no idea!"

"It isn't enough to understand it though. You have to be able to apply it and that takes constant practice."

"Yes, I remember, the observers and the characters, state of awareness and the Witness," recited Matilda as if in class. "In order to become an observer, you have to develop the opposite habit. Now, as soon as anything comes up, instead of getting immersed in my passions and losing myself in the dream, I'll wake up and start taking conscious action. The slightest waft that something is 'off' in my personal space and I'll make myself wake up. The moment I get a sense of anything, I'll activate my Witness and start asking questions. Now I own myself and am my own self."

"Well done, Matilda!" said Itfut praising her like a pupil. "And can you remember what the most important question is? What do you have to do to awaken your inner witness?"

"Pay attention to where I'm placing my attention and to whom it belongs: it is with me or have I given it away to the movie. Basically, you have to track reality and as soon as anything pops up, instantly activate the inner witness. If something goes wrong, you have to be able to see reality and yourself within it."

"And the same goes for when things are going right. You have to ***see*** more often like the seers in my world do: you have to be able to say, 'I see myself and I see reality'."

"To avoid turning into a glamrock?"

"Yes, yes, that too."

"It's strange," said Matilda. "They were savages, but they transformed instantly into Carmelites. How do you explain something like that?"

"Yes, it's strange," Itfut agreed. "It must be a quirk of the mirror. Everything is bizarre in the dream space. So, have you decided what you're going to do with them?"

"So far their transformation is purely external. In essence, they're the same old glamrocks. They haven't fully woken up yet. We need to show them the difference between good and evil."

"How?"

"You'll see. I'll switch on my skills for entertaining the masses. First, though, we should feed them. They must be starving."

Matilda approached the black cylinder, adjusted her bow with the usual movement and whispered something. Segments immediately began to emerge from the cylinder holding baskets of flat breads and baked fish, large jugs and ceramic cups and plates. Itfut watched with interest and peered into the baskets.

"Tili, why bread and fish?"

"It's a classic!"

"What, what is? In what sense?"

"You'll see."

"And what's in the jugs, Tili? It's not that happy drink again is it?"

"No, it's grape juice, also a classic."

The diva and the priestess began carrying the food outside. Itfut prudently materialized a large tablecloth to lay the food upon. The nuns walked up and observed the preparations with curiosity pointing to things and discussing it all among themselves. Once the whole à la carte service was transferred to the tablecloth, Matilda gave the order.

"Right, darling sisters, come and sit down!"

The nuns obediently arranged themselves in a large circle and the diva and the priestess sat at the center next to the covered tablecloth.

"Now, we're going to learn a special action," said Matilda addressing them all, "it's called 'doing something nice for others'."

"Others? Nice?" the nuns asked. "Why others? The others aren't one of us!"

"Who are you calling 'others'?"

"Those who might arrive!"

"And what will you do with them if they do?"

"Eat them!"

"And how many have you already eaten?"

"None! None!"

"And why is that?" asked Itfut.

"We plan to eat them but when we're about to start they leave instantly," Mana-lisa answered on behalf of the group.

"What do you mean, they leave? Where do they go?" asked Matilda.

"They disappear. One minute they're there, and the next 'poof', they're gone."

"I see," said Itfut. "The others are dreamers. They appear here when they are having a dream. It's the standard nightmare: the dreamer is attacked by savages and just as they are about to be eaten alive, the dreamer wakes up from the terror."

"Why do you treat aliens like this?" Matilda asked the nuns.

"It's how it's meant to be!" the nuns replied.

"Who says? What's the point?"

"We don't know. That's just how it is!"

"If you carry on like this, you'll stop being manas and turn back into glamrocks. Is that what you want?"

"No! No!"

"Then remember, doing bad to others is not allowed! You're not allowed to hurt anyone. What have Mana-fata and I ever done to hurt you?"

"Nothing, nothing! The manas are kind!"

"And what about you though? You were going to eat us!"

"You are one of us now! The others aren't!"

"Mana-lisa, come here," Matilda called out. "You are you. The others are all the rest and not just 'our own or not our own'. You must never hurt another. You have to look after people, otherwise, Mana-lisa will stop being a mana and go back to being an ugly glamrock again. Is that what you want?"

"No! No! I want to be a mana!"

"And what about you?" said Matilda turning her gaze to the others. "This goes for all of you! Do you all understand what it means to be a mana? It means to do good for others."

"But how, how?" the nuns stammered. "How do we do good for others?"

"We're about to show you." Matilda placed a fish and flat bread on the plate and nodded to Itfut to fill a plate, too. Then together, they went up to one of the nuns and handed her the plate of food.

"There, we are doing something good for you but before you dig in you have to do the same for one of your sisters."

The nun was surprised but she did as she was told and passed a plate of food to the nun sitting next to her.

"And now you," said Matilda to the recipient. "Pass it on and do something good for another. There is enough food for everyone!"

The diva and the priestess each passed their plate to one of the nuns who passed in on to another going around the circle until everyone had a plate of food.

"Is everyone feeling good now?" asked Matilda.

"Yes! Yes!" the nuns answered in unison.

"There, you see! And why does everyone feel good?"

"Why? Why?" the nuns said answering her with a question.

"Because when you do good to others, it comes back to you. Understand?"

"We understand, we understand!" the nuns said nodding.

"Okay, you can eat now. Enjoy!"

TAKING ACTION INSIDE THE DREAM

They all began tucking into the food, the diva and the priestess included. While they were eating, Matilda turned to them all again and said, "And now, just for the sake of comparison, let's try doing something bad to others and see what happens." Then, picking one of the nuns, she turned to her and gave her a good slap round the head.

"There, I did something nasty. Not that painful but still unpleasant, right?"

"Yes," the nun replied.

"Now do the same to the sister next to you."The nun did the same to her neighbor who copied her and so on around the circle.

The nuns began slapping each other vigorously round the head and got so carried away that Matilda had a job getting them to stop.

"Enough! That's enough! Stop! Does everyone feel bad now?"

"Yes! Yes!" the nuns answered in unison.

"Why does everyone feel bad?"

"Why? Why?"

"Because if you make someone else feel bad, it comes back to you. Understand?"

"We understand, we understand!" they said nodding.

"You see how doing good and doing something bad to another comes back to you? What conclusion should you draw?"

"What conclusion? What conclusion?"

"I've already told you. You must never hurt others. You have to look after others. Got it?"

"Got it, got it!"

"And just to reinforce the lesson, we're going to learn to kiss each other. That's what we promised. Do you want to?"

"Yes, yes!"

"You, then," said Matilda turning to one of the nuns. "Touch your lips to your sister's cheek and she will do the same to the nun sitting next to her and so on around the circle. Go!"

The diva and the priestess observed for a while watching the transfigured nuns absorb the new experience. The nuns appeared to enjoy it and once again, it was not easy to get them to stop.

"Now," said Matilda, "we're going to repeat what we've covered so far. What must manas do in order to remain manas?"

"Do good for others!" the nuns responded amicably.

"And what will manas turn into if they are bad to each other?"

"Glamrocks!"

"Do you want to be glamrocks or manas?"

"Manas, manas!"

"Excellent!" Matilda announced with a sense of accomplishment.

"That's not all, though," Itfut chipped in. "What else do manas do?"

"What they want?"guessed the learned Mana-lisa.

"They do whatever they choose to do," the priestess added. "You, Mana-lisa, what do you do of your own choosing?"

The nun thought for a moment and then it seemed to dawn on her.

"I sew!" she exclaimed in delight.

The others stared enviously at the lucky nun.

"And what about us? What do we do?"

"Not you altogether but each one of you individually!" Itfut corrected them.

"Ask yourself!" Matilda said trying to help them.

"You, Mata-tasha," said Itfut addressing the nun, "Ask yourself, what do you do?"

"What do I do?

"And answer straight away without hesitating!"

"I do the washing," she answered at first perplexed but then more confidently. "I do the washing! Because I choose to!"

"And you, Mana-bela, what do you do of your own choosing?"

"What do I do? I do the clearing up! Because I choose to!"

"And you, Mana-lina?"

"I cook! Because I choose to!"

"And you, Mana-tana?"

"I take care of others! Because I choose to!"

All the Carmelites were interrogated in turn and it turned out had each had chosen her own occupation. Meanwhile, the sun was already beginning to set. Another difficult and eventful day in meta-reality was coming to an end. Finally, the diva and the priestess decided to ask the inhabitants of this strange world what they actually knew about the place.

"So, sisters," said Matilda addressing them. "I hope, now, you will no longer attack anyone else who turns up here."

"We won't! We won't!" They responded.

"And what will you do with them?"

"We're going to be nice to them!"

"Bravo! But Mana-fata and I are also strangers here and we need to leave now."

"No! No!" the nuns called out. We want the manas to stay!"

"We have to go," said Itfut. "We don't belong here. And you will manage fine without us. You have the food the megalith gives you. Mana-lina, do you know how to get food?"

"Yes, yes!"

"And also, you all have your own activity," said Matilda. "You'll all have something to be getting on with now."

"We will, we will!"

"And before, what did you do when you were glamrocks?" asked Itfut.

"We read gibberish!"

"That's it? That's all you ever did? Just that?"

"It's all we ever did."

"The dream was stuck on it," Itfut whispered to the diva. "It's roughly the same thing as a still image where there are no observers, and everything has stopped moving."

"Yes, the only difference here is that dreamers have arrived," replied Matilda.

"What is this city?" Matilda asked the nuns. "When was it built? Who built it?"

“We don’t know,” answered the nuns. “It’s always been here.”

“And what about you? What do you remember about yourselves? How did it all start?”

“We don’t remember. We’ve always existed. Everything’s always existed.”

“And always the same thing, identical?”

“Always the same thing, identical.”

“Tili, that’s how it should be in an individual sector of meta-reality where there are no observers,” said Itfut. “It is like a segment of the film strip: what’s filmed is what’s there. Here, eternity and a single moment are equivalent concepts.”

“It’s obviously pointless questioning them about it,” said Matilda. “But hang on a minute! They used to be glam-rocks and then they became Carmelites. That must mean we’re already on another film roll, right?”

“Quite possibly.”

“But how did that happen? Did they fell asleep as glam-rocks and just wake up again as Carmelites?”

“Yes, you could say that we woke them up.”

“So that means that they have all woken up in a different dream”

“They are still sleeping characters, but their dream has changed, yes.”

“So, what would it take for something to change for us?” asked Matilda.

“Wait!” said Itfut startled. “You’re saying we need to fall asleep and then wake up again? But we’ve already done that.”

"Yes, once, only that time a dream which had stopped was being relaunched. What would happen if we fell asleep and woke up inside a dream that was already running? At least something ought to change, didn't it?"

"The question is what. Although in our position there's probably no other option."

"Which means we've got to try."

The nuns meanwhile had diligently returned all the crockery to the megalith and were now huddled together looking inquiringly at their top manas.

"So, sisters," said Matilda addressing them. "The day has come to an end. Do you ever go to bed?"

"Yes, we go to bed!" the nuns replied.

"Then you wake up and everything is newly similar again?"

"Yes, new again!"

"Well, from now on, everything's going to be different. It'll be better, more fun. It might be that Mana-fata and I disappear tomorrow like the others before us."

"No! We don't want you to! We want the manas to stay!"

"Don't be sad, sisters!" said Itfut trying to cheer them up. "We might return yet and see each other again."

"Yes! Yes!" shouted Matilda. "We will definitely come back and visit you! We just need to figure out first how to move about in this reality."

"The manas will figure it out! The manas are clever!" said the nuns.

"In the meantime, we have another present for you," said Matilda throwing up her arms in a sign of invocation. "May there always be stars!" she said.

At that moment, the dark, empty sky was lit with a myriad of stars in all different colors. The nuns burst into shouts of rapture. Even Itfut was surprised.

"Wow! Tili!"

"And now, let's say farewell, sisters!" said Matilda.

"Bye for now, dear friends, see you again soon!" Itfut said waving at them.

The nuns exchanged glances and then simultaneously bowed speaking in chorus:

"Thank you, Mana-tida! Thank Mana-fata! Thank you!"

And with that, they all scattered wandering off in the direction of their houses.

* * *

"Just one more question, Futi," said Matilda once they were alone, "perhaps the most important of all."

"What super important question is that, Tili, Tili?"

"After we've fallen asleep, could you and I end up in different worlds?"

"Well, the last time we fell asleep together in the same place we woke up together too."

"Yes but firstly, we did not wake up together in the sense of it being at the same time, and secondly, when we woke up, the previous dream had stopped, so I'm wondering what might happen this time?"

"I don't know but for some reason I think we will stay together. We are already in the dream space and not in the everyday physical reality from which people usually depart when they dream."

"Did you dream last night?"

"No."

"Me neither. I'm still scared though! Why don't we ask Threshold about it?"

"He's not very forthcoming with his answers but, all right, let's try it," Itfut agreed. "Hey! Threshold, are you there?!" shouted Itfut looking up at the sky. A rustling wind picked up as usual and a whisper arose which seemed to come from all directions at once.

"I am here and everywhere...here and everywhere..."

"Just one question!" shouted Matilda. "Only don't fly off straight away! Answer us! Please! Will we be separated if we fall asleep here or will we still wake up in the same place together?"

"You'll wake up together...together..." came Threshold's whispering response.

"And is it possible for us to return to the material world and if so when?" asked Itfut.

"All in good time...time…," the wind whispered.

"And can we both return to the same world?" Matilda shouted. "Please! We want to be together!"

"It's not enough to want it... not enough..." came the windy whisper again before beginning to subside.

"What else will it take, then? What else?" Matilda shouted after the wind but there was no answer.

"There you go, same as always..." said Itfut. "More questions than answers."

"The most important thing is that it answered our question. We will wake up together," said Matilda.

"Seems like it. Come on, let's go get some sleep, Tili. I'm so tired!"

"Me too, let's go."

The priestess and the diva entered the megalith and fell straight into bed without even stopping to undress.

"Let's not undress, Tili," said Itfut. "You never know what will be awaiting us when we wake."

"I was thinking exactly the same thing," said Matilda. "I'm still scared though, Futi. Let's push the beds together and hold hands."

"Yes, let's."

Only once they had repositioned the beds and lay down did they notice that the dome of the megalith had become transparent and through it shone a myriad of beautiful multi-colored stars. The diva and the priestess stared silently up at the twinkling night sky too tired to chat any longer. A minute later they were both asleep.

PUSCILLA

Beast ran as fast as he could, winding down the narrow city streets, complicating his route, trying to throw the pursuers off his trail. Just as he had in the past, he carried his woman across his shoulder who had by some incomprehensible turn of fate ended up here in the current era. Only now his woman was clothed not in animal skins but in a civilian-style dress. Beast looked very different to his former, cave man self, too, as well as to his more recent animal form.

He was a handsome young man now with brown shoulder-length hair dressed in a black velvet frock coat with large gold buttons, the same style trousers and a snow-white shirt with a frill. All that remained from his former appearance were his big sad eyes and shaggy loafers that were quite incongruous when matched with his aristocratic looking suit. There was still something about his countenance that remained the same and by which those who knew him could accurately recognize him as the Beast they knew.

Beast did not know exactly where he was dragging his woman, but he was totally clear on the reason why. If a woman is in danger and if it is impossible to eliminate the cause of the danger, you pick up the woman and carry her as far away from the source of the danger as possible. Moreover, this time, his woman was not kicking and screaming for the whole forest to hear as she had done in the past. On the contrary, this time she was making quiet, you could even say, contented sounds reminiscent of a purring cat.

'Weird, why is she purring?' thought Beast. No sooner had he formulated this thought than the woman once again made a sound that far from resembling anything human was more like a loud, protracted 'Mi-i-ia-a-ow!' Only then did Beast to his immense surprise discover that it was not a woman he was carrying but a large cat the size of a panther. Yes, it was quite something, but Beast had no real call to be surprised considering that just a few minutes earlier he had been nothing else but Shaggy Beast. The young Beast-man continued to run without stopping carrying his burden on his shoulder.

At that moment, having heard the relict call, all the cats and tom cats across the entire neighborhood appeared out of all the nearby alleys, entrances and gates and ran after the fugitives, meowing desperately, each in their own way.

The catty horde swelled all the time as new members joined it all continuously yelling 'Miaow-Miaow!' The big cat lying across Beast's shoulders echoed in turn with her own 'Miaow-miaow!'

And who knows how long this would have gone on for and how it would have ended had not the young Beast-youth run into a small square, finally dropped his cat to the ground, given himself a good shake and suddenly transformed back into Shaggy Beast. All the cats and tom cats who had gathered around froze in surprise. And then Beast roared at them, 'R-r-r-a-a-ahhh!' at which point all the cats and tom cats ran away again scattering in all directions making 'Miaow-miaow!' noises as they went. The big cat, who was now sitting on the ground with its tail wrapping around its legs blurred into a catty smile and purred with great satisfaction, 'Mia-a-a-oow!'

* * *

Meanwhile, the female doctor, the nurses and the 'expedition' team only managed to recover from their stunned stupor once the kidnapper had disappeared around the corner.

"What on earth was tha-a-at?!" screamed the doctor.

"Under below!" cried Yellow Submarine.

"Help!" shouted Orange Cow

"Company, reveille! Alert! Alert!" shouted Eejit Green.

"In the car! Quick!" ordered the female doctor. "After them!"

Grumbling, the male nurses climbed into the ambulance.

"Catch them up!" shouted Eejit while wedging his club beneath one of the vehicle's back wheels.

"Heal them, heal them!" shouted Submarine hooking her anchor up against the curb and gripping onto the back of the ambulance.

"In hot pursuit of a bloody maniac!" shouted Cow jumping ahead of the vehicle.

"In pursuit of a savage sadist!" shouted Eejit, waving his hands about. "Faster, what are you hanging about for!"

Only the warrior Brunhilda remained calm looking about her appearing to be listening for something. Meanwhile, the ambulance came to an abrupt halt skidding from side to side.

"What is going on?" The doctor said as both she and the nurses piled out of the vehicle to take a look. Submarine quickly jumped to the side and Eejit thrust his hands into his trouser pockets.

"Oh, what a paradoxical discovery!" he exclaimed. "There appears to be a piece of driftwood of unknown origin stuck right under your wheel. So that's what's hindering the successful dispatch of emergency assistance!"

"It's a terrorist, one of your gang! And you, it seems, are all in it together!" said the doctor gripping the entire crew with a hard stare.

One of the nurses pulled the club from out under the wheel while another took a pair of handcuffs from his belt.

"What on earth do you mean!" said Eejit. "We are extremely supportive of the supremacy of the rule of law over all manner of illegal initiative, as well as the full recovery of all accountable members of society."

"You can't fool me with your smooth talk!" yelled the doctor. "Go on, out with it! Who is the subject and with what aim has he abducted our patient?"

"Most honorable colleague," answered Eejit. "As we have already stated, we have the honor of being employees of the Red Cross and Crescent, or more specifically, trainee confabulating inventors... uh-h, I mean investigators sourcing and researching all manner of means and methods for the cure of all manner of disease. We cannot say what motives drive our comrade. We too find ourselves lost in a mad fog of conjecture and insinuation. However, you may find one reliable assumption to be the following:..."

"That inventor of yours is a dangerous love maniac!" the doctor shouted impatiently. "And you are all his accomplices or worse, an entire gang of love maniacs!"

"Excuse me, dear colleague, but in the unfounded accusation aimed at our decent selves, you make mention of a medical determinant currently unfamiliar to us. Could you not enlighten us... wherein lies the quintessential significance of the term 'love maniac'? Or perhaps you meant 'erotic dreamer' or 'amorous prospector', or even 'romantic harasser'?"

"Harassers are of no interest to us whatsoever. Our profile is strictly limited to the affliction of love. Love mania is the same disease in its most pernicious form. You, my darlings, are just trying to sweetly pull the wool over my eyes, again!"

"Not at all sweetly! I mean, not at all! We simply wish to understand..."

"That's enough! I haven't got time to stand here splitting hairs with you lot!"

"But I have not yet put forward my significant supposition concerning the motives of our comrade's hasty act. Said supposition is as follows..."

"Get to the point!"

"Well, in brief, the real meaning of the supposition is this: Our comrade is not at all the kind of pathetically drooling admirer who would plan to exert love over the patient, but rather an overly zealous natural scientist who, yielding to his exorbitant zeal, decided to, so to speak, run circles around you by successfully treating the patient via the method of her abduction, thereby hoping to bring on a state of stress as a result of which, according to his strictly scientific hypothesis, the patient ought to make the swiftest of recoveries...

"Well, we're going to catch your inventor-investigator and then we'll get to the bottom of things," said the doctor interrupting Eejit's deep and meaningful speech. "Right, everyone in the car. Let's get a move on!" she ordered to the nurses.

"We're all for it!" came the voice of Brunhilda who had just whispered something into Cow's ear. "You have our full cooperation!"

"Yes, yes, you can rely on our multilateral and unlimited complicity!" said Eejit affirming Brunhilda's position.

"Why don't I fly ahead and show you the way," offered Cow spreading her wings. "From above I'll be able to see more clearly than you can which way they went."

"Okay, launch your drone," agreed the doctor. "We'll follow him."

The roaring ambulance engine, the flashing light and terrible-sounding siren all set off at great speed to where the kidnapper was hiding while Cow rose up into the air to lead the chase off the trail.

* * *

Beast stood looking at the big cat and the cat sat looking back at him. She had black fur with white socks and was smooth-haired with the exception of a luxuriously fluffy tail which was a ginger color with white spots the same color as her ears. She was not exactly a rare breed, but she was still a beautiful cat.

They looked and looked at each other and then, without saying a word, they simultaneously assumed human form. Beast was a young man again and, in the cat, he saw his woman. Neither seemed surprised by this series of metamorphoses.

"Is it you?" he asked.

"It's me," she replied.

"Did you recognize me?"

"Yes, my lord."

"How come you are here? What are you doing here?"

"I don't know. I'm here, that's all I know. And what about you, my lord? How did you come to be here?"

"I don't know either. Do you remember?"

"Yes."

"All my life I have regretted how I behaved back then, and I still do."

"It's all right, my lord. It was my fault and I have been punished for it."

"As have I. Nobody loves me. How have you been punished?"

"Everyone loves me, but they all leave me."

They were both silent for a few moments.

"Do you metamorphose?" asked Beast.

"When, what do you mean, when I suffer or when I stop suffering?" answered the woman. "When someone dumps me, I transform into a woman. And when someone pick me up, I turn back into a cat. But this is how I usually look."

In that moment, right in front of Beast's eyes, she transformed into something halfway between a cat and a woman. She was wearing a black, fur jacket with three quarter length sleeves and knee-length trousers. Her attire was very similar to the clothes Beast had sewn for her when they were together in the cave. Her head was adorned with a thick shock of black hair, and she was wearing a pair of white booties and white gloves. She had a pretty face and there was something distinctly feline about her features. Aside from that, an exotic, fluffy, bright ginger tail with white spots protruded upwards from behind and there were a set of little ears on the top of her head. In everything else, her appearance was entirely human and altogether quite chic.

* * *

It was in this form that Brunhilda, Eejit and Submarine found the Beast-youth and the cat-woman sitting on the bench. They came running up to the pair and stared at them in surprise as they caught their breath. The howl of the crazy ambulance siren could be heard somewhere in the distance from which they concluded that Cow had successfully confused the chase.

"At last, we've found you," said Brunhilda breaking the silence. The queen barely took her eyes off Beast clearly intrigued by his new guise.

"I was categorically correct by the way insisting that we should set our course on the sound of that Godless, inveterate miaow," said Eejit.

"This is right out of some carnival masquerade!" exclaimed Submarine. "Or a masquerade carnival?"

"Beast, perhaps you could introduce us?" said Brunhilda.

"My woman," said Beast getting up from the bench and pointing at the cat-woman. "At least, she was once. And these are my friends," he said. "Queen Brunhilda, Eejit Green and Yellow Submarine."

"You forgot to add 'my' to queen," said Brunhilda throwing jealous glances at the cat-woman. "Is that really you?"

"Yes, my queen, it's really me. My appearance has changed but I don't know why. This isn't the first time it's happened either."

"And who are you, oh miracle of miracles?" said Eejit, addressing the cat-woman.

"I'm Puscilla," she said getting up.

"She also changes form," Beast explained on his woman's behalf.

"So, are you pussy or are you Puscilla, oh miracle of miracles?" asked Eejit.

"It's quite obvipuss that I am both Puscilla and Puscilla," the cat-woman replied as she walked back and forth in front of them taking great pleasure in showing herself off.

"So, that's how it is," the queen remarked. "And who were you before?"

"I was a woman, before that a cat, then a woman again, and then again a cat, and so on many times."

"And everyone adores you, I suppose?" Brunhilda continued.

"Not really. First, they love me, then they dump me."

"And what happened? Why did you end up in the ambulance?"

"I was dumped again."

"Who dumped you?"

"My purrfect."

"Tell us more."

"He was so striking, whiskered, large-tailed and striped! A real puss-in-boots! How imposingly he paced about me!

How he tickled my ears with his tail! Oh, how he rubbed his chin against my neck! And how seductively he purred! And I, catty-eyed than I am, was completely taken in by it all.

At first, we lived in feline friendliness and moggy harmony but then he started disappearing more and more often. He got caught up with some catty-bandits and started trading in catty-band traffic. Then he was hunted by moggy fraudsters who wanted to get him locked up in the pussy pound. He hid for a while in a cat-a-crypt and was rarely seen. The last time he came by, he collected all his catty-clobber announcing catty-strife and pussy-split because, he said, I didn't look good enough."

"'What did he mean, you don't look good enough?' asked Submarine.

"That's what I said, 'What do you mean I don't look good enough?' I mean judge for yourselves; don't I look good?"

Puscilla spun around flaunting her figure and moving her hands like front paws.

"Yup! You could definitely say that!" said Submarine.

"There! It is completely obvipuss that I look great. And he went ahead and dumped me! Imagine, the moggy mess I was in!"

"Did you try stroking his fur and saying, 'My purr-fect, don't go to the cat-a-crypt, you'll catch a cold'?" The phrase came from somewhere above them and at that moment, Cow plopped down to the ground.

"Phew, I almost did not manage to break away from them. Then I caught the end of your conversation and hung in the air. I didn't mean to interrupt."

"Oh! And who might you be?" asked Puscilla in surprise.

"This is Orange Cow," said Beast.

"Cow managed to lead the chase off our trail," added Submarine.

"He-e-ello-o!" smiled Cow.

"And why do you ask? Hi, I'm Puscilla."

"I might be wrong, but I think the reason people always dump Puscilla is because Puscilla has a tendency to think only of herself," replied Cow.

"You're right! But how did you guess? I admit it is a weakness I suffer from. I'm far too ailorouscentric," said Puscilla looking across as Beast. "I am trying to change."

* * *

In the meantime, the howl of the siren that had until now sounded far away was getting closer.

"Uh, that crazy ambulance!" Submarine exclaimed. "What are we going to do?"

"We'll have to find somewhere to hide," said Cow.

"We can't hide forever," said Brunhilda.

"This is all my fault," said Puscilla. "Let's not run anymore. I'll deal with them myself."

"But how?" asked Beast.

"I've got myself fit and can look after myself."

"But how?" asked Eejit. "I don't think I can pull the wool over their eyes any longer."

"I won't let them hurt anyone or me for that matter." With these words, Beast grabbed Eejit's club.

"My friend, this tool is an extreme measure and should only be used as a last resort and anyway, it looks totally out of place with your sophisticated outfit," noted Eejit.

"If this was something that could be decided by force, I would have settled it a long time ago," said the queen raising her skirts to reveal a hidden sword. "But we'll only cause ourselves more problems if we go that route."

Before they could finish, an ambulance came hurling around the corner and pulled up sharply with the sound of screeching brakes, its siren still howling. The doctor jumped out of the cabin and put her hands on her hips.

"Right. Got you, inventor-investigators!"

"We were just about to inform you of the good news. The patients are recovering," said Eejit, gesturing in the direction of the runaways. "Your assistance is so swift and merciless that the sick recover instantly at the mere sound of your graceful siren."

The doctor gave a squint and a pout.

"Save your breath, darling and your graceful eloquence." She waved for the others to turn off the siren. "The sick don't recover just like that. Any patient has to be healed. Properly healed! But this farmyard of yours, well, healing isn't the word for it! Right," she said and nodded to the nurses who had meanwhile gathered beside her, "bring in those two!"

Beast stood in front of Puscilla guarding her and still gripping the club.

"Like that is it!" shouted the doctor. "Rendering resistance at the moment of execution! We'll call for back-up and get your entire crew-stew on the books!"

"Just a minute," said Puscilla, who came out from behind Beast's back. "You're under pen arrest. Should I launch liquidation?"

The doctor's manner changed, and she turned instantly pale.

"What...? How so...?" the doctor stammered struggling to find her words. "And who might you be?"

"I'm a writer," replied Puscilla. "I'll write you now and you'll disappear."

"Writer...! She's a writer...!" the nurses spoke first in a whisper and took a few faltering steps backward.

"My dear, why on earth didn't you say so?" said the doctor in a very different tone. "So, you're feeling better already? We wanted... we thought... we wanted to help you! You looked so unhappy!"

"You think?" inquired Puscilla in an indifferent tone and playing with her tail. "No, I can assure you, I'm totally and very catty happy."

"Really? So, there's been a mistake. But you must understand that our duty obliges us...! Our task is to return patients to a state of happiness after all."

"And my task is to write and eliminate fictional characters. So, should I start the liquidation?"

"No, no, of course not! I can see that you really are better! Anyway, we must be going, we're in a terrible hurry!"

The entire ambulance team rushed back inside the vehicle.

"We'd like to express our manic gratitude!" Eejit shouted after them.

The doctor threw him a dirty look and slammed the ambulance door. The vehicle screeched into motion and hurtled off down the road.

DO YOU KNOW WHO YOU ARE?

The moment the crazy ambulance had disappeared from view, the others gathered around Puscilla and started bombarding her with questions.

"I have to admit, oh miracle of miracles, that you surprised even me, someone who has been surprised by so much, I stopped being surprised long ago," said Eejit.

"How did you do it?" asked Cow.

"What did you do?" asked Submarine.

"What did you mean when you said that you created and eliminated fictional characters?" asked Brunhilda.

"Since becoming a writer," Puscilla answered, "I've become convinced that things written in books often manifest in physical reality and it's particularly true of this local reality. Whatever you write, practically everything comes true."

"What do you mean, 'this local reality'?" asked Brunhilda.

"Aren't you from here? Don't you know?" asked Puscilla in surprise. "Ah! But what am I saying! Of course, you're not from here. So, where are you from?"

As it turned out, this question caused some confusion among the general company.

"How do you mean, where are we from? I mean, where are we from?" said Submarine to himself.

"Well, we're from the place we're from..." said Cow.

"Eejit, go on, articulate. Tell her where we're from." Brunhilda said, at a loss to answer the question herself but not wanting to show it.

"Well, it's obvious isn't it?" said Eejit making a vague gesture with his hand. "We're from over there." He too was thrown by the question it seemed.

"My lord," said Puscilla turning to Beast, "Might you be able to answer?"

"Yes and no," said Beast thoughtfully. "We set off with the aim of finding out about the lid that is hanging over us. But it's all very strange... I can't actually remember where we set out from. My mind's all a bit of a fog..."

"It looks like none of us can remember," said Brunhilda. "It might be somehow connected to where we are now. Maybe you can explain it to us, Puscilla?"

"I don't really understand myself, where I am or how I got here," Puscilla replied. "All I know is that this world... somehow is not real."

"What do you mean 'isn't real'?" said the others in amazement.

"Well, it's kind of moggy... How can I put it... I feel like I've ended up in a puppet show. It's as if it does not exist of itself and is being played out somehow. And the people here, it's like they aren't really real. They're more like puppets."

"In what way like puppets?" asked Brunhilda.

"Literally. They don't know who they are."

"They don't?" asked Submarine in surprise.

"No. They don't know their own self. It's as if they're being directed by someone. Puppets in a puppet theatre don't know their own self either. Naturally, they act like ordinary people but there's something wrong with them. It's like they are mentally able but not entirely aware. You must have noticed it yourselves, haven't you?"

"Well, yes, we did notice something," said Eejit. "We do have some notion... You could say that the people here seem to be completely lacking in any notions of their own. They're in their right mind but at the same time, they can be easily wound round someone else's little finger, although that might not always be easy to achieve."

"That's exactly it!" Puscilla confirmed. "They're not fully consciously aware! If I weren't a writer, I would struggle to know what to call them but now I know. They're more like fictional characters than real people. Imagine! It's as if some author made them up. And I've met my own characters here, too, by the way. The whole experience was a huge shock! I'll tell you about it sometime."

"I don't want to seem impolite," Cow interrupted, but don't you think Puscilla that there might also be something wrong with you, even just a little bit?"

"Are you referring to these?" Puscilla asked touching her tail and ears.

"Partly. The manner in which you express yourself is not entirely normal and you have what one might call interesting habits, if you don't mind my saying so."

"My manner and habits and completely catty, I agree but there's not much I can do about it. It's my personality."

"Let's leave our personalities out of this, shall we," said Brunhilda. "We've all got one and they're all a bit on the exotic side to say the least. What I really want to know is why don't these people know who they are? What does it mean?"

"It's like I said, it's as if they were somehow not entirely conscious. They look like they're thinking about what they're doing and yet they're not consciously aware and can't really account for their actions. They're being directed like puppets."

"This is all very strange."

"It's not just strange, it's eery. I ask everyone I meet, 'Do you know who you are?'"

"Why do that?"

"To try and find at least one person who is consciously aware."

"And have you?"

"No, there's no-one like that here. You're the first."

"And how do they normally reply?"

"They don't. They'll do anything to avoid answering the question and they get irritated and angry."

"Why haven't you asked us then?" asked Brunhilda who continued to quiz Puscilla and was clearly concerned.

"Because you know who you are, don't you? I could sense straight away that you're different to them. And aside from that, I've known my lord here for a very long time."

"But that's what bothers me. I don't think I can say I know who I am."

"Come on! What do you mean you can't say who you are?" Puscilla froze open-mouthed in surprise.

"Eejit, do you know who you are?" asked Brunhilda.

"Your Majesty, at the risk of behaving like a fictional character, I'd have to say that I'd prefer to avoid having to answer the question, too."

For a moment there was complete silence. Eejit, who had the reputation of never being stuck for a response was probably lost for words for the first time in his life.

“So, I’m not the only one. What about you, Submarine, do you know who you are?”

“How could I not know who I am? Of course, I know who I am!”

“So, what exactly can you say you know?”

“I’m Yellow Submarine!”

“That’s it?”

“Um, well, yes...that’s it. But...?”

“And you, Cow?”

“I think I can say that I know myself.”

“Wait! Wait! I am remembering something!” Submarine fussed but then became thoughtful and fell silent.

Cow had also drifted into reverie. And then another transformation took place, this time involving these two of the casting crew. In front of their very eyes, Cow was transformed into an attractive-looking, plump woman with ginger hair dressed in an orange knee-length dress and black garish shoes. The outfit was accessorized with large, blue beads at the neck and wrists. Cow’s wings had vanished into thin air. Meanwhile, Submarine was transformed into a frivolous-looking blonde dressed in a yellow trouser suit, but she was wearing the same orange boots as before. Both newly appearing young women gazed about them looking totally perplexed, as were their companions. Despite the fundamental changes in their appearance, they were still the same beings somehow unmistakably recognizable as Orange Cow and Yellow Submarine.

“Right,” said Brunhilda breaking the silence. “Now we have four werewolves in the team. Fabulous!”

“Oh, something weird is happening to me!” Submarine exclaimed. “Pinch me!”

Eejit instantly fulfilled Submarine's request.

"Ow!"

"Well you did say to pinch you. You look much better like that, by-golly. Anyone else needs a pinch? Except me, of course."

"I'm not that surprised actually, for some reason," said Cow. "I've always had this knowledge about myself... or imagined myself like this... I don't know exactly."

"So, which is it, you know, or you don't know?" Brunhilda asked.

"I can't say I know with total certainty as I don't remember the past and I don't understand the present."

"And now you, Beast, do you know who you are?"

"Well, yes and no, my queen." Beast spoke finally having kept silent up until now.

"You've already said that. What does 'yes and no' mean?"

"I've experienced many transformations in my life. I remember all of them but this time, now, I feel like I have been born anew. Not reborn perhaps so much as manifested. It's a very strange feeling. It's like I know who I am and at the same time, I don't."

"And the rest of you, how are you all feeling?" asked Puscilla.

"I feel like a blank sheet," said the queen. "All I know is that I am Queen Brunhilda but that's all I can say about myself. And I don't remember when I stopped knowing anything else about myself."

"There! It's the same with me!" Submarine exclaimed. "It's as if I only just appeared right here and now, and I have no idea wherefrom."

"All I can say is that I am me," said Cow, "but that's it, nothing more."

"So," said Brunhilda summing up, "what have we got? We don't know who we are or where we came from. But we do know why we came. Our goal is the lid, right?"

"Yes, yes!"

"We want to find out what it is and what it's doing there. And three of us have experienced a metamorphosis. If I'm not mistaken, only Eejit and I have retained out former appearance. My sword and everything else are still there," she said, placing her hand on the weapon hidden beneath her skirt. The queen was wearing a medieval-style dress made of rough cloth and her long, brown hair was braided into a plait, a plain gold hoop crowning her head. Everything about Eejit was the same, too. He was green like Shrek and wore a green shapeless hoodie. He looked a total barbarian, the only difference being that he always wore a pair of sunglasses.

During the expedition Submarine had constantly badgered him saying, "Take those glasses off! The lid's blocking the sun out, you moron!" and Eejit would reply, "The radiance of my eyes carries enlightenment which will blind those who wander helplessly in the dark."

"You look a complete idiot in them!"

"Yes, but an idiot with authority."

"And what are you wearing that ridiculous robe for? Are you playing Osho?"

"There is only one thing I can humbly say to that: time spent with me will bring you a magical moment of enlightenment and what's more it is a great honor."

"Yeah right, go to hell!"

"Eejit, do you still have your eloquence?"Brunhilda asked.

"I dare to hope so, Your Majesty."

"Okay. The key thing is this: how can we reclaim the things we don't know about ourselves?"

"I know who you are!" said Puscilla.

"How? Where do you know me from?"

"I read about you. Your Majesty, you are a living legend. Orange and Submarine are also famous characters. And I've known my lord since the beginning of time. Eejit is the only one among you whom I have not yet had the honor of meeting."

"That is because that my glory follows me modestly not daring to outstep me," Eejit stated.

"So, that means that we aren't real either?" asked Brunhilda.

"No! It's totally obvipuss that you're real!" replied Puscilla.

"But from what you're saying, we're fictional characters."

"You are real because you're capable of asking yourselves that question and because you are self-aware i.e. you can say, 'I am me' or 'I am my own self' and that proves that you are real individuals and not fictional characters."

"Do you remember you said that you would write the local characters down and make them disappear? How does that work?"

"Very simply. When you create their image in a book, they materialize and when you strike them out of any given plot, they are liquidated and leave the stage. That's the catty-magic of it all..."

Wowzaz!" Submarine exclaimed. "So, can you write us out of the casting crew, too?"

"How could you even think such a thing! No! I want to be on feline-friendly terms with you. Quite the opposite in fact. I wanted to ask if you would consider letting me join your gang. I'm worried about the lid, too."

"So why can't you just write that the lid disappears?" asked Cow.

"I've tried that, but it didn't work. It's a bit trickier dealing with reality than it is with these local characters. Will you let me come with you?"

"Of course! How can we not take a cat, a Puscilla like you with us? You can be our Catty-Puscilla," said Eejit.

"And since when have you been the one in charge around here?" Brunhilda objected.

"Your Majesty, humbly at your service."

"My Queen," said Beast joining the conversation, "I too request that you agree."

"Me, too!" said Cow.

"Me, too!" said Submarine.

The Queen was thoughtful for a moment.

"I will come in handy!" Puscilla continued. "I can be your catty-intel specialist, for example."

"Our whatty-who?" asked Brunhilda.

"I can carry out pussy-espionage, take part in pussy-spying operations. I can catty-charm secrets out of anyone and even Puscilla-kill if necessary."

"What do you mean, Puscilla-kill?" laughed Brunhilda.

"Well, if you'll excuse the language, it's when you fling, hoodwink, bewitch and spin heads."

"I don't doubt you know how to do all that. As long as you don't use your skills against us, particularly when it comes to 'spinning heads'," said Brunhilda throwing Beast a sidelong glance.

"Totally out of the question! My lord knows me, and he'll tell you, I'm fundamentally harmless. I liquidate my characters in the case of extreme necessity only, but to liquidate someone else's characters, well, professional etiquette and all that... to say nothing of real people."

"What have you decided, my queen?" asked Beast.

"All right, we'll take Puscilla with us," said the queen.

"Hooray!" shouted Cow.

"Hooray! Hooray!" shouted Submarine.

"Welcome to our team," said Eejit.

"Thank you, all of you!" said Puscilla happily. "That's just moggy-marvellous! Only you won't abandon me, will you?"

"We won't abandon you," Beast assured her.

"We need to think about what action we're going to take next," said Brunhilda.

"If I might make a suggestion, Your Majesty, if you will allow me?" said Eejit.

"What?"

"Well, for starters, a bite to eat would not do us any harm."

"I know a great cafe nearby," said Puscilla.

"Lead on."

And with that, they set off again behind Puscilla.

SURREALITY

Puscilla, who was standing at the head of the procession, moved with a cat-like gait waving her tail about and pedaling her 'front paws'. Beast walked alongside her.

"So, this is what you're like now? You've changed a lot since back then."

"Yes, as have you, my lord."

"I feel a bit embarrassed about what happened back then and just now."

"Me too, my lord."

"And still, you talk to me in the same way you did before, monosyllabic in your own unique manner."

"In your eyes, my lord, I am still the same."

"And yet, we are different now. We've both been through a lot, I suppose."

"Yes, now we have something to talk about."

"There'll be time for that yet."

"Cow, how are you doing without your wings?" asked Submarine. "Can I still call you Cow? It doesn't seem to fit with your current image."

"And your name fits perfectly with yours?" replied Cow. "Are you Submarine or someone else?"

"Me, I'm still Submarine!"

"Well, I'm still Cow. What else are we supposed to call each other if we don't even know ourselves who we are? And as far as the wings go, for some reason I get the feeling that I will be able to transform back into my old self at some point, I just don't know how yet."

"I think the same. Wouldn't it be great if we could shapeshift back and forth whenever we wanted to?"

"And you, Beast," asked Brunhilda, "do you plan to change back into Shaggy Beast?'

"Would you like that, my queen?"

"No, stay as you are."

"Whatever you say, my queen."

"Stop, stop!" shouted Submarine.

"We've never imagined that Beast can be the self he is now, all young and attractive," Cow added.

"Yes, I know, and you're not bad yourself, although you weren't bad before.".

"Oh! 'Not bad' from the lips of our monosyllabic friend here has the ring of the finest compliment," said Eejit.

"Thank you, thank you!" said Cow and Submarine coquettishly.

"Beast wasn't bad looking back then, either," interjected Puscilla. "Back when my lord embodied his first external formand we lived in the cave. And what about me, my lord, was I not bad looking then, too?"

"Yes, Puscilla," Beast replied in his own crisp style.

"And now? And now?" asked Puscilla, still fishing for a compliment.

"Yes, Puscilla. Only why are you still calling me 'my lord'?"

"I can't help it. Old habits die hard! It's my own little mogism."

The friends did not quite understand what 'mogism' meant but it ceased to matter as they had arrived at a premises with a sign above it saying ‘Cafe’. Inside, a motley assortment of customers stared at the crew suspiciously for a bit as usually happens when strangers appear in a close-knit community. A minute later they went back to whatever they were doing, some eating, others drinking, only glancing back over at the newcomers from time to time and then whispering to each other.

The friends found a free table with enough chairs for them all, sat down and waited trying not to turn their heads round too much, so as not to be caught staring too hard at the interior and the other visitors. Although nothing particularly stood out, there was something odd or you could say uncharacteristic about the people and their environment. The friends did not have time to work out wherein this uncharacteristic quality lay as a waitress who did not look very friendly headed over to their table.

She was wearing a blue uniform with a white apron on which the question Anything else? was printed in large letters. She held an order pad in one hand while the other hand gripped the beak of a heron which she led behind her. In this position, the heron had no choice but to follow the waitress obediently, hastily moving its feet.

The waitress stood at their table and asked casually, “Whachavin?”*

Madam, we aren’t ‘watchavin’ anything but would like to eat something, in other words, to have a spot of lunch,” said Eejit.

---

* The question ’what are you having?’ pronounced quickly sounds like ’watchavin’.

"Which is why I'm asking politely for now: whachavin?"

"Miaow! For now?" the guests repeated in surprise.

At that moment, an eccentric-looking gentleman in a Latin American style coat who had evidently overheard their conversation, shot up to their table in a nonetheless ungentlemanly fashion and interrupted them.

"Wait till you visit Honduras.They don't stand on ceremony there, that's for sure!"

The waitress waved the man away with her notepad as if he were an annoyingly persistent fly and he left them alone.

"Right," said Puscilla. "I'll have moggy-coffee without the catty-caffeine please."

"O-key do-key!" exclaimed Eejit. "I'll have something ailorous-alcoholic without the ailorous-alcohol."

"And I'll have milk without the milky way," joked Cow.

"Water without the aqua, for me," said Submarine playing out the joke.

"Right," replied the waitress. "We don't serve coffee, same goes for the other drinks."

"What do you mean, you don't serve coffee?" asked Puscilla in surprise. "You are called a 'Cafe' after all."

"Exactly," the waitress retorted. "If we were called a 'coffee' then coffee is what we would serve. You can go outside if you like and read the sign syllable by syllable. I think you'll find it says 'Ca-fe'."

"What do you have, then? Cafe?" asked Puscilla.

"There is no such drink. For your information, it doesn't exist. I recommend our signature house cocktail."

"What's it like?"

In that instant, another customer shot up to their table, a dirty looking lady with a long feather boa, who exaltedly exclaimed, "It's divine, absolutely divine! I love it! Love it! Love it!"

The waitress waved her book at the woman and she was forced to retreat.

"So, would you like to order some?"

"My dear," said Eejit, "umm, sorry, what is your..."

"I'm a stavardess actually," the waitress replied in an arrogant tone.

"Aha... okay, well, we will, let's say 'risk' what you have to offer."

"Right," said the stewardess. "I'm writing that down."

She took a pencil from her pocket, placed it in the heron's beak, clasped it shut again with her hand and began carefully writing in her pad the word "Cocktail". The bird squeaked plaintively but did not dare resist. Our guests observed this elaborate procedure in astonished silence. Finally, Eejit decided to ask a question.

"Madam... uuh, stavardess, why are you tormenting that bird?"

"It's what we do here," she answered sharply and then gestured to her apron.

"What?" asked Eejit, raising his eyebrows in surprise and even taking off his glasses.

"Here is it, the same question that I am sick of having to ask over and over again. Read it for yourselves."

The guests at the table were about to express their indignation but Eejit interrupted them taking the initiative.

"My dear, first of all, with your permission, we would like to see the menu."

"We don't have a menu. We don't keep one."

"What do you mean? How will we know what to order?"

"You'll either make an order or you won't. There are separate price lists for special requests."

"What kind of special requests?"

"If you make one, you'll find out won't you."

"Okay, as I said, we'll risk the cocktail."

The waitress turned around without uttering another word and headed over towards the bar dragging the bird behind her. No sooner had she stepped away from the table than a gracefully aged old man in a tracksuit jumped up to their table and in a loud voice said,

"You guys like taking risks, don't you! I spotted it straight away. We should organize a race! Definitely!

"What race, what are you talking about?" asked Eejit answering on behalf of them all since no-one else knew what to say.

"A competitive race! Combative! A very vigorous race with obstacles, if you like! It'll be even better with obstacles! It's an excellent way of getting you going. Definitely! Definitely!

"And I'll tell you something else!" the familiar gentleman joined in. "You just have to visit Honduras! Have you ever been? It's a very invigorating country! They confiscate your documents the moment you get off the plane and throw you straight in jail and they sort it all out later. We could go there, right now! Immediately!"

"First, we'll hold a race, though! Definitely! A very vigorous race!" the old man continued.

"Hang on!" the woman with the boa joined in. "They've got to try our cocktail first! It'll take your breath away! Love it! Love it!

Who can say how long this cacophony would have continued had not the queen stood up, shot the pests a menacing look and without saying a word, made an imperious gesture of the arm indicating that they should go away. This they did without delay nonetheless repeating, ‘Love it! Love it! Honduras! We’ll hold a race!’ Once they had finally sat back down at their own tables, they calmed down again.

In the meantime, the gracious stewardess promptly returned. In one hand she carried a tray with six tall glasses, still gripping the unfortunate heron by the beak with the other. Having placed the glasses on the table, she began to play with the tray not letting go of the bird for a moment.

The glasses were filled with a greenish liquid and had all the extras you would expect: straws sticking out, cocktail umbrellas, slices of this, that and the other… There was also one less than usual attribute, to put it mildly, amidst the other bits and pieces which, as soon as they spotted it, sent our entire casting crew into shock.

Live frogs were sitting on top of the glasses gripping hold of the rim. They opened their mouths from time to time as if trying to say something. Only now did our friends realize that all the glasses on the other tables were exactly the same.

“Excuse me” said Eejit, barely able to contain himself, “but what is this for!?”

“A frog’s front feet are like flippers,” the waitress replied, “they’re good for mixing the cocktail.”

“We’re supposed to stir the cocktail with frog’s legs?” exclaimed Eejit, who was astonished by what he was hearing despite having boasted earlier that nothing could surprise him anymore.

“Would it not be simpler just to bring us a spoon? They’re cute amphibians and everything but their legs are also soft which makes them unsuitable for the purpose, and anyway, they're alive!"

"Did you expect us to fry them for you? Fry your own frogs!"

"Excuse me but do you really consider it normal to stir anything with a frog? How do you actually see that happening?"

The group's old friends looked desperate to jump up and offer valuable advice, but the queen stopped them in their tracks with a sharp gesture of the hand.

"A cocktail has to be stirred before it is consumed," the waitress snapped. "House rules. Our customers should be informed although in your case, I'm prepared to make an exception taking into account that you're obviously not from these parts." The waitress softened a little.

"Oh, please do make an exception!" Eejit did not dare launch into a more extensive tirade not wanting to irritate the waitress any more than they had done already.

"Easy. You see the table is set with toothpicks. All you have to do is tickle the frog's tummy and it'll start kicking its feet and mixing the cocktail itself."

"How awfully charming! Delightful!" exclaimed Eejit.

The remaining members of the team preferred to remain silent, but their feelings were quite clear from the expression on their faces. The queen who was almost beside herself with rage was on the verge of walking out, but Cow whispered to her:

"Your Majesty, let's stick it out a bit longer. I'm interested to see what happens next."

"My dear stavardess," Eejit continued, "be so kind as to tell us what else we might order?"

"That's more like it. You're learning," the waitress replied condescendingly and pointing to her apron. "You can place your order."

"But what? What exactly?"

"I repeat. You either make an order or you don't. If you are going to order something, then order what you want."

"But how can we know what we want if we don't know what is available?"

"Are you going to order something or not?" The waitress was becoming impatient again.

"Miaow! We're going to order," said Puscilla who decided to answer for them all.

"Okay, I'll write it down, then."

The waitress took a pencil from her pocket with her habitual movement and, placing it in the heron's beak, began to write the word "order" in her notepad.

"Just one more question, if you'd be so kind?" said Eejit.

"Go on?"

"Why this complex writing procedure? What's the bird for?"

"It's absolutely ridicupuss!" Puscilla burst out.

"Why the hell should she eat for free? Birds have to earn their supper too, you know."

"You are deeply mistaken, miss. This bird owes you nothing. Let her go and she will feed herself," said Eejit.

"Now we're getting down to your special requests." The waitress was livening up. "So, you insist I set the bird free?"

"Yes, I insist."

"As you wish. Pay according to the price list and the heron will go free."

The waitress threw a sheet of paper onto the table and pointed to a number in the list.

"Really?" said Eejit who was surprised yet again. "Well..."

He took out his wallet, counted out the required sum and handed the notes over to the waitress who took the money and finally let go of the bird. The heron opened its beak but dare not move.

"There, you bird, take that." Eejit pulled the frog out of his glass and placed it in the bird's open beak. "You are free!"

The bird swallowed the frog, flapped its wings and hurried towards the door which happily had been left open.

If you have any other special requests, please, go ahead." With these words the waitress left the group's table to deliver someone else's order.

Once alone again our friends sighed with relief.

"Bravo, Eejit!" said Submarine.

"A noble act," said Beast.

"I would not have thought of that," said Cow.

"Special requests, hey? So that's how they scam money off their customers!" shouted Puscilla.

"There'll be others," Eejit suspected.

"But haven't you been here before, Puscilla?" asked Brunhilda. "You said you knew this place?"

"I knew of it, but this is the first time I have ever come in."

The friends did not even touch their cocktails but before long the waitress returned with empty crockery and set plates on the table before assuming an expectant pose.

"Any other special requests?"

"Not yet, dear," said Eejit. "We are just waiting longingly for our order."

"There it is right in front of you."

"What do you mean? The plates are empty?"

"That's your order. What else would you like?"

"We'd just like something to eat if you don't mind."

"Well, tuck in then."

"How can we if there's nothing there?"

"Start, I said!"

Eejit, who was by now tired of being surprised, picked up his knife and fork and touched his plate as an experiment. In that instant, a large piece of meat appeared on his plate — Eejit's favorite dish. He cut off a slice of meat, chewed, swallowed. Then he removed his glasses and looked around at the others giving them an encouraging look. The others followed his example and the dishes they would have liked to order appeared on their plates. They prudently refrained from making any comment and tucked into the food before them. The waitress rolled her eyes to heaven, rotated her finger at the side of her temple and then silently turned and walked away.

"Right then," said Eejit as soon as the meal was over. "Something to drink would be nice."

"Thinking of trying the house cocktail?" asked Submarine in a sarcastic tone. "That's all they have."

"No, I want to test a hypothesis."

Eejit called the waitress over.

"My dear, could I trouble you for six empty glasses?"

The waitress grunted, walked off and returned carrying a tray. Without saying a word, she placed the glasses in front of each guest and then stood with her hands on her hips. Eejit took the glass and tried carefully taking a sip. The glass immediately filled with a liquid of some kind that Eejit took great pleasure in gulping down in one go. The rest followed his example as was becoming the custom.

"Thank you," said Eejit.

"Thank you very much!" added Submarine.

"And now the bill, please," said Brunhilda.

The waitress brought the bill over and the queen settled the amount leaving a generous tip. This time, everything went as expected and all that remained was for our friends to get up from the table and leave. But Puscilla stopped them with a movement of her paw and asked the waitress her favorite question.

"Can I just ask; do you know who you are?"

"What are you trying to say?" the waitress answered warily.

"What do you think, are you playing the role of another or is someone playing yours instead of you?"

"You're trying to insult me?"

"No! We simply want to know whether you are genuinely you."

"No, I can see that you're trying to insult me."

"We really don't have the slightest desire to offend you," added Eejit. "We are just curious and would not ask if we did not have the deepest respect for you."

"I have nothing against insults either. They relate to the special requests category. We always try to meet our clients' requests. Here's the price list. You can familiarize yourself with it in the meantime.

The guests looked with interest at the list of bad names and swear words each marked with its own price.

"Only I should warn you that you will have to pay for my own rude response, too. It's included in our range of services. Everything is charged strictly according to the price list."

“No, dear stavardess,” Puscilla explained, “you have our total catty respect and the last thing we want is to argue with you. Can you simply say, ‘I am me’?”

“That insult isn’t in the list, but I can add it now,” replied the waitress decisively reaching for her pencil.

“No! No! That’s not an insult! It’s a game we play. Each of us is going to say ‘I am me’ in turn and then it’ll be your go. That’s all!”

The waitress became even more wary than before but before she could say anything else each of our friends said in turn, ‘I am me’. But no sooner was the round complete than something extraordinary happened. Before she even had time to open her mouth, the waitress froze mid-pose. A wax coating covered her face and hands and she literally turned into a wax figure.

The friends also froze totally dumbfounded. Having recovered, they looked around. Everywhere they saw the same motionless scene. The people in the cafe, or rather their mannequins since all the faces were lifeless wax, had frozen in unnatural looking poses, as if they had been caught suddenly in a freeze-frame.

This was another shock for the team no less powerful than the one they had just experienced. They wandered confused from one table to another, cautiously touching the mannequins.

“Hey!” they said, but there was no reaction.

Outside, the scene was exactly the same. All the cars and passers-by had frozen still. Everything froze into a lifeless scene. In this new world, our friends were the only ones who remained alive.

THE CRAZY WRITER

"Oh, my goodness, what's happening! What's happening?! What's going on? What's going on?" exclaimed Submarine.

"Has anyone ever seen anything like this before?" asked Cow.

"I've never seen anything like this in any of my lives," replied Beast.

"Miaow! I told you this world wasn't real! And the people here aren't real either. They're like puppets!" said Puscilla.

"But they were real just a minute ago even if they were a bit weird," said Eejit. "And the food in my stomach is telling me it's completely real, too."

"Puscilla, I think your question Puscilla-kaputted them, just as you said it would," said Brunhilda.

"It wasn't just me! If anyone Puscilla-kaputted them, it was all of us put together!" Puscilla objected. "Remember, we all said,'I am me' in turn and immediately afterwards they froze all in their own pussy-poses."

"That's putting it mildly," said Eejit. "They haven't just frozen. It's more like they've transformed into mannequins, an exact wax copy."

"Yes, Puscilla's question has nothing to do with it." Beast stuck up for his friend. "Nothing happened as a direct result of her asking the question except that the waitress misunderstood us. She did not seem to get what it meant. And she did not understand what 'I am me' means either."

"My dear friend, that's the longest explanation I have ever heard you give," said Eejit. "And the key to the mystery lies somewhere in what you just said, although I don't know where exactly."

"That's it," said Puscilla. "Why don't they understand the question and why do they find it so difficult to say the simplest phrase?"

"But Puscilla," said Brunhilda, "you asked another question after that which completely threw the waitress. Even I did not understand it at first. Remember? You said, 'What do you think, are you playing the role of another and is someone playing your role instead of you?' What did you mean by that?"

"I said back when all this started that the people here reminded me of puppets as if they were being controlled by someone else and their actions weren't self-motivated."

"It is an interesting question, philosophical even," said Eejit. "Perhaps if we can discover the answer to it, we'll understand what's wrong with them and what's going on here in general. If you think about it though, it's a reasonable question to ask any real person."

"Really? What if someone had asked you that question, Eejit?" asked Submarine.

"I would definitely have to think very hard and I'm not certain I would know how to answer."

"And what about you, Puscilla, do you think of yourself as a puppet?" asked Brunhilda. "I don't mean to offend. I mean, of course you are real it's just I don't understand what you are doing here. How did you end up here? Where did you come from?"

“I don’t know. I don’t remember. And you don’t know or remember how you ended up here, either, do you?”

“We don’t have time for philosophy and reminiscing,” said Cow. “The fact of the matter is that everything froze immediately after we all took turns to say, ‘I am me’.”

“The question is why?” said Submarine. “What happened exactly? Oh, look! What’s that?”

Submarine, who was standing behind the waitress, suddenly spotted something woven resembling a plait protruding from the back of the waitress’ head. It was giving off a white glow although quite faintly, which was why Submarine had not noticed it earlier. She went up to the waitress and touched the glimmering object only to discover that rather than being made of any tangible substance, the plait appeared to be some kind of energy form. No less surprising, the plait which came to an end between the waitress’ shoulders merged into a fine blue ray of light which traveled downwards in a vertical line, and rather than leaving a spot of light on the floor seemed to disappear into the ground. Submarine put his hand through the blue ray but rather than glaring on her skin, it passed through her hand and came out the other side.

The friends set about examining the other mannequins, who all turned out to have the same kind of plait that transformed into a ray of blue light. The friends then studied each other but none of them showed any sign of having anything similar, the only exception being the queen whose hair was woven into a real plait.

“How could we not have noticed this straight away?” asked the queen in surprise.

"We were too stunned by their immobility and waxy appearance to notice anything else," Eejit replied.

"So, you're saying that these glowing things only appeared when they became mannequins?" asked Submarine.

"Miaow! I bet my tail they did not have anything like that while they were still alive," said Puscilla. "I would definitely have noticed if they did. The stavardess was hovering around us turning this way and that. We would surely have noticed."

"Right. So, what does this all mean?" asked Brunhilda.

"I have absolutely no idea, my queen," replied Beast.

"Me neither," said Eejit, who on this occasion could find nothing else to say.

"So, what are we going to do?" asked Submarine.

"Let's take a wander around the town and take a good look at things," said queen.

The left the cafe and set off down the street. The buildings and surrounding objects all looked the same as usual, the only difference being that the leaves on the trees hung completely still without the tiniest waver. There was not a breath of wind in the air or any other movement. All was deathly silent. The mannequin 'passers-by' they met along the way all appeared to have the same attribute, a luminous plait which disappeared into the ground.

A little while later, the friends came across an even stranger object. It was a rectangle, or rather a construct of some kind with a black stripe running around it half a meter wide. The sides of the rectangle extended as far as the eye could see both along the ground and across the full breadth of the sky. The band only looked like a black strip, but it was in fact a void that cut through everything that crossed its path. Across the ground it was a bottomless pit, across the sky and sides, a gaping black hole. It was as if a strip of space and everything that it crossed had been cut away and thrown into nowhere.

The entire casting crew peered into the void in the ground careful not to allow a hand or a head to cross over into the area of the void. It was impossible to make anything out. Eejit threw in a pebble which sank into the nothingness without a sound. This time, there was nothing to discuss since when the mind is confronted with things that are beyond any conceptual understanding, it genuinely finds itself with nothing to say and so the team just stood at the edge in alarmed silence. Beast was the first to show daring. He tentatively pushed a branch through the black emptiness. As nothing untoward happened to the branch, Beast decided to jump across the abyss himself, which thankfully was not very wide, and he landed safely on the other side. The rest of the team were afraid but followed on after him.

Looking back, they all sighed with relief. Examining the construct again, this time more carefully, the friends discovered a curious detail. The empty strip that cut into the nearby building had not in fact eaten away at the bricks. There were fragments remaining on either side of the strip which could have been neatly realigned. It turned out that the space inside the construct had not been destroyed so much as just torn apart. Nonetheless, this discovery did not explain anything, and the phenomenon appeared no less strange for having made the observation.

The friends decided to move on. After a while, they heard noises and what sounded like screams. They immediately set off in the direction the noises were coming from. Having walked to the end of the block they found themselves in a small square. There was a bookstore on one side of the square and there were lots of people rushing about, real, living people.

Some were running into the store reappearing moments later with a book in their hands. Others were milling about the square trying to dodge a very odious-looking figure who ran about pursuing them. The figure was a rather disheveled, wild-looking youth who was carrying a pile of books and chasing after the others screaming,

"I will write you a-a-ll! How dare you read my books without my permission! I'm going to buy up every copy, you'll see!"

The wild-looking youth caught up with one of his victims and after a struggle ripped the book she was holding from her grip. The victim leapt up with a screech and ran back into the bookstore. No one paid any attention to the fact that the friends had appeared on the scene and the running about, screaming and screeching continued unceasingly. Amidst the general chaos and confusion there stood the occasional motionless mannequin and there was no way of knowing why some of those in the square were living and others were not.

"Miaow! I recognize him!" shouted Puscilla. "He's one of my characters!"

"One of your characters?" The others were astonished.

"Yes, from one of my books. He's a crazy writer and those are his readers."

“Now things are beginning to make more sense,” said Eejit. “So that’s why they are living! We can at least assume that your characters are living because they are yours and because you are also alive.”

“Looks like it. None of the other characters here are mine and they are all mannequins. Although I still can’t understand why that should be the case.”

“Puscilla, perhaps you should go and do something about your writer, then” suggested Brunhilda. “Why is he causing all this trouble?”

The team ran up and stood around the madman.

“Young man, can I ask you something? It’ll only take a minute,” said Puscilla.

“Are you readers?”

“What us? No, never.”

“Okay, I’m listening, only be quick.”

“What do you write about?”

“I write about how reality works.”

“And how does it work?”

“How should I know?”

“How can you write a book about something you don’t know?”

“The book writes itself. I just hammer away at the keyboard. Anything else? I’m busy! Very busy!” The writer had clearly run out of patience.

“Please, please, just a moment more!” Puscilla continued her efforts to distract him. “Why are you forbidding your readers from reading your books?”

“To stop them from finding out how reality works. Once they find out, nothing will interest them anymore and they won’t want to read anything else.”

"But you're stopping them from reading as it is!"

"I'm stopping them from reading my book so that they won't stop wanting to read anything else."

"You have an unusual, I would even say paradoxical approach to the writer's craft." Eejit joined in the conversation. "Is it all right for us to take a quick look at your book, as we're not readers?"

"Yes, all right, only you won't get it from me. Hey, you! Wait!" The crazy writer suddenly leapt forward and started chasing a girl who had just run out of the store.

He caught up with her, grabbed hold of her book and started tearing it away from her. The girl held onto it stubbornly squealing at him to stop. Then Beast ran up to the writer.

"Wait a minute, dear boy, that's no way to treat a woman."Beast grabbed hold of the book himself and hurriedly flicking through the pages only to discover that they were all blank.

"But there's nothing in it!" exclaimed Beast in surprise. "It's totally empty!"

"These bastards will try and learn from a plain page!" shouted the writer. "I try and keep the information to a minimum!"

"Well, you couldn't get any more minimum than this!"

"Excellent! Now leave me alone." The writer was about to launch into another pursuit, but our team surrounded him in a tight circle.

"Your Majesty," Cow whispered to Brunhilda, "have you noticed that the living don't have the plait with the blue ray?"

"Yes," the queen replied, "but you could not see it in our former living acquaintances either. I want to ask him something about that."

“Young man,” said the queen to the writer, “does it not seem strange to you that some of the people here are alive and moving while, at the same time, others stand motionless like mannequins?”

“What mannequins?” the writer muttered.

“Well, look,” said Brunhilda and pointed to the mannequin standing nearest to them. “How do you explain that?”

“Explain what?”

“Explain why he is standing there not moving.”

“Who do you mean? Standing where?”

“Right here,” and the queen and led the writer up to the mannequin standing nearby. “And there’s another one and another.”

“What are you playing at? There’s nothing there!” The writer was genuinely perplexed.

“Ri--i-ight,” said the queen who was now just as confused. “Puscilla,” the queen said, “are you going to ask your question?”

“Yes, only I hope it won’t catty-kaput him.”

“Let’s see. He’s no use to us like this anyway.”

“O-catty-kay. Hey, you! Do you know who you are?” Puscilla asked the writer who was already stunned by what was happening.

“Of course! No-one knows me better than I know myself!” the writer declared arrogantly.

“So, you, are you?”

“I don’t understand, what are you trying to say?”

“Can you say, ‘I am me’?”

“I still don’t understand the question,” the writer said, clearly very puzzled.

“We have this game, you see. We are each going to say, ‘I am me’ in turn and then you have to repeat it too, that’s all.”

"I don't understand the question," the writer continued but the team had already begun casting their 'spell'. As soon as they had gone around everyone in the circle, Puscilla turned to the writer again.

"Now it's your turn. Are you you?"

"I don't under..." Before the writer could finish his sentence, he gave a jolt and then froze becoming completely covered in wax. Exactly the same thing happened to his readers who had been running about nearby but now came to an abrupt standstill as if caught in a freeze-frame. And just as suddenly, they all grew a plait with a ray of light extending from it.

"And now these are all catty-kaput!" Puscilla lamented.

"Not to worry," said the queen. "For some reason, I'm certain it's temporary. They'll all de-kaput later. Anyway, we would not have got anything useful out of these ones when they were living either."

"What's the title of this book?" asked Eejit. "Let's see… 'Surfing Trans-reality'. And what might that mean, I wonder?"

"We'll never know now," said Cow. "The pages are blank."

"No! This is too much! This is all moggy-monstrous! It defies comprehension!"

"And my imagination," added Beast.

"And my immersion," Submarine chipped in before asking her favorite question, "what are we going to do now?"

"Let's move on," said the queen.

And with that they carried on down the same street as there seemed little point in turning off anywhere. Things were not getting any better for our friends, who soon found themselves coming across the black construct again. This time they jumped more boldly across the abyss and continued on their path. From time to time, they came across motionless mannequins, and to everyone's surprise, some of them they had seen before. The next surprise our friends encountered was even more astounding. They found themselves back at the same cafe they had visited earlier despite the fact that they had walked in a straight line continuously never having turned off the main street.

It seemed best to go in. What they saw once they were inside plunged them once more into a mild state of shock. The interior remained unchanged and the mannequins were all the same too, only this time, they had adopted different poses. In some cases, the mannequin's pose was only marginally altered but the change was distinctly noticeable nonetheless. Without asking each other any more questions, the friends hurried toward the exit and once again made their way down the street heading in the same direction as before.

Quickening their step impatient with curiosity, they passed the construct for the third time and reappeared by the bookstore at the square. Instead of the former chaos, the square was filled with the already familiar mannequins led by the same crazy writer. Here, too, the poses of all the figures had quite clearly changed.

"I can't make it out," said Eejit. "Maybe they're moving too slowly for us to spot it. Let's watch them."

The team sat down on a bench and observed the mannequins attentively but did not detect the slightest movement. Already tired and deflated, the friends sat in silence for a long time. Eventually, Eejit spoke.

“There’s one terrible thought that torments me. It’s unthinkable and yet there can be no other feasible explanation.”

“There’s no need to scare us!” said Submarine. “Things are weird enough as it is!”

“Go on, out with it!” said Cow. “What could be more incredible than what we are looking at already?”

“Do you realize where we are?”

“Where? Where?”

“In a movie.”

“What movie? What do you mean ‘we’re in a movie’? Why do you say that?” The others bombarded him with questions with the exception of the queen who maintained her usual dispassionate composure.

“More specifically, we’re on a film strip that has stopped turning,” Eejit continued. “Have you ever seen a film strip? It’s made up of individual frames separated by blank strips. Minor changes are captured in each subsequent frame. It looks like our film roll has stopped turning and all the characters in the movie have come to a standstill. We’re the only ones walking about. Do you understand what I’m getting at?”

The other members of the team stared at Eejit openmouthed. Only the queen spoke.

“You’re right. It’s unfathomable but that’s how it is.”

“But what about the writer and his pets?” asked Cow. “Why were they able to move about in the frame?”

“That’s a little harder to explain,” said Eejit. “It’s probably because one movie can take place inside another. But that’s not important. Guess what the most essential question is now.”

“What is it? Go on, tell us.”

“The critical question now is how we get the film roll moving again?”

METAMORPHOSES

Judging by the improbability or even the total incredulity of the things that were happening to theheroes, it might appear to the reader that this story is too far-fetched to contain any grain of truth. But this is not the case. Firstly, the mind could never come up with stuff like this and secondly, when did you last come across a fantasy novel in which the heroes themselves were surprised by what was happening and considered it all highly improbable?

This tale is an account of reality, albeit reality in an unfamiliar guise or, you could say, the hidden side of reality. Just because some things seem beyond belief does not mean that they can never actually happen. And even the incredulous is never totally, categorically and indisputably impossible.

Mankind has too little knowledge of the world to even hope to assert with any authority what is possible and what is not. As soon as you look at things outside the context of the usual stereotypes, you have to acknowledge that we live in a very strange world, which seems extremely reluctant for us to come to understand it fully. What do we know of the Universe, for example? Very little.

The observable universe extends for 12 billion light-years. This is the temporal limit of the cosmological horizon beyond which nothing else can be seen. But what does lie beyond? Presumably, the rest of the universe that cannot be observed by the human eye.

As far as we know, the universe came into being 14 billion years ago. Assuming that the Big Bang theory of 'how it all began', is correct, this is an absolute past in relation to the current point of observation.

Beyond the limits of the cosmological horizon, a huge number of invisible galaxies stretch for another who knows how many billion light years. But what lies beyond that? Infinite emptiness? Hard to believe, particularly taking into account the fact that only a tiny fraction of reality is revealed to the eye. Everything else remains the endless unknown.

There are more stars in the Universe than there are grains of sand on Earth and there are more atoms in one grain of sand than all the stars put together. Inside a single grain of sand there is an entire universe of atoms. And how many separate universes are to be found inside a single atom, is beyond calculation because the internal plane goes on as infinitely as the external.

In the light of all this, what can the mind really know of the Universe or, let's say, everyday reality? Moreover, our everyday reality is just one aspect of reality. Reality in its entirety includes everything that ever was, that is and that could ever be. Relatively speaking, the first and the third in this list, what was and what could be, relate to meta-reality. The second, what is, relates to everyday physical reality. So, what could you say is the fundamental difference between one reality and the other?

The heroes of our story have yet to work out how the world of dreams differs from the everyday, physical world. For now, they are experiencing 'the impossible' in meta-reality. But who would dare state unequivocally that such things could never take place in everyday reality? The 'possible,' and the 'impossible' are only determined from the point of view of the rational mind. But what is 'real' or 'not real' is quite another matter altogether and bears no relation to the rational.

* * *

After we left priestess Itfut and diva Matilda asleep in the megalith, they woke up in a different space. They also woke up in a condition that it would not normally be possible for them to experience.

"Tili, what is this, your dream?!" exclaimed Itfut.

"Sorry what? I don't understand," Matilda replied.

"I was asking whether we're inside your dream. What were you thinking about just before you fell asleep?"

"I don't remember. Where are we?"

"I'm on a plate. Where are you? What can you see?"

"Ooh, I think I'm on a plate too. Futi! What's happening?"

"You're a complete gourmet, that's what!"

"Why?"

"Because I could not have made this up if I tried. Do you realize who we are?"

"No, who are we?" Matilda mumbled not yet fully awake.

"I'm halva!"

"Have you lost your mind?"

"And you? Look at yourself!"

"Ooh lala, Futi! I'm a cookie!"

In the reality that is visible space, there stood a table lit from above. Lying on the table were two plates, one displaying halva with a diamond-like rim and another holding a cookie tied with a pink bow. Nothing else could be seen.

"Ah, ha, ha, ha!" Matilda giggled.

"Still having fun?!" Itfut shouted at her. "Congratulations! You're a cookie wrapped in a bow!"

"And you too, something preposterous with a collar! Ha, ha, ha, ha!"

"At least I'm tasty!"

"I'm tastier than you are!"

"No, I'm tastier than you are!"

"No, I'm tastier!"

For some reason, the friends started to argue and almost ended up having a fight as if they were not quite themselves, although, it was obvious from their appearance, that they were indeed not themselves.

"Alright, Futi, let's calm down. How do you feel?"

"I'm halva, I like to crumble, disintegrate and make everything sticky."

"I'm a cookie. I'm round, made of sweet dough and sprinkled with sugar and nuts."

"I'm halva!"

"I'm a cookie!"

"And I'm halva!"

"And I'm a cookie!"

"Okay, that's enough!" said Itfut. "Tili, there's something wrong with us. I feel like I'm losing consciousness."

"Me too, my mind has gone all foggy," Matilda said. "How did we end up looking like this?"

"I told you, we ended up inside your dream, gourmet you!"

"Why in my dream and not in yours?"

"I'm guessing because I had not fallen asleep before you started dreaming."

"How are we ever gonna get out of here? Fall asleep again?"

"There must be another way. We need to learn how to move about in this space. It's too difficult to control exactly when we might fall sleep."

"We've tried travelling about using the trigger-jigger and visualizing our 'destination'," said Matilda. "Remember when we got flattened?"

"Back in the megalith." Itfut replied. "The megalith responds too powerfully."

"Where are we now then?"

"I have no idea. I can't see anything beyond your plate and mine but we're definitely not in the megalith."

"And we tried shifting about when we were at the mirror but all it did was show us a film as if it were a screen."

"Maybe that's all it does?"

"And we tried relaunching the dream from where it had stopped and that time it did not work until we fell asleep. Maybe that's the best thing we can do now?"

"There's no time, Tili!" Itfut shouted. "I'm about to get eaten!"

At that very moment, a spoon scooped off a piece of halva and was quickly carried upwards.

"Futi, no way!" Matilda said excitedly.

"I'm, I'm... being eaten, eaten!" Itfut cried.

"Futi! Quick! Activate your trigger and get us out of here!"

"Okay, I'm trying. I just hope we leave together."

"Imagine us together! Then we'll disappear together! Quick! Before they finish y-y-you!"

"I'm doing it now, right now!"

The spoon came plunging downwards once again to scoop up another portion of halva.

"Hurry, Futi!"

In that moment everything around them began to spin, twisted into a dot and then began moving in the opposite direction until it had literally transformed into a whirlpool. When the diva and the priestess came to, they found themselves in a deep, deep sea. Evidently, somewhere not far from an atoll reef judging by the corals, crystal clear water and abundant, colorful fish.

"Futi, are you okay?" asked Matilda instantly.

"I think so." Itfut replied.

"Where are we? Why the sea?"

"Sorry, pure coincidence. The sea happened to be the first thing that came into my mind."

"Honestly! You could at least have landed us on the shore! What are we going to do now?"

"Anything's got to be better than being a sweet treat that could get gobbled up at any moment."

"And you think we won't get eaten here? Ooh! How are managing to talk? How are breathing?" Matilda asked in a whole run of questions.

"And how did you manage to talk and breathe when you were a cookie, Tili? We're in the dream space if you hadn't forgotten?"

"Oh, it was quite something being a cookie! But it's nothing to how I feel here. This is amazing!"

The diva looked herself over, flipped her fins, flapped her tail, gaped her mouth open, gnashed her strong teeth, and seemed altogether quite pleased with herself. The priestess, on the other hand, could not get used to her new guise at all and just stared at her friend, her mouth gaping.

“Tili, for the sake of all the Gods, who are we?!”

“We’re huge fish, Futi! Mega-huge fishes! Barracudishy-fishes! I’ve seen something like it in the oceanarium.”

“So, is this my dream or yours?”

“I don’t know. Maybe it’s somehow a shared dream...”

“We still haven’t learned to travel about. It’s not good.”

“Oh, Futi! Let’s go for a swim! When will we ever get another opportunity like this? Look at yourself. You look great! You’ve even got your little collar still.”

“And you’ve got your bow.”

It was true, the priestess had a diamond rim just beyond her front fins and the diva had a pink bow on her tail.

“Does anyone down here in the chain eat us?” asked Itfut.

“No, no-one eats us. We eat everyone else, anyone smaller than us that is.”

“Hey, then let’s eat! Since someone tried to eat me, I’ve been feeling quite up for eating someone else!”

“Okay!” The fish-priestess looked around in all directions while the fish-diva, making the most of the moment, swam up behind her friend and nibbled her tail.

“Oy! You cow! You bit me!” Itfut cried and chased after her wretch of a friend.

"I could not help myself, Futi-i-i!" Matilda was in full swing, wiggling her bow.

The two friends messed about, chasing after each other and some of the smaller fish.

"Who are you swallowing there without sharing with me?" asked Itfut.

"Oh, I see, I have to consult with you now on who I should or shouldn't swallow?" Matilda replied. "Um!"

"It's important to share!"

"How am I supposed to share with such a voracious fishy as you?"

"Look! There's an octopus between the stones! I bet that's scrum!"

"Don't touch the octopus. She's nice! Let's swim over there. Look! There's a shoal of stupid herring! Shall we attack them instead?"

"Yes!"

Having swum to their heart's content and eaten their full, the barracudishy-fishes rested on the sandy sea-bed.

"What next then, Futi?"

"We need to think about getting out of here. We don't belong here."

"It's been so much fun swimming and hunting! Let's come back here again some time, shall we?"

"Tili, we need to get back to the material world. We ought to be thinking about that not swimming about here."

"But how?"

"I don't know but we have to try. We have to learn to travel through space. Now it's your turn. Try and shift us into a more familiar environment."

"Familiar to whom? We lived in completely different worlds, before we met, remember."

"Okay, well, to your environment then. Most importantly, be careful that we end up in our own mannequins, otherwise we'll turn into something weird again."

"Right. I get it," said Matilda. "We have to travel back to our mannequins, our own mannequins, yes, we should be in our own mannequins..."

At that, the marine space swirled in a giant whirlpool, curled up into a point and then span in the opposite direction.

The shopping center was dimly lit. It looked as if it was nighttime and there was not a soul to be seen. Two mannequins made of white plastic were standing behind a glass showcase. Dressed in ladies' outfits of the latest fashion, among other things, they had two distinguishing accessories: a diamond-studded collar at the neck of one mannequin and a large pink bow at the lower back of the other.

MANNEQUIN CATWALK

The mall was filled with deadly silence. The circular gallery was immersed in semi-darkness and only the motionless mannequins in glass showcases were lit, albeit very faintly. One of the mannequins stirred, the one displaying a dark evening dress with a diamond-studded collar and hat. It turned its head toward its neighbor and spoke, although the expressionless, white, plastic face made no change at all.

"Matilda! Where have you brought us?"

The second mannequin dressed in a jump suit with an incongruous bow tied to the back, started moving its hands and feet, and turning around to face the first mannequin, responded with the same mask-like expression.

"Futi! I got it slightly wrong. I tried to get us back into our own mannequins, but we ended up like this."

"Who are we? Where are we?"

"We're literally mannequins and it looks like we're in a clothing store."

Both mannequins stepped down from the plinth and wandered up and down the racks and rails. It was a strange sight, if not downright disturbing — two mannequins moving and talking, their plastic, faces remaining completely motionless.

"Wow, nice things. Gotta try these on!" squealed Matilda rummaging through the suits hanging from the rails.

"Tili! You've picked a fine time!" said Itfut dampening Matilda's enthusiasm. "We need to transform back into our normal appearance and our own clothes."

"Well, I think I look normal. Normal enough for all the shoppers to look up at me enviously when they walk by."

Matilda continued looking through the suits and dresses without a care in the world and then Itfut started doing the same as if Matilda's mood was catching.

"They might envy you, but they admire me!" Itfut said while straightening her snazzy hat. "See? How do I look?"

"Why are you dressed better than me?" Matilda suddenly answered aggressively. "I hate you!"

"So that's how it is, is it?!" The priestess gave her friend a shove. Matilda stumbled and knocked over a rack as she fell. The diva picked herself back up and lashed out at the priestess tearing at her dress. The priestess began mauling back at her rival, no less wound up than she was.

"You just touched my bow, you slut!" Matilda yelled having lost all sense of self-control.

"My diamond collar is simply stunning!" Itfut shouted even louder. "You'll never look anything like as good as me, you ugly cow!"

"I'll break your hand off!"

"Oh yeah? And I'll twist your head off!"

With that, the priestess twisted the diva's head off, which fell to the ground and rolled across the floor. With some force, the diva pulled off the priestess's arm and lobbed it to one side. Paying no attention to their losses, they continued to torment each other with unfailing frenzy. Suddenly their fury subsided just as swiftly as it had appeared.

“Okay, okay, I don’t need to win,” said Itfut her voice unexpectedly calm.

“The relationship is more important, if it’s a good one,” answered Matilda, despite the fact that she was still missing her head.

“Yes, no victory is worth sacrificing a good relationship.”

“You have me, and I have you, that’s all that matters.”

“I’m sorry, I’ve put your head back on. You look good as new.”

“I’ve fixed your arm back on. It looks even better now than it did before.”

They straightened each other’s clothes with a conciliatory, albeit useless gesture, since all their clothing was torn to shreds.

“Hatred is a good feeling. Indifference and apathy are the really negative emotions,” Itfut continued.

“Yes, hatred is cool,” Matilda agreed.

“I hate you, which means I’m not indifferent to you, and that must mean that you aren’t indifferent to me either.”

“One of our great writers said, ‘She who is incapable of hate will never learn to love.’”

“Yes, I love you hatefully.”

“And I hate you lovingly.”

“What?!” said Itfut beginning to get worked up again. “So, you hate me, do you?!”

“No, of course I don’t hate you.” Matilda replied raising her voice. “I’ll just kill you, the next time I see you!”

“Well, consider that this time! Do you want me to rip your head off again, stuffed bird?”

"You don't stand a chance. I'll knock your block off, bitch!"
"Oh, you animal!"

They grabbed hold of each other again, toppled over, shrieking and rolling around on the floor and then stopped just as suddenly as they had started.

"Futi, what are we doing?" Matilda was coming to her senses.

"It's a thin line between love and hate, Tili," said Itfut.

"And from hate back to love," said Matilda. "But what would we want with hate?"

"I don't know. It's as if we're not in our right minds." said Itfut.

"Yes, something's wrong with us."

They both stood up, disheveled and confused as if shaking off the grip of delusion.

"Let's say that you will be yourself and I will be myself," said Itfut.

"We'll just stop getting at each other," said Matilda.

"More specifically, we'll stop making demands of each other all the time."

"And having expectations of each other."

"I'll let you be yourself."

"And me, you."

"You are free, and I am, too."

"We are free, and we are together."

"You have me, and I have you, that's all that matters."

"I need you and you need me."

Itfut went quiet after that.

"Or maybe you don't?" asked Matilda with uncertainty.

"Why can't you just be how I want you to be?!" Itfut started complaining suddenly.

"And why can't you just do what I tell you to do?!"
"I can't bear you when you're being like this!"
"Piss off! I don't want to see you ever again!"

Once again, they were about to start fighting but Itfut stopped suddenly and shook her head.

"Ilit! Wake up!"

"What did you call me?"

"Remember your second name!"

"I'm Ilit and you are Tufti. You're Tufti and I am Ilit! What is wrong with us?"

"We keep falling asleep. We're drifting into the mannequins' dream and forgetting who we really are. Say to yourself: I am me!"

"I am me!" Matilda gave a start and then woke up too. "Futi! What a thick, boggy dream that was!"

"Yes, it really sucks you in," said Itfut. "And your conscious awareness gets clouded and lost. We must stay aware!"

"I can't believe that just happened to us! We behaved liked monsters! What crap!"

"That is what happens when you get immersed in a dream, especially someone else's dream. You forget yourself completely, but I've never experienced that kind of madness and lack of awareness before."

"Exactly. That was not like me at all! And it wasn't even my dream. It was like I had possessed someone else's body or was myself possessed. I've never been inside someone else's dream before, either."

"Yes, you have, you have," Itfut exclaimed. "Have you forgotten how you turned into a cookie and then a fish?"

"Oh yes!" Matilda said remembering suddenly. "When I was a cookie and you were halva, we were so empty and stupid but that was nothing compared to the mannequins. They're completely braindead and nasty, too!"

"It's more like they're soulless."

"But why are they so nasty? I never imagined they could be like that. And we behaved just like them!"

"We behaved more adequately and more like ourselves when we were fish."

"It turns out the mannequins really are dumb. It's such a good thing we managed to get away from them."

"We aren't in the clear yet, Tili. We managed to escape their movie and their roles, but we still haven't reentered our own bodies."

"Oh yes!" said Matilda as the truth dawned on her again. "We need to get back into our own bodies, our own mannequins as quickly as possible! I can feel my awareness drifting back into sleep again!"

"Don't drop off! Remember! What does it mean to have self-control?"

"To have self-control means to control where your attention goes."

"And what else?"

"And whenever you do anything, ask yourself, 'is it really you deciding to do this or is someone else in control of you?"

"Right. When your attention is driven by the script you become immersed in the dream — in the movie. We became immersed in the movie and lost ourselves. Now, in order to wake up inside the movie, we have to switch our attention back to ourselves."

"Okay, Futi, I've woken up at last!" said Matilda. "Now it's your turn to take us somewhere."

"The most important thing for us now is to be able to reoccupy our bodies, our own mannequins again."

"Then let's stay here for now and start moving about again when we're back in our own bodies."

"Yes, I'm going to focus on that," said Itfut and began to carry out her magic pass. She dropped her chin and bent forward slightly, and then, with a single action, rose her arms to the level of her shoulders, elbows bent and then straightened them up and out, at the same time, speaking her invocation.

"OO-OO-OO-OO---LA!"

In that moment, both mannequins transformed fluidly into two eccentric-looking individuals. One was dressed in an ankle-length dress of dark-blue velvet and was wearing a neck collar studded with diamonds. Her face was covered in crimson war paint and the cheekbones beneath her green eyes were decorated with a row of white spots. Her black hair was cut into a bob. She was a priestess, scary and yet beautiful and graceful at the same time. The other figure was dressed in a dark-green jumpsuit and was wearing pink platforms. Her face was covered in blue face make-up and there was a huge pink bow attached to her lower back. Her hair was wild-looking and dyed light blue. She was a quintessential diva, or you could say, a larger than life doll but rather than having the normal, cute, doll-like prettiness, there was something extraordinary about her beauty. Peering into the mirror, the red brunette and blue blonde delighted quietly in their original appearance, which they had begun to miss so much. The priestess laughed and twirled about while the diva jumped up and down clapping her hands together.

"Futi! We're ourselves again!" Matilda shouted. "Hela!"

"Hey, hey! And I've got my shoes back!" Itfut yelled. "I'm all back!"

They spent a few minutes longer enjoying the fun but then stopped as if suddenly remembering something. They still didn't know where they were. Looking at one another, the diva and the priestess silently climbed up onto the plinth in the shop window and looked around through the glass not daring yet to leave the shop.

Then, suddenly, loud techno music started playing and, in that instant, the mannequins in all the shop windows came alive, stepped down from their plinths and poured out into the gallery in a motley crowd. Moving in a kind of dance, they made a phantasmagoric march around the gallery's entire circumference. The shopping center was still submerged in semi-darkness but now it was filled with music and movement.

I got the eye of the tiger, a fighter,
Dancing through the fire,
Cause, I am a champion and you're gonna hear me roar!
Louder, louder than a lion,
Cause, I am a champion and you're gonna hear me roar!
O-o oh, oh, oh, o-o! O-o oh, oh, oh, o-o! O-o oh, oh, oh, o-o!
You're gonna hear me roar.*

The mannequins were a whole variety of different colors: white, black, beige, some wearing wigs and some

---

* Song by Katy Perry,'Roar'.

without, their faces motionless and impassive. Some of those displaying bikinis had no head and stumps in place of missing arms and legs. Others, those displaying trousers, were missing a torso. The absence of various body parts did not seem to stop the figures from dancing although it made for a horrible scene. All in all, the mannequin catwalk created an alarming, ominous impression, their movements awkward, mechanical and jerky.

The diva and the priestess froze. They watched the entire scene without moving an inch, trying not to give themselves away. When the music stopped, the mannequins stopped dancing and began to disperse in all directions. Some made for the shops taking up positions behind the counters like shop assistants. Others adopted the manner of shoppers choosing and trying on clothes. Another group arranged themselves in the cafe sitting behind the tables pretending to eat and drink while other mannequins served them. Another group positioned themselves in the play zone and make out that they were playing games, some billiards, others bowls. All the others simply wandered about the gallery.

"Futi, they're copying real people!" Matilda whispered. "They're doing everything exactly as we do, when we go to the mall. Can you imagine?"

"Quiet, don't move," Itfut replied. "Let's watch them for a bit longer."

Aside from everything else, the mannequins were somehow communicating with each other. They would turn their heads towards each other giving out a loud, indistinct whisper, all the time their faces and lips remaining frozen as if in a stiff mask. The result was a cacophony of unintelligible, unconnected words coming from all sides, sometimes fading but then becoming louder again.

"Futi, let's do something," said Matilda impatiently. "We can't stand here like statues forever."

"Okay," said Itfut. "Let's try and leave the mall.

They stepped down from the plinth and made gingerly in the direction of the exit not knowing what to expect if they were spotted. The moment they entered the gallery area, all the mannequins stopped moving and went quiet. Then, as one, they turned sharply to face the friends and rushed towards then with blatant hostility.

The diva and the priestess both made a run for it. The mannequins, who were now completely silent, took unhurried but assured strides stretching their arms out towards the runaways, including the ones with missing torsos and legs.

"Futi, what do you think they want from us?!" asked Matilda.

"I don't know" Itfut replied as she ran.

"What will happen if they catch us?"

"Best not to find out!"

"We've got to find the exit! We're going around in circles!"

The chase continued all around them with mannequins appearing everywhere. In whatever direction the friends turned, they were launched at by animated and yet lifeless statues. Dodging their pursuers, the diva and the priestess ran the full length of the gallery, but the exit was nowhere to be found. It looked like the nightmare would never end.

Then came the critical moment. As if having planned it beforehand, the mannequins arranged themselves in rows on two sides of the gallery cutting off the path to retreat. Spreading out their arms, they formed a ring. The friends were trapped.

Noticing a small niche in the wall, the priestess took a dive towards it and dragged the diva along behind her.

"Tili, stand still!" Itfut whispered and with that she stood as still as she could.

Matilda did not ask questions and did the same.

The mannequins were instantly confused. They started turning their heads to each side and mumbling indistinguishably to one another. There was clearly no point in continuing the chase anymore. The mannequins started wandering randomly in all directions, their arms outstretched in front of them as if they were blind. They even walked past the friends without noticing them, and finally dispersed in one direction, although not altogether abandoning the search.

"Tili, they can only see us when we're moving!" whispered Itfut.

"Yes!" Matilda replied quietly. "How did you work that out?"

"Pure intuition."

"What are we going to do now?" Move on to somewhere else?"

"No, I want to try something else."

The priestess closed her eyes focusing her attention and then she sharply opened them again and...

Everything around them stopped. The mannequin figures walking past stop as if in a freeze-frame. The entire scene froze and tiny, glistening flakes that mysteriously appeared out of nowhere hung suspended in the air, like snow that had suddenly stopped falling.

Matilda was the first to start moving again and emerge from her amazement.

"Futi, what did you do?"

"I stopped the movie," Itfut replied, also beginning to move.

"How did you do it?"

"Simple, I activated my trigger-jigger and imagined that everything around us froze."

"So, that means the mannequin movie stopped but we didn't? We can walk around here freely? Awesome!"

The friends stepped out of the niche in the wall and took a few steps through the gallery. The mannequins remained still.

"Something like this happened to us once before," said Itfut. "Remember? It was when the dream stopped and the glamrocks froze."

"That was a bit different to this though," said Matilda. "They were still moving, just in very slow motion. There was some trick with time going on."

"Maybe the same thing is happening now? There weren't any of these little flakes back then though... Hey! Look, what's that?"

The priestess pointed to the mannequin standing closest to them. She noticed something woven in the shape of a plait coming out from behind the mannequin's head. It glowed with a white radiance and stopped roughly between the shoulders at which point it flowed into a fine, blue ray of light that ran vertically down into the floor. The same thing could be observed in the other mannequins, even those with missing limbs and those whose plait seemed to extend from the spine or the waist.

"Futi!" Matilda said excitedly. "You've got one the same!"

"What? I've got one?" Itfut asked in surprise and suddenly, as if struck by lightning, she exclaimed, "Oh my Gods! You've got one, too!"

They could see now that they both had glimmering plaits with the same blue rays extending down as far as the floor. "Tili, I've remembered!" shouted Itfut who had suddenly become extremely excitable.

"What?"

"What is your attention focused on, right now?"

"What?" asked Matilda, perplexed.

"Bring your attention back to yourself! Say to yourself, 'I am me!'"

"I am me!" Matilda said repeating the words.

"I am me!" Itfut repeated.

In that moment, the blue rays disappeared from both friends leaving just the glowing plaits.

"I understand it now. I remember!" Itfut shouted again.

"What?! What did you remember?" shouted Matilda.

"I know what the trigger-lever is!"

CARAMILLA-MARAVILLA

We left our 'expedition lid' members at the square, where they sat feeling totally lost because the movie had stopped, and all the characters led by the crazy writer had frozen like statues.

"What are we going to do now?" Yellow Submarine asked her usual question, but this time provided the answer herself. "What if we were to rewind the film strip to the frame where everything stopped and then a bit further still?"

"That could be interesting," said Eejit Green. "Even more interesting is how a superficial blonde comes to have such profound thoughts."

"And you're such a smart-fart, we'd be lost without you!" Submarine replied.

"It's all very catty-curious," said Puscilla. "What do you hope to find on the previous frames? After all, we'll just see ourselves, won't we?"

"Maybe, and maybe not," said Orange Cow. "If Eejit is right and we are wandering through a movie set on pause, then we must have left the film which means we shouldn't be anywhere in the frames after that point."

"Quite, it would be illogical if we rewound the roll and find ourselves in it," said Beast.

“But if we aren’t in the frames prior to when the movie stopped, that would be illogical too. We were there, inside it after all.” Cow added.

“Whichever way it turns out, if something illogical is going to happen, maybe the film roll will start moving again,” said Eejit. “We’ve passed three frames, so that means we need to go back to the fourth frame and see what happens there.”

“Let’s go,” Queen Brunhilda commanded.

They decided to go back on themselves despite the fact that they were all very tired. The friends crossed three gaps between frames and ended up in the frame where the movie had stopped. They looked in on the cafe again, and everything there was as before: motionless mannequins frozen in the same poses. Finally, they crossed the fourth gap between frames. Nothing had changed there either. Everything was totally static, like in a photograph. Our friends continually had the sense that they were walking about in a photograph, only this world was three-dimensional. It was a peculiar feeling and they all found it eerie and uncomfortable.

Suddenly, the space around them began to move and a light breeze appeared. The leaves rustled in the trees and other sounds could be heard as mannequin pedestrians came back to life and cars started driving down the road, first in slow motion, then quickening until everything eventually reached natural speed.

“Wow!” Submarine uttered.

No sooner had he spoken than the others let out similar exclamations and sighed with relief. “We’re not going to ‘catty-kaputt’ anyone anymore except in extreme circumstances,” said Brunhilda.

“Yes, of catty-course!” Puscilla agreed.

The friends arrived at the square. With the exception of the occasional passer-by, the square was empty, and the bookstore was closed. They walked another block and then stopped at the doors of the familiar cafe.

“Shall we take a look?” suggested Eejit.

Once inside they found that all the visitors had already left. The only person there was the cleaner who was washing the floor and moving chairs about. The same waitress as before appeared and announced, “We’re closing! Did you want to order something else? Come back tomorrow.”

“Really?” Eejit replied on behalf of the group. “Okay, thank you, goodbye.”

They turned and walked outside onto the street.

“Wow, she was very matter of fact, all things considered!” said Submarine in surprise.

“Yes, as if nothing had happened or as if she did not remember,” said Cow.

“And the movie had somehow been fast-forwarded,” said Puscilla.

“At least it hasn’t been rewound,” Beast noted.

Meanwhile, it was already getting dark.

“We need to find somewhere to stay,” said the queen.

“I would invite you to stay at mine,” said Puscilla hesitantly, “but I don’t know whether you’ll be comfortable. It’s quite small and I live as quite a frugal-mog, if you see what I mean.”

“Don’t worry, Puscilla, we’ll find a hotel somewhere,” said Cow setting Puscilla’s mind at ease.

“Then I’ll come with you, too,” said Puscilla. “I think there’s a guest house over there.”

Not far away, a town house shone invitingly. It was decorated in grandiose fashion with balls, ribbons and bulbs. Above the front porch in large neon letters were the words, ‘Villa Maravilla.’*

They rang the bell and the door opened automatically. Once inside, the group found themselves in a spacious hall, in the middle of which stood a large heavy table with similarly grandiose chairs arranged around it. An equally grandiose chandelier hung from the ceiling, and a fireplace burned cozily in the far wall. An imposing wooden staircase led up to the balustrade on the second floor.

A middle-aged lady with a self-important manner leisurely descended the stairs wearing a magnificent dress trimmed with beads and all manner of ribbons and ruffles, and her hair, which had been piled up about half a meter high, was styled in a manner more grandiose than everything else put together.

“What a weird catty-collage!” Puscilla blurted out.

“Shh!” Cow hissed at her. “You can see how impressive everything looks.”

“Rather a ceremonial entourage!” the woman proclaimed. “I’m Caramilla, your hostess at Villa Maravilla!”

---

* Spanish: ’Maravilla’ meaning a marvel, something wondrous, astounding.

Brunhilda stepped forward.

"Hello, we were wondering whether you might have rooms for the night?"

"Are you majestic?" the woman asked.

"What?" asked the queen not quite understanding what the woman meant.

"To the extreme!" said Eejit, who was quick off the mark, evidently having sensed something. "Look, this is Puscilla-Puss."

He stepped aside, shoving Puscilla forward. Puscilla lifted up her paws, fluffed up her tail and made a long face.

The hostess examined Puscilla from both sides staring at her intently and seemed satisfied.

"Yes, you do appear to be majestic. Well then, I am gracious Caramilla and I welcome you most indulgently to Villa Maravilla!" The woman spoke in a high, throaty voice, doing her best to emphasize all the apparent pathos of the moment. "Do follow me, follow me!"

Gracious Caramilla floated up to the table and then circled it in a manner of upmost formality while our friends followed her.

"An aspirational waltz!" said gracious Caramilla. "Please, sit at the table, all to the table!"

The friends took their places while the hostess observed them with her arms folded. Brunhilda sat at the head of the table closest to the fireplace. The others sat along the sides. Beast scratched his head not knowing where to sit, next to the queen or beside Puscilla. He decided it best to remain neutral and so sat between Cow and Submarine.

"A fine balance!" said gracious Caramilla with obvious satisfaction. "Quite ornamental! I would ask you to wait a little without sorrow. You will be offered a light, ethereally-unobtrusive dinner!"

"Thank you, incredible, simply astronomical, gracious Caramilla, for such a radically hospitable welcome!" said Eejit.

The hostess nodded as far as it was possible to given her hairstyle and then she withdrew with a flamboyant gait, moving her shoulders back and forth, her arms raised at the elbows. As she was leaving, she added another equally incomprehensible phrase.

"Official fashion!"

"Well, Eejit," said Cow, "it looks like you've found a companion worthy of your eloquence at last."

"Talk quietly, they might hear us," Brunhilda warned.

"What a strange individual!" Submarine exclaimed softly.

"Well, if you ask me, better bombastic politeness than rude directness like that other waitress," Eejit said.

"Yes, so far so good," said Puscilla.

"You could have sat here to my right, Beast," said the queen a note of reproach in her voice although formerly, such a desire would have been uncharacteristic on her part.

"Or next to me, my lord," Puscilla interjected.

"I'm sorry, my queen and you, Puscilla." Beast found himself making excuses. "I have not yet settled into my new appearance and feel a bit like a fish out of water."

"Allow me to express my gratitude for the honor, Your Majesty." Eejit likewise felt he should justify himself.

(Eejit sat to Brunhilda's right and Cow to her left.)

"It doesn't matter," said the queen.

In the meantime, gracious Caramilla was swift in returning to their table. She brought huge, flat plates with her and ceremoniously placed them in front of each guest taking advantage of the table's huge proportions. Then, in contrast to the sizeable plates, she covered the rest of the table with light snacks and biscuits served on numerous, tiny saucers. The cutlery she laid out was just as numerous and varied. In conclusion, the hostess brought out a hefty teapot and a collection of small teacups.

"An epic concert!" gracious Caramilla exclaimed as she finished serving. "You will find that everything is magnificently exquisite at Villa Maravilla!"

"Quite so, gracious Caramilla," said Eejit in a similarly highfalutin manner. "Your table is simply dazzling, mesmerizing, breathtaking!"

"Ornamental," added gracious Caramilla indulgently. And as she was about to leave, she threw in another phrase for good measure.

"Fleeting influences!"

"Sorry, what exactly are these influences supposed to be influencing?" asked Submarine unable to restrain himself. The hostess turned around in surprise.

"Carelessness of course!"

"And whose influences, are they?" continued Submarine in the hope of comprehending at least something of what his hostess was saying.

"Astral influences!" retorted gracious Caramilla, shocked that her guests were ignorant of such basic notions. "But if elevated, philosophical conversation is more to your taste than my offerings here, I can always set you a philosophical problem to solve."

“What kind of problem?” asked Submarine stunned by her reply.

“Well, a problem such as this: ‘restore the volumes of an ambitious dream’.”

“No, no, there’s no need. Really, many thanks, gracious Caramilla,” Cow interrupted. “We’d much rather become acquainted with your delicious-looking offerings!”

“As you wish!” said gracious Caramilla and then withdrew, thankfully, before the situation became any more complicated.

The friends began to eat and took unhurried pleasure in their evening meal. The whole atmosphere at the villa turned out to be highly conducive to comfortably passing the time despite their hostess’ extravagant behavior. Moreover, gracious Caramilla was considerate enough to go about her own affairs without intruding on the company of her guests and so our friends had the opportunity to quietly talk things over at last.

“So, what are we going to do?” asked Submarine.

“In what sense?” Beast responded.

“The essence of the problem is clear,” Eejit said, taking it upon himself to answer for the others. “Aside from the lid, we now have another riddle to solve — the movie.”

“And why a movie might suddenly freeze?” Cow added.

“And those strange luminous, woven extensions the mannequins have, like plaits, and the blue rays that disappear into the ground... what is all that about?” Puscilla interjected. “I’ve never seen anything like it.”

“The most important thing is for us to try and work out where we are?” said Brunhilda.

"The question is whether the world we have ended up in is real or an illusion?" Eejit continued.

"We've ended up in a different world...?" asked Submarine. "We might not necessarily be in a different world. It might just be that something weird is happening to our own world. The whole issue with the lid began in our own world, after all"

"Yes, but our reality has never stopped like this," Cow noted. "And never in our world did we come across strange, impenetrable objects. Remember the invisible wall with the sea splashing behind it?"

"Puscilla was saying that something is wrong with her local reality, too," said Beast.

"Puscilla, have you ever seen the wall?" asked the queen.

"No, I have no idea what you're talking about, Your Majesty," answered Puscilla.

"That must mean that you haven't ever been there. Have you been here long?"

"No, not long but I don't actually remember how I got here."

"What can you tell us about this place?"

"Nothing really apart from what I've already told you. It is like this world is not real and the people in it aren't real either. In a word, it's a 'puppet theatre'. It doesn't fit any other cattology."

"You mentioned that characters can appear and then disappear depending on what's written in a book..."

"Yes, here, whatever you write, it all comes true down to the smallest detail. The only thing that didn't work for me was writing about the lid. For some reason, nothing you write can influence the lid."

"On the other hand, everything here looks very real with the exception of the strange behavior of the local inhabitants," said Eejit. "Take the food, for example. Seems pretty real to me."

"Yes, but when you dream you are eating the food seems real to you then, too," Cow said.

"So, you're saying that all this is a dream?" asked Submarine. "We can't all be having the same dream at the same time, though, can we?"

"Maybe only one of us is dreaming," Beast surmised.

"Even better," Submarine exclaimed. "So, you're saying for example, that you're the one having a dream and I'm not really real. I'm just a fragment of your dream?"

"None of the characters in a dream are real including the person whose dream it is," Cow said. "No, this is all nonsense. We need to find out where we are. It's totally obvious that we aren't in our own world."

"I'm definitely not in mine," Puscilla confirmed. "I'm telling you, this world isn't real, that's totally mogious, although highly catty-concerning."

"And there's one other thing we need to do!" said Submarine. "We need to remember who we are!" The others did not respond quietly contemplating for a moment all that had been said.

Eejit finally broke the silence.

"I feel like a completely clean sheet as our esteemed queen put it."

"And as Beast said, I feel like I've been born again," said Cow. "Especially as I'm no longer an orange cow but a chubby red-head, transformed without rhyme or reason."

“And for no apparent reason, I’m no longer a submarine but a blonde,” added Submarine.

“And Shaggy Beast is no longer a long-haired beast but a mysterious young man of interesting appearance,” added the queen.

“I’m flattered, my queen,” said Beast with a bow.

“And I’ve already told you about myself and my catty-likeness,” said Puscilla closing the circle.

“As far as I understand it, we stopped being able to remember ourselves the moment we came across the wall object,” said Brunhilda. “At least, that’s the impression I get.”

“So, it would seem,” Eejit agreed. “We do vaguely know ourselves, though, don’t we. I mean, we definitely have a rough sense of who we are.”

“Yes,” said Cow. “For example, I know that Eejit is the smartest and most rational of us all and that Queen Brunhilda is the wisest and most judicious.”

“Cow is the politest and Submarine the most frivolous,” continued Eejit.

“No, not frivolous but light of mind!” objected Submarine. “It’s just that all my thoughts are light, not like you, the philosopher.”

“Whatever you say,” Eejit said agreeing again. “I would not dare argue with a blonde.”

“Beast is the most uncouth, although now it’s the opposite. How do you explain that?” Cow continued. “And Puscilla... is probably the most refined.”

“The most sophisticat,” said Puscilla happily.

“We know ourselves in one sense and at the same time, we don’t,” said the queen.

“In short, we need to determine where we are and how we’re going to get out of here,” Eejit said summing up. “Maybe we’ll remember ourselves, then.”

“Maybe we should go home?” Submarine suggested.

At these words, they all fell silent again.

“But will it work?” said Cow expressing the doubt they all felt.

“Do you know which way to go?” asked Puscilla. “I mean, I don’t.”

“I don’t think I could even remember how to get back to the strange object,” said Eejit. “Does anyone remember?” No-one answered.

“I can’t help this time either,” said Cow, “now that I am without my wings.”

“But what would be the point?” asked Brunhilda. “We did not come all this way to return with our tails between our legs, did we? Let’s first sort out what we came to do.”

Everyone agreed and they shifted their attention back to the purpose of the expedition.

At that moment, gracious Caramilla was kind enough to reappear.

“Any desires, strivings or expressions of will to hand, perhaps?”

“Expressions of will are hardly appropriate in a guest, gracious Caramilla.” As usual, Eejit took on the role of spokesperson. “Firstly, we are filled with gratitude, and secondly, a humble request: we are tired and would like to rest, now, if you will.”

“Do you have cash to hand?” inquired the most gracious Caramilla.

“How much is it?” asked Brunhilda.

The gracious Caramilla reached into the elegant pocket of her full skirt, pulled out a scrap of paper, turned her back to her guests and handed the note ceremoniously to the queen. The queen glanced at the note, agreed and then counted out the necessary sum and handed it over to their hostess.

"Then in Villa Maravilla, you will be triumphantly laid out in encompassable beds for unencompassable rest! Please, follow me, follow me!" said gracious Caramilla and led the group up the stairs to the second floor.

The beds were indeed triumphal. On heavy iron bases covered with lush mattresses and blankets, rose entire pyramids of pillows in all different sizes. Given that there were only five guests rooms, and Cow and Submarine said, 'we can share, we'd prefer to share,' they were given one room which meant that the others all had a room each. So, everyone was happy. The day ended well.

BEAST'S DREAM AND AWAKENING

Beast tossed and turned for a long time overwhelmed by the events of the day to say nothing of his unexpected transformation. Tired of turning from side to side, he decided to stretch his legs in the corridor. There were two rest rooms, one for the gents and one for the ladies. He bumped into Cow as she was coming out of the Ladies.

"Can't sleep?" she asked.

"No, my thoughts stop me from falling asleep and my dreams prevent me from sleeping soundly," Beast replied.

"As bad as that? What do you dream?"

"I have a recurring dream." For some reason, Beast decided that he could trust Cow with his secret. "Foreign women come up to me, sometimes individually, sometimes several at once, and they're looking at me with coldness and contempt."

"What do you mean 'foreign'?

"They're trying to emphasize that they are not my women."

"Do you fancy them?"

"No, of course not!"

"So, they just come up to you and stare at you?"

"No, then they start talking."

"And what do they say?"

Beast began to recount more of his dream.

"A woman came up to me and spoke.
'I'm not yours,' she said.
'Really?'
'Yes.'
'Go away, then,' I said, and she left.

But why did she come and what did she say that for?

Another time, a different woman came up to me and put her hands on her hips and just stared at me.

'What are you staring at?' I asked.
'I don't find you attractive.'
'Why do you feel the need to say that to me?'
'Just because.'
'Go away.'
'I'm going to come back and watch you,' she said and then she left...

And then, a group of women came and stared at me, crossing themselves and watching silently.
'What do you want? Why aren't you saying anything? What are you looking at?' I asked.
'We don't love you,' they said.
'That's it?'
'Yes, that's it.'
'Go way.'
'We'll come back and say it again,' they said and with that they left."

Cow was surprised by Beast's dream but listened with genuine sympathy.
"But what's the underlying reason for the dreams, do you think? What's it all about?" she asked.

"I'm being punished," he replied.

"For what?"

"For being a bad person."

"That's nonsense! You're not bad at all, quite the opposite. You're a good person!"

"No, I'm bad. Nobody likes me and nobody ever loves me. It's a punishment."

"It's just some foolish complex you've got! Everyone likes you and liked you even before you started to look like this. And with your new appearance, even more so. You realize that there are two particular females who have their eye on you, don't you?"

"What females?"

"Right! As if you didn't know! Queen Brunhilda and Puscilla."

"I still can't believe it."

"You're so stubborn! No-one is punishing you except yourself. It's your choice and you're living with it!"

"Why are you being so hard on me? It's tough enough as it is."

"You deserve to be beaten for having thoughts like that, not just a telling-off! Me and Submarine will get together and give you a really good beating, definitely! For now, go back to bed, get some sleep and get rid of those women once and for all!"

"I don't know how to. They just keep coming back."

"The next time they come to you in a dream, just say 'So what?'"

"Okay, I'll try."

Beast and Cow returned to their separate rooms. When Beast fell asleep, the strange women returned and said,

"We don't find you attractive. We don't love you. We aren't yours."

And Beast replied,

"So what?"

"We will never be yours."

"So what?"

"What do you mean, 'so what'? Won't you suffer?"

"No."

"We'll go now then."

"Go then."

"We'll go and we'll never come back. We're leaving, right now."

"Go, leave."

And they left and Beast began to feel better.

* * *

The next morning, 'expedition lid' woke up, got washed and dressed and gathered at the table in the dining room.

"So, did your women come to you again?" Cow whispered.

"Yes, same as usual," Beast replied.

"So, did you say it?"

"Yes. They were surprised and then they left."

"Well, there you are, you see! That's the last you'll see of them."

"I hope so."

Soon, gracious Caramilla appeared in the living room, prim and ceremonious as usual and delivered another ostentatious phrase:

"I would like to give to our guests a rostral-to-coudal welcome at Villa Maravilla!!"

"And we return the greeting, most highly and most profoundly, gracious Caramilla!" Eejit replied.

"Good morning!" the others said.

"Morning is neither good nor evil. It just happens as it always does," said gracious Caramilla. "Did you sleep, my dear, amiable guests?"

"Yes, well, thank you!" they replied.

"You need not thank me for sleeping well. I simply enquired whether you slept, or you did not sleep?" Gracious Caramilla was unmercifully categorical. "And now, here at Villa Maravilla you will be offered breakfast inspired by the most coveted trends!" With that, she turned, lifted her arms upwards from the elbows and retired with the same characteristic flamboyant gait.

"Here at sodilla-Maravilla!"

"Here at soddin-Maravillanin!" As soon as she had disappeared behind the door, Cow and Submarine started laughing at her.

"Yes, our sodilla-Maravilla!"

"Our soddinilina-Maravillinina!"

"Mocking others, are we?" Eejit reproached. "Not good, don't you think?"

"My dear Eejit, we would not presume to laugh at Villa Maravilla, we simply supposed to express our good humor," said Cow imitating Eejit's manner of speaking.

"I see, well, so be it, then."

"It's good here, isn't it?" said Submarine.

"Yes!" said Cow.

"It's purring-perfect!" said Puscilla joining in.

"We have serious matters to discuss," said Brunhilda addressing them all.

"What are our plans, Your Majesty?" asked Eejit politely.

"I think, for starters, we should talk to the hostess and find out what she knows."

"Is that worth it? She clearly isn't fully there, like everyone else in this town."

"By the way, what's the name of this town?" asked Submarine. "Puscilla, you live here, don't you?"

"Pomponius," Puscilla replied.

"Oh-ho, the name is pompous, too, just like its essence," said Eejit.

"Essence of what?" asked Cow.

"The fact that everyone here seems to think they are so important, whereas in essence, they are all slightly loopy."

"Abso-catty-lutely!" Puscilla agreed. "As we established. They don't have a sense of their own individual self and so they're not their own person. What town are you from, by the way?"

The question was followed by an awkward pause.

"Puscilla, there you go again!" said Cow. "Didn't we say that something was wrong with our memory ever since we arrived here?"

"I remember, though!" Beast responded.

"What? What did you remember?" the others asked excitedly.

"We're not from a town, we 're from a land, the land of Zealand."

"Oh yes! That's right!" said Submarine.

"Why did not I remember that myself?" asked the queen in surprise. "We really are from the Kingdom of Zealand, where our queen rules."*

"Yes, I remember now," said Brunhilda.

---

* The term "Zealand" has a number of geographical meanings, including a hypothetical continent.

"I've never heard of the place," said Puscilla.

"But how can that be? I mean, we're from there and we're not made up characters!" Cow said, surprised again. "It's all very strange! Although, what is there to be surprised about. Everything that is happening to us is strange and surprising."

"Looking at the characters here, I have that same feeling that we are inside someone else's dream," said Beast. "Which is why we are all slightly less consciously aware than normal, and it explains why we know who we are and at the same time, we don't."

"But we're not asleep!" Submarine objected. "I know for definite that we are not asleep!"

"Well, I'm not sure of anything anymore," said the queen summing up. "Whatever the case, it's worth talking to the hostess."

Meanwhile, gracious Caramilla arrived just in time with a tray of food.

"Right, now I'm going to have you for breakfast!" she declared.

"Us?" said the guests in surprise.

"Yes, since you are the objects of my breakfast."

"But gracious Caramilla," objected Eejit, "I would say that we were more like totally conscious subjects!"

"But in relationship to mine, I mean, to the breakfast I have prepared, you are objects," the hostess insisted as she set out the plates.

"We won't argue with you, gracious Caramilla," Eejit said. "On the theme of objects, we were hoping to ask you whether you know anything about the lid that is covering the sky?"

Caramilla was instantly wary.

"What did you want to know specifically? And why does that interest you?"

"You see, the lid is a matter of great concern to us, and we have set ourselves the task of finding out about it, where it came from, for example, and how to be rid of it."

"Is that right, my dears?" Caramilla stopped fooling around and became enlivened as if she had suddenly woken up. "Oh, you have no idea how long I've been waiting for someone like you!"

"Why, gracious Caramilla?"

"Just call me Caramilla," the hostess continued and began serving her guests with even greater diligence. "Eat! Eat, dear ones! I'll just go and get the teapot and then I'll tell you everything!"

UNSCIENTIFIC NATURE

Caramilla returned with the tea and sat down at the table next to her guests.

"And so, my dears, you want to know how lid appeared, do you?"

"Yes, yes! We do!" They all replied.

"Then listen while you eat."

There was not a trace of Caramilla's former ostentatious arrogance. Their hostess had transformed into someone who communicated simply but with great awareness and vivacity of mind.

"The lid appeared as a result of vigorous measures our scientists undertook against the sun. According to their "strictly scientific" calculations, they argued that the sun was beginning to have a detrimental effect on the weather, the ecology and our health."

"How did they come to that conclusion? Since when has the sun been harmful?" Our friends showered their hostess with questions. "Why did they decide that the sun was harmful?"

"It is just what they decided. Human health has been significantly weaker in recent times, the environment is very polluted, and the weather is all over the place. The scientists decided that it was all because of the sun and increased solar radiation."

"As if! Did the sun pollute the planet's ecology, too?"

“That was the conclusion they came to,” Caramilla continued. “If the sun is emitting harmful radiation then it makes sense for us to send harmful radiation back. According to their scientific concepts, every action has an equal and opposite reaction and the reaction should suppress the action.”

“So, what did they do?”

“The scientists, scrambled together an apparatus at the Academy called an ‘electric telegraph’, and used it to send powerful rays of electromagnetic radiation into the sky aimed at the sun.”

“As far as I am aware, it is not possible to create any kind of radiation capable of affecting the sun,” clever Eejit remarked. “They’d never have enough energy.”

“It did not affect the sun but it did have a side effect. A lid-like formation appeared in the atmosphere.”

Our friends burst into indignant exclamations.

“They don’t have the right!?”

“We tend to believe that the authority of science is unshakable and unquestionable,” said Caramilla.

“Well, electricity, yes, but why the ‘telegraph’?” asked Eejit.

“They thought they could influence the sun by sending it instructions.”

“In what way?”

“Very simply, by using Morse code.”

Eejit’s eyes opened wide in surprise.

“Are they complete idiots?”

“It’s not for me to judge,” replied Caramilla and carried on telling them how it had all come about.

* * *

The scientists gathered at a round table once as part of a scientific conference. One of the participants went up to the podium and made a short but significant speech:

"Well, something is not right," he said.

His colleagues responded with a round of applause. When the applause had died down, the speaker bowed, left the rostrum and returned to his place at the table. The chairman was the next to take the floor.

"Right. The scientific paradigm in the report is clear but according to the methods of science, we must clarify the subject of our research. What do you consider to be your strictly scientific conclusions?"

"It's not a bubbly."

"It's not a gadfly."

"It's not a medley," those present declared.

"Please express yourselves scientifically," the chairman said. "There are grounds here for an article at a scientific conference."

"In some sense, it's become worse." Similar comments followed.

"Yes, in extrapolative manner, worse than before."

"Previously, things were better in a number of ways."

"One could even say that things were better in a certain way."

"And now, insufficiently wide."

"Deeply so."

"To summarize the scientific conclusion then: generally speaking, it has become unscientific. Correct?"

"Yes! That's correct! It's become quite unscientific!"

"Further, considering the conclusion through the prism of the angle of this point of view, we undertake to look deeply into the causes of the current situation," the chairman continued.

"The causes are inconceivable yet obvious," one of the scientists stated authoritatively. "The sun is entirely to blame."

"Yes, we can completely and recklessly assert, it's the sun's fault," confirmed another scientist no less authoritatively.

"And what are the scientific grounds for this statement?"

"It's a strictly scientific hypothesis."

"No, it is a scientific paradox."

"No, it is a scientific postulate. We reasonably postulate that the sun is to blame for everything."

"Right. This last sentence would appear much more scientific. However, in accordance with scientific procedure, we are required to provide some kind of explanation, however approximate. It should at least be something one can grasp with the imagination."

"How about, the sun is above everything, which means it's guilty of everything?" one participant suggested.

"Yes! Yes! That's a truly scientific truth!" the others present joined in.

"A brilliant scientific extrapolation!" said the chairman summing up. "Everything is ingeniously simple, as they say. Who is in favor of attributing this conclusion the status of scientific discovery?

There was general disconcertment.

"Without doubt, a great discovery," one of the scientists dared say. "But who made the discovery?"

"We all did! All of us. This is a discovery birthed not by one individual member but a collective organ."

"Well then, that sounds like a very reasonable inference to me. Given that everyone present here today has been fully engaged in academic enquiry, you will all receive the subsequent next degree status. Correct?"

"Yes! Correct!" the others agreed enthusiastically.

"And now, our task is to scientifically influence the sun," the chairman continued. "Such is our duty. What scientific proposals do you suggest?"

"Carry out a scientific experiment."

"It must confirm the authority of science."

"But how? How?"

"Scientifically."

"How exactly should we approach the task so that it is scientific?"

"It doesn't matter. Everything we do is scientific. We are science."

"Dear colleagues, our truly scientific discussion is turning into a very useful, extremely constructive allogenesis. However, a congruent brainchild should emerge as a result of our intense scientific scrutiny, which will have the ambivalent effect of neutralizing the solar-based products generated by the decay of our luminary."

"Dear chairman, dear colleagues!" One of the scientists began to address the participants. "My own intellectual genius tells me that this brainchild could and should represent an electronic telegraph, which has been scientifically invented, and which represents a powerful, universal means of influencing unscientific nature."

"Yes, true!" the scientist's colleagues responded noisily. "It's true and what is more, it is also correct!"

Having made this decision, the scientists began preparing for the monumental 'experiment of science'. It did not take them long to prepare, after all, what was there to stop and think about? They had to act and fast, off the cuff, on the spur of the moment before nature seized the initiative and prevailed over science, which would have been completely unacceptable.

As expected, the whole scientific scene unfolded into the makings of a scientific laboratory. It was basically a spacious hall with all kinds of equipment arranged around the sides and an impressive aggregate-unit at the center, consisting of an intricate interweaving of pipes, cables and other mind-boggling structures.

An operator sat at the controls in an armchair. He was dressed in shiny overalls and a helmet with protruding antenna and was surrounded by an endless buttons and lights. The action was led by the presiding officer, positioned in an elevated, glass bunker. The other members of the academy were there too and followed what was happening to the scientist, reflecting the action, in the conventional manner, with their facial expressions.

"Get ready!" The chairman shouted into the microphone "We are beginning the experiment of science."

"The electric telegraph is ready!" the operator answered.

"Caution! Telegraph... Transmission... Go!"

"Launching command mode!"

"Holding mode! Come on damn it!"

"Got it! Giving it full whack!"

"I'm transmitting! Sun, Sun! This is Earth. It's unbearable down here! Limiting heat! Limiting heat!"

"Wiring the command!"
"Destination: solar central axis!"
"Sending command to axis!... Command dispatched!"

A moment later, there was a deafening crash and everything around them shuddered. Then all was quiet again and everything became very still. The academic board also froze from fright and confusion, all standing with their mouths inappropriately dropped open.

"Show monitor readings!" the chairman ordered.

A large screen lit up with an image of the sky or rather, what had become of the sky. Above the earth there was now a dark, heavy surface blocking out the rays of the sun.

No-one dared utter a word not knowing how to interpret what had happened. Finally, one learned scholar took it upon himself to speak.

"Well, we've not just reduced the sun but, completely... So, there you have it."

"Yes, quite correct!" the others joined in.

"And that's just as it should be!"

"Science has been validated!"

"But more importantly, humanity is saved!" said the chairman in conclusion. "I congratulate you all on the overwhelming victory of science over nature!"

"It's a new science-experiment-record!" they all chanted in chorus. "It's a new science-experiment-record!"

* * *

"And there you have it, my dears," said Caramilla finishing her story.

"How do you know all these details, Caramilla?" asked the queen.

"Because I was part of the Academy. I was the only one to oppose the whole disgraceful affair and they had me banned."

"So that's how it works!"

"And they're still disrupting the atmosphere with this 'telegraph'?"

"Yes, totally carefree!"

"But what about the public, the authorities, common sense...?"

"It's advantageous for the authorities to put the whole cock-up down to the influence of various external factors, even to the sun. The public are being deliberately misled by the authorities and as for common sense, well, only those who have woken up seem to have any."

"So, in your opinion, society here is asleep?" The friends continued asking Caramilla questions.

"Yes, deeply, hopelessly, my dears," Caramilla answered.

"We also wonder if we have ended up inside a dream."

"Really? You know, it is not just a matter of humanity being asleep in a figurative sense. Humanity has always been asleep in that sense and will never fully wake up. The issue here is whether there is a difference between dreaming and waking."

"Caramilla! What are you saying ?!" Submarine was getting all excited. "I don't understand what you're talking about! And when I don't understand something, I start itching all over!"

"Shh! Be quiet." the queen reprimanded her. "It's not like it's the first time you don't understand what's being said."

"Gracious Caramilla, we've had so many adventures here recently, that we don't understand anything anymore," said Eejit.

"But seriously, what do you mean when you say a 'difference between dreaming and waking'?" asked Beast.

"There is no fundamental difference between the two. When I was working at the Academy, I spent a long time researching the question but never came to an intelligible answer. It is a curious issue but for some reason, nobody seems to attribute it any importance."

"I think it's important!" said Submarine. "I just don't get it... when I start thinking about it my head starts to hurt! And so, for the nth time, I ask, are we sleeping right now or not? We're not asleep right now, are we?"

"No, we're not asleep," said Eejit comforting her.

"So why are all these incredulous things happening that usually only happen when you're dreaming?"

"I have the same feeling as you do, as if I had woken up inside a dream surrounded by strange characters and with something weird going on with reality," Caramilla said.

"Right! You call them characters, too!" said Puscilla very pleased. "What is it about their behavior that you find strange?"

"It's difficult to explain," said Caramilla thoughtfully. "I often get the impression that people are being controlled by something else. They are not really aware of what they're doing. I also sense that they vaguely suspect that they are someone else's characters, but they don't want to acknowledge it."

"Bravo!" said Puscilla. "You've hit the nail right on the head! "When you ask them the question directly, they'll do anything to wriggle out of giving you a direct answer."

"What question?"

"Puscilla!" The queen made a warning gesture and Puscilla guiltily covered her mouth with her paws.

"No, really, what question?"

"Something tells me that you could ask Caramilla that question," said Beast. The queen glanced at Caramilla and then gave Puscilla a nod.

"Do you know who you are?" asked Puscilla.

"Of course, I do! I am me," replied Caramilla calmly.

"Hooray-hooray-hooray!" cried Submarine. The friends all expressed their admiration.

"What are you all so happy about?" asked Caramilla.

"This is the first time since we've been here that we've met anyone who you could call consciously aware," said Eejit answering on his friends' behalf.

"I see. I feel the same way, as if I have finally met other… others, who are completely compos mentis. I almost said characters then! Although, I have to say, I'm not entirely certain that I'm not a character myself. What about you?"

They all exchanged glances but said nothing.

"After everything that's happened, we aren't certain of anything either," said Cow breaking the silence.

"What happened to you, my dears?"

The friends started to recount all the strange adventures they had experienced since entering this strange reality. They told Caramilla about the mirror-like object, their miraculous metamorphoses, the eccentric characters they had come across, the paused film strip and the frozen mannequins with luminous plaits. Caramilla listened to them all with unveiled curiosity.

NESTED REALITIES

Caramilla sat with her elbows on the table and her chin resting in her hands for another minute or two after the friends had finished their story contemplating all she had heard.

"It all sounds just as far-fetched and it does sound realistic, my dears," Caramilla responded finally. "Only I don't advise you to tell anyone else what you have just told me. No-one else would believe you."

"We would not expect anyone to, gracious Caramilla," said Eejit. "Why do you believe us, though, and why do you think our story sounds in some ways realistic?"

"Something that seems totally inconceivable in one reality is sometimes distinctly possible in another."

"What do you mean? In another reality?" asked fastidious Submarine.

"Yes, in a dream for example."

"In a dream, yes, but a dream is not real!"

"Are you certain that the reality in which you find yourselves now is actually real?"

"Of course! Take this table... it's solid and we are all alive and well. We can touch each other."

"Everything looks and feels like it's physically real in a dream, too, as if you can reach out and touch it all. So how can you tell the difference between what is actual, physical reality and what only appears to be a physical reality?"

"It's obvious!" said Submarine. "We live our lives in physical reality, whereas a dream is something we only see when we are asleep!"

"By the same token, you can fall asleep in a dream and you can wake up inside a dream," Caramilla replied. "In that case, the first dream would be the real dream, whereas the second would be a nested dream, not a real one, right?"

"Um, I don't know..."

"Well, I'm not at all sure that this reality is genuinely physical reality," said Puscilla. "The people here are more like dolls. Of catty-course, with the exception of yourself, Caramilla. I have even met characters from my own books here. Surpurrprising, but a fact nonetheless!"

"We have to assume that if the present reality can be paused like a film strip then it can hardly be considered physical reality," remarked Brunhilda.

"I have no idea which reality I would call physical reality," said Caramilla.

"Oh, interesting. What do you mean by that Caramilla?" asked Submarine.

"I suppose I don't know what physical reality is really like. I have no way of knowing. Do you know?"

"Caramilla, all your questions have us completely stumped!" said Cow.

"They scare me," added Submarine.

"When a person falls asleep, they shift into a different reality. When they wake up, they return to this reality. But how did they enter this reality originally? When they were born, presumably, but where did they come from to get here? Probably from the same reality a person goes to when they die. Then where, in turn, did they come from before appearing in that reality? And then you have to ask yourself, which one of all those realities is the ultimate reality? The reality of dreaming or waking reality? The other world or the world beyond the other world? And you could go on like that forever."

After these words everyone was quiet busy processing their own thoughts.

"It seems clear that all realities have to be considered genuine." Eejit was first to speak. "Otherwise, they are all just an appearance of reality. It all depends how you look at it."

"And you could also look at it as if there weren't lots of different realities, just one consisting of separate layers, like an onion. And as we fall asleep and wake up again, as we are born and as we die, we pass through the layers like a series of nested dreams," said Caramilla.

"So, what might be the original source of all those nested realities, and where are they?" asked Beast. "I can remember several of my own incarnations, but I have never noticed how the process actually happens."

"Metoo," said Puscilla. "My metamorphoses are like a shift from dreaming to waking life and back again. It's a kind of weird moganimation."

"It's the same with me," said Cow, "spontaneous transformation."

"Me too!" said Submarine.

"The original source of all realities lies in the hands of the Creator," said Caramilla. "Just as all the secrets of reality lie in his hands. Reality is the strangest of jokes. We are all so used to looking at what's happening on her stage that few ever think to look in the wings."

"The most important thing for us is to work out which reality we are in now: our own or some other, foreign reality," said Eejit.

"Although the lid appeared when we were still in our own reality," noted Cow.

"Maybe the lid penetrated into our reality from inside this reality," Beast suggested.

"And there's one more enquiring question that's important to us," added Submarine. "How do we get home?"

"Caramilla, have you ever seen the mirror-like object we told you about?" asked Eejit. "What do you know about it?"

"Yes, I've seen it," Caramilla replied. "It appears to be some kind of boundary between two worlds or two aspects of reality. But I don't know any more than that. Science is incapable of providing an explanation for the phenomenon either."

"Not that your science would know!" Puscilla exclaimed. "It's a complete pussfranity!"

"What Puscilla is trying to say is that it's an absolute profanity," Cow explained.

"Yes. Precisely. It's total mogsense!"

"And what direction is the object from here?" asked Submarine. "We seem to have forgotten how we got here or where we came from, but we might remember if we can get back to the object."

"To the south. This street will take you southwards if you turn left as you leave the villa," Caramilla replied.

"But before we do anything, we have to deal with the lid," the queen stated. "Caramilla, is it really true that no-one here is worried that there's a lid across the sky? I mean, it's a catastrophe!"

"Everyone has accepted the lid, like they've accepted the state of the ecology and they don't want to change anything," Caramilla replied. "Planes have stopped flying but everyone stubbornly pretends that the lid is nothing to be worried about and everything is just as it should be."

"So, there's an airport here and you can fly to other destinations?"

"There used to be but not anymore. Everyone travels by train now."

"Do your pseudo-scientists really not understand what they've done?"

"At the moment they're working on producing scientific proof that the lid is totally harmless, quite beneficial and even essential."

"So, is there nothing that can be done?" asked Brunhilda.

"I do have an idea," said Caramilla. "I could send you to the Academy as representatives of the supervisory board. You would inform them that you are closing the lid project and demand that they stop sending radiation into the atmosphere."

"But Caramilla," said Eejit in surprise, "we all look so eccentric, no-one would believe we bore any relation to an officialdom."

"Oh, I'll cook you up the kind of document that no official would dare disobey. Please, follow me, come on my dears, follow me!"

Caramilla led the guests into her office, where their gaze was met by a strange apparatus representing an intricate interweaving of pipes and crude metal constructions in combination with sophisticated electronics. Caramilla turned on the machine. It made a humming noise and its light bulbs began to blink.

"This is my baking machine. It's my very own invention!" she said. "It will concoct any document or certificate you like. Our system's bureaucracy is as vast as our society's sleep is deep, so this machine makes life much easier."

"Wow!" said Eejit just as amazed as his friends.

Caramilla pushed various buttons and pulled a number of levers until an inscription lit up on the screen that read "supervisory board". The machine puffed, made internal creaking sounds and after a short period of productivity issued a ready-made document. The sheet of paper marked with a letterhead and bearing an official stamp read in the following manner:

"This certificate genuinely certifies that the bearers of said certificate are members of the Supreme Supervisory Board and are vested with the relevant powers authorizing them to empower other relevant officials, as well as to deprive them of said powers."

"Dear Caramilla," asked Eejit, "if I might clarify, what specific powers does this document gives us, and what kind of official can it be presented to?"

"It's right there: 'relevant powers in relation to relevant officials'," said Caramilla.

"And that should be enough?"

"More than enough. The most important thing is that the document is written in a style concordant with official understanding."

"And what if they ignore the document? What then?" asked the queen.

Caramilla thought for a moment.

"Do you think you could stop the movie like before?"

"Abso-catty-lutely!" replied Puscilla.

"Then listen up. The electric telegraph has a self-destruct mechanism. On the right of the control panel, you will see a red lever beneath the glass bearing the inscription 'PES'. When you stop reality, smash the glass and turn the lever all the way. That will initiate the self-destruct program and the entire scientific gizmo will go up in flames."

"Caramilla, what is 'PES'?" asked Eejit.

"It's an abbreviation for 'end of the experiment of science'."

"So why does is start with a 'P'?"

"They say 'pend' instead of 'end' to make it sound more scientific."

"Pussy-pend, my tail!" exclaimed Puscilla. "We'll give them a complete apo-catty-lypse!"

"Just be careful," said Caramilla. "If you have to draw on the last resort, do it because when the movie starts playing again, they'll sound the alarm and launch a raid to find you."

"Don't you worry, Caramilla," said the queen. "We'll get it right. Thank you for everything."

"Thank you, my dears! All hope lies with you now!" Then Caramilla gave them directions to the Academy and accompanied them to the porch.

"When it is over, we'll come back and tell you all about it," Submarine assured her.

"I'll be waiting for you, my dears!"

SCIENDOLOGISTS

And with that the 'expedition,' the prime objective of which was to liquidate the lid, set out on the ultimate leg of their journey. Heading the procession was Eejit Green, who was literally green, dressed in his shapeless hoodie and signature sunglasses minus the club which he had left behind having decided that it was superfluous.

Second was Queen Brunhilda, a regal-looking lady in a medieval-style dress made of rough linen, her red hair arranged in a plait, a golden hoop crowning her head and a battle sword hidden beneath her skirts.

Orange Cow went third in her new guise as an attractive-looking woman of ample proportions with red hair dressed in an orange knee-length dress and garish black shoes.

Next came Yellow Submarine also donning her new guise as a frivolous-looking blonde dressed in a yellow jumpsuit and orange boots.

Then there was Puscilla, and whether she was mostly woman or mostly cat, she was definitely a spectacular-looking brunette with a shock of wild hair dressed in a black fur jacket and pants, white boots and gloves, a luxurious fluffy tail and a set of feline ears.

Bringing up the procession was Shaggy Beast, now a young man of pleasant appearance, big, sad-looking eyes and brown hair to his shoulders, elegantly dressed in a black velvet suit with large gold buttons and a snow-white shirt with lush frills, but strangely, shod in woolly moccasins.

Soon, this colorful team appeared in the square in front of a tall, grandiose building arrogantly flaunting the large-lettered inscription 'ACODEMY OF SCIEND'. The letters O and D looked distinctly newer than the others suggesting that they had been added recently.

The friends entered the building and found themselves in a spacious hallway with a grand high ceiling. Despite its spaciousness, the room was stuffy and smelled of old books. Individual letters similar to those on the plaque on the outside of the building were propped up against one wall arranged to create the word 'MANAGAMENT'. The decrepit parquet floor creaked underfoot. A wide-fronted staircase lined in a battered old carpet led up to the next floor. Beside the staircase stood a table with a worn, cracked surface. Behind the table, facing the entrance sat a wizened old man in thick-lensed glasses wearing a threadbare suit with long sleeves. He sat with his hands clasped together and his fingers interlaced.

"And where do you think you are going? You're not allowed up there!" the elderly man shouted out without even stopping to ask the guests the purpose of their visit.

Puscilla stood in front of the others resting her paws on the table. She leaned forward and purred.

"Yes, we ar-r-r-e!"

The old man was taken aback but quickly recovered.

"And who might you be? Guests aren't allowed beyond this point! This is a place of sciend!"

“Puscilla!” Cow hissed.

Eejit pulled Puscilla back, who was trying to hypnotize the old man with the gaze of a panther and addressed the man himself.

“Sir, we have come to the Academy of Science on an official mission and would like...”

“We have sciend here, not science!” the old man interrupted him pointing his finger upwards. “Sounds a lot more impressive, doesn’t it?”

“Of course,” Eejit replied removing his glasses. “We would like to meet with the scientists to discuss ...”

“And we’re not called scientists anymore but something much more representative — ‘sciendologists’! And we’re not the Acodemy, we’re the Managament, see! We’re in the middle of changing the sign.”

“And for what purpose might I ask?”

“Because we have come to the conclusion that sciend is not to be studied but managed.”

“Why is that? Have you already studied everything?”

“Precisely! We know everything there is no know about sciend.”

“And how do you intend to manage it?”

“However, we think fit but in a strictly sciendific manner, naturally.”

“Quite correct. Just as it should be,” said Eejit. “That being the case, we would still like to meet with the scientists... the sciendologists…”

“You can’t. They’re busy.”

“What with?”

“They’re thinking.”

“What about?”

“About sciend!” the old man replied raising an upward pointing finger again.

“What is there to think about if you already know everything there is to know?”

“We don’t just know everything. We know more than everything!”

“More than everything?”

“Yes. But there is still work to be done on classi-si-fication and prinsci-pili-ali-zation of whatever there is.”

“Something resembling an inventory then?”

“Precisely. There is still a lot of work to be done in classi-sci-fi-ying what relates to sciend and what does not.”

“And the criteria for distinguishing between the two?”

“Very simple. Anything that does not lend itself to sciendific explanation is not sciendific. We negate anything we do not understand.”

“But inexplicable phenomena do not cease to exist simply because they have not yet been explained,” Eejit objected.

“Right, please clear the premises! We have sciend! What have you got?”

“We’ve come with sciend too!” Cow decided to join in the conversation. “We have a strictly sciendific hypothesis which we wish to put to you personally.”

“What hypothesis and why me personally?”

“Because I can see straight away that you are a luminary of sciend.”

“So, what is this hypothesis of yours?” The old man asked softening a little.

"Well, for example, do you know where sciend originated in the ancient civilizations? After all, they were ancient and undeveloped."

"There was no such thing as sciend then, nor could there have been," the old man smiled condescendingly. "We are the only ones who have ever had sciend!"

"But what about the surviving megaliths, alphabets, ancient drawings and artifacts?"

"I repeat, none of that can be explained from the point of view of sciend which means it's all strictly unsciendific."

"I completely agree with you! But you could turn it all into sciend if you strictly sciendifically substantiate our hypothesis."

The friends glanced at each other in confusion not understanding what Cow was driving at. Meanwhile, Cow was transformed, excited and suddenly acquired her former appearance as an orange winged cow. She flapped her wings and rose up into the air singing as she went.

"Once upon a time, when there was no such thing as sciend, the cows came out of the sea and taught people writing, astronomy and all sorts of other sciends! Then the cows returned to the sea, and people began studying and developing sciend, taking it to its limits with no perfection as well as to a state of perfection, which has no limits, as a result of which, a modern sciend appeared, which was perfectly limitless and outrageously perfect!"

The sciendologist stared at the wondrous sight equally stunned and entranced. But when Cow landed and transformed back into a fat girl, the old man returned to his senses.

"What I have just seen and heard is impossible because it's not sciend," he uttered.

"But you saw it with your own eyes," said Eejit.

"It's not enough to see it. It requires sciendific substantiation," he replied.

"Substantiate it then, strictly sciendifically," said Cow. "And our hypothesis will become a sciendific discovery."

"Yes, indeed, if I do it, then it will be sciend," the old man agreed after taking a moment to think about it.

"Naturally! You alone, no-one else!"

"In that case, I will go this instant and start writing my dissertation." The old man fussed and was about to rush off when he suddenly hesitated and turned back.

"But you're still not allowed in here. There's sciend here!"

"Excuse me, but with whom do we have the honor?" asked Eejit.

"I am the sciend desk clerk!"

"We too are directly related to sciend. We represent a supervisory board commission and have come on an official visit."

"We have more than enough of our own commissions and committees. But if we require another one, we'll create it ourselves. We don't need anyone else's."

"We are especially authorized persons, endowed with special powers to withdraw the powers of relevant and other officials, and we thereby relieve you of the powers of sciend desk clerk. You are free to go and immerse yourself in the abyss of sciendific knowledge. See? Look!"

Eejit held out the document for the old man to see and having studied it attentively, the old man reluctantly agreed.

"I have not plunged into the abyss for a long time."

"Well, you can plunge now but before you do, take us to your top sciendologist."

"The top sciendologist is busy at the moment. He's carrying out a very weighty sciend experiment."

"Wonderful. We will observe."

"Well, if ... you take full responsibility." The old man finally stopped deliberating and led the whole company upstairs.

They entered a laboratory which they recognized from Caramilla's description as the room in which the electric telegraph was stationed. An operator was sitting at the controls pressing buttons from time to time from which one could assume that the electrical contraption was actively functioning. In addition, preparations were clearly underway for something extremely important, since everywhere people in white coats and shiny overalls were scurrying this way and that. The friends climbed up into the glass bunker to join the director sciendologist, who was in charge of the whole operation as well as a few other sciendologists.

"And who might you be? You aren't allowed in here. This is sciend!" shouted the chairman.

"We are a commission from the Supervisory Board," said Eejit, waving his piece of paper. "We are authorized to observe and attend, as well as to attend and observe."

"Well, observe then. But don't get in the way of proceedings. This is a crucial moment."

The chairman appeared to be so focused on the activity at hand, he had neither time nor inclination to stand and bicker.

"Right. Attention please! Everyone in their places!" the director shouted into the microphone. "The invention experiment is starting!"

The people in gowns and overalls fussed more than ever.

"Get ready!" The chairman continued to give the orders. "Overview... maneuvering... control!"

The people in the laboratory started running about even faster but finally, they calmed down and took their places at the controls and monitors.

"All devices set for control!" reported one of the operators.

"Placing special specimen for experiment!" The next command came. A door opened and a man in a white, anti-radiation suit entered the laboratory.

The figure was also wearing impressive-looking boots, gloves and a helmet with a small, glass window as an eye hole. He was carrying a rat which he gripped by the tip of its tail, his arm fully outstretched,

"Insert screening container!" the chairman ordered.

A second door opened and another man in the same type of suit entered the room holding a saucepan, likewise, his arms outstretched.

"Insert anti-safety lid!"

A third door opened, and a third participant appeared holding the lid to the saucepan.

"Attention! Lid modelling in process!"

All three cosmonauts turned to face one another and with an efficiently coordinated set of actions placed the rat in the pan and covered it with the lid.

"Prepare prototype of nature!" sounded the next command.

Only now did our friends notice a microwave arranged on a pedestal at the center of the room. The three astronauts approached the pedestal. One opened the microwave door, the second inserted the saucepan containing the rat and the third closed the door.

"Enrage prototype of nature!"

One of the astronauts plugged in the microwave, the second set the time and the third extended his finger ready to press the Start button.

"Right, beginning miscalculation!" the chairman proclaimed solemnly.

All those present in the room noticeably tensed staring at their monitors which evidently showed the course of the experiment.

"Your cocotte is about to explode," said Puscilla disturbing the solemnity of the moment.

"Sh-h-h!" the sciendologists hissed.

"On my command!" shouted the director about to begin the countdown. "Nine, eight, seven, six, five, four, three, two, one, zero ... Lift off!"

One of the astronauts started the microwave and then all three stood around it motionless in anticipation. The microwave buzzed, sparkled, then smoked and finally exploded shattering into hundreds of pieces. All those present in the hall ducked instinctively but no one was hurt. Surprisingly, the saucepan and the rat remained untouched in its original place.

"Confirm sciend!" ordered the director after a short pause.

The astronauts approached the pedestal. One removed the lid from the saucepan, and another took out the rat, which turned out to be alive and well.

“Sciend has defeated nature! Congratulations to all on a successful experiment!” proclaimed the director. Vigorous applause followed.

“The invention experiment has shown that our lid is not only harmless, but also anti-safety! And now it is strictly sciendifically proved!”

“And we, on behalf of the supervisory board, congratulate you on your successful experiment,” said Eejit taking the floor. “And now, if you will, permit me to declare, on behalf of the aforementioned board the successful pend of the sciend experiment.”

“What do you mean, the pend?” asked the director perplexed.

“Just that. We declare its successful pend and with that hereby close the sciend experiment. You may turn off the electric telegraph.”

“But the Supreme Supervisory Board ordered...”

“That was the Supreme board. We are the Supereminent.”

“But we have sciend here!”

“And we have the authoritative powers,” said Eejit shaking his piece of paper under the sciendologist’s nose.

The sciendologist hesitated but then spoke resolutely.

“No, we cannot stop the experiment. This is sciend after all!”

“Why don’t you learn to live in harmony with nature instead of trying to influence it?” asked the queen joining in the conversation.

"What do you mean? I don't understand what you're trying to say."

"This is your world, your home. Why should you have to do anything to it? Why all this effort to toy with it, rake it over, stir, change and rebuild?"

"What do you mean, why? To conquer nature, of course, to bring about the final victory over the natural world!"

"But why is it so important to conquer nature? Why can't you just live in harmony with the world?"

"Because we are smarter than nature. We are more inventive!"

"And you think you know everything there is to know about nature and how this world is ordered?" Brunhilda asked refusing to let up although Eejit was already waving at her and preparing for plan B.

"Of course! We already know everything there is to know about sciend!"

"And what does your sciend have to say about the mirror-like object beyond the city?"

"What object?"

"The invisible wall it is impossible to pass."

"That is not sciend!" laughed the sciendologist.

"But it is a part of this world about which you claim to know everything there is to know. So how do you explain it?"

"Very simply. There is no such object."

"How can you say that if it's right there?"

"If we can't explain it, it is impossible. And if it is impossible, what other conclusion can we possibly draw?"

"I don't know, what?"

"It does not exist!"

"Your Majesty," whispered Cow to Brunhilda. "It's useless trying to talk to them. It's time to stop the movie."

Submarine decided it was time she intervened.

"Watch me carefully!" With these words, she transformed her appearance in front of them all appearing as before, as a yellow submarine wearing orange boots. "Is this impossible, too?"

The sciendologist was taken aback but recovered himself quickly and continued defending his standpoint.

"Of course!"

"But I'm right here in front of you! I'm no cartoon character, I exist!" said Submarine giving the sciendologist a poke with her anchor.

The director was completely unabashed and continued to insist on his own point of view.

"That cannot be because according to sciend, it cannot be!"

"Miaow! Not only do you know nothing about your own mogology, you know nothing about yourself!" Puscilla intervened.

"I refuse to participate any further in this unsciendific argument."

"You got so immersed in inventing newfangled gizmos, you forgot yourself," Puscilla continued.

"We have to have gizmos. We can't cope without them." To their surprise, the sciendologist began answering in a more amenable manner.

"That's true. You couldn't manage without them." Puscilla was staring intently at the sciendologist as if she were hypnotizing him.

"You need gizmos."

"Yes, we need them."
"Answer me this, do you know who you are?"
"Do I know myself?"
"Can you say, 'I am me?"
"Can I say... what?"
"We are all going to say, 'I am me' in turn and then you say the same afterwards."

The friends surrounded the sciendologist and began repeating their incantation. No further questions were required. As soon as the last in the circle had spoken, the sciendologist became totally still and covered with a wax coating. Everything else around them froze.

Without hesitating for a second, Beast rushed straight towards the sciendologists' infernal machine, quickly located the sign "PES" on the control panel, smashed the glass and turned the red lever all the way.
"Everyone run!" shouted the queen and the friends ran to find the exit.

THE FLIP SIDE OF REALITY

Submarine tottered along in her orange boots barely keeping up with the rest still donning her cartoon-like appearance.

"Wait for me, I can't go that fast!"

The friends dashed down the long corridors of the Academy building trying to remember the way to the exit. The movie stopped in the same manner as before only this time something was different. In the air hung tiny, shimmering specks that looked like snowflakes that had suddenly stopped falling. It was as if not only reality but space itself had frozen. All the objects around them looked somehow unnatural as if they no longer belonged to this world.

When the team finally ran outside onto the street, they were greeted with a truly grandiose phantasmagoria. The entire surface of the earth had become transparent, revealing a black abyss underfoot. At the bottom of the depths were myriad, parallel luminous paths that seemed to go on for infinity. The paths looked like they were made up of separate frames like filmstrips. The filmstrip located directly underfoot shone brighter than all the others.

The friends cried out in surprise and losing their balance, fell down on all fours. Submarine was so frightened, she transformed back into a blonde girl instantly. Stunned by the transformations taking place in reality as well as in her own appearance, Submarine let out a shout worthy of Puscilla's lexicon.

"Capooey! Complete Capooey! Completely and utterly Capooey!"

"Complete or not, I don't know, but it's definitely catty-osmic!" Puscilla responded.

"Cosmic!" added Cow.

"Cosmological!" said Eejit.

Beast and the queen remained unperturbed looking about them without saying anything. They were the first to get to their feet.

"Look! What's going on?" shouted Puscilla. "You've all got pussy-plaits! Have I got one? Have I got one, too?"

They all looked at each other. A luminous, plait-like plexus now extended outwards from the back of the head of each, similar to the protrusion they had seen on the frozen mannequins only without the blue rays.

"Perhaps not entirely, Puscilla," said Eejit, "but there is something strange there. You have one too for that matter."

"I can't feel anything!" said Submarine, running her hands down the back of her head.

"Me neither," said Cow.

"Now look at the mannequins' plaits!" Puscilla exclaimed.

Only now did the friends notice a passerby a short distance away who had frozen mid-step. His plait had transformed into a long blue ray, which extended downward right into the luminous path below. They looked around and witnessed the same phenomenon in another mannequin and another, until they had convinced themselves that it was an attribute common to all those in the square. The rays appeared to be attaching the motionless figures to the paused filmstrip below.

"What is this?!" shouted Submarine, "it is like we are being shown the structure of reality."

"I get the feeling that reality is trying to show itself to us in its true form," said Eejit.

"Puscilla, this is the perfect illustration of your idea that the people here are like puppets in a puppet theater," said Cow.

"More like characters in a movie," said the queen.

"But not us!" said Puscilla. "Our pussy-plaits are free! They're our own!"

"We chose to stop the movie. We're wandering around this movie live," Eejit explained.

"Yes! We're alive in a movie that's been paused!" exclaimed Submarine. "Colossal!"

"So that means, we're just taking a stroll here, whereas they live in the movie permanently?" mused Beast. "Yes, they live here while we're taking a stroll. Interesting..."

"The other interesting thing is whether the whole world stopped moving or just the movie we're in," said Cow.

"We would hardly be capable of stopping the entire world," the queen replied.

"As we've seen, the movie can be local and nested at the same time," said Eejit. "Remember how we stopped reality in the cafe and then saw the other part of reality along with the crazy writer and his disciples continuing to move about."

“Judging by the flakes that are hanging in the space around us, it looks as if all the local filmstrips have been paused. They weren’t here before,” Puscilla pointed out.

“And not just judging by the flakes,” said Eejit. “Look at those luminous paths. Those must be like filmstrips and the reality that surrounds us is the picture projection. None of them are moving.”

“Just what are these plait things?” asked Submarine looking puzzled. “And why have they appeared now when they weren’t there before?”

“My queen,” said Beast turning to Brunhilda, “you alone have your hair dressed in a plait but it is different to the luminous one. The luminous plait falls at an angle to your back and ends roughly one handspan’s width from your shoulder blades.”

“Whatever it is, we don’t have time to stop and work out what’s happening to us and reality right now,” Brunhilda replied. “We should make a run for it before the filmstrip starts moving again.”

“But maybe we shouldn’t run,” suggested Eejit. “What will the sciendologists see when they wake up if we do? Just that we suddenly disappeared. We were there and then ‘whoosh’, we were gone.”

“Yes, from their point of view that would be unsciendific!” said Cow.

“And if it is unsciendific, it is impossible!” concluded Submarine. “Which means, we were never there!”

“Nothing is quite that simple,” said the queen. “The most important thing is that they’ll see the collapse of their sciendific gizmo and want to know who could have launched the liquidation. It could only be us because we disappeared afterwards. Rather than going looking for trouble, we'd be better off getting as far away as we can from the 'scene of the crime'."

"You're right, Your Majesty," said Puscilla. "We need to cat-it right out of here."

"Yes, but where to?" asked Submarine. "What about heading back to our good old Villa Caramilla?"

"We can't go back there," the queen replied. "If we get caught Caramilla will come under suspicion. We need to hide out in the city somewhere and observe what happens."

"That's right. After all, we don't know what might happen next," said Eejit. "Look, that's the tower of the city hall. That would make a great viewing platform. Shall we head for the tower?" said Beast.

"How will we get in?" asked Submarine.

"Easy!" replied Cow. "While the filmstrip is on pause and all these people are like mannequins, we can go wherever we want."

"Right, time to go," said the queen.

They ran across the square and climbed the tower of the town hall via the internal staircase. At the top there was a viewing platform with a clock and a bell that opened up onto a panoramic view of the entire city. More precisely, the panorama consisted not of one city but of many copies of the city's image repeated over and over again extending far into the distance in the direction of all four of the cardinal points.

The entire, visible landscape was marked with lines like a chessboard. When the friends looked in one direction, there were two or three nearby blocks in one square. These were repeated in the next square, and in the gap between stretched the same kind of yawning emptiness, with which our friends were already familiar — a kind of black construct which descended downwards and overlapped the same gap on the luminous path far below.

In the more distance squares, it was hard to tell whether the contents were another copy of these same blocks or the next set of blocks, but overall, it was like an optical illusion in which everything was repeating itself, each image embedded in the next. The overall picture resembled a series of mirror reflections that went on into infinity with decreasing scale, so that in the distance they could see endless individual copies of the entire city. The whole scene was like a complex hologram, which equally represented a projection of the frames in the filmstrips below. The sky, however, was still obscured by the lid's dark, solid surface.

The friends tried ardently to make out which object was being reflected where, but the illusion constantly slipped away from them, revealing one facet after another. Eventually, they abandoned their attempts to comprehend the incomprehensible, exhausted with frustration, not knowing what to say. Moreover, the surrounding picture of reality appeared mythical, somehow unreal as if they themselves had been cut out of a different reality and inserted into this one, like living figures placed inside a still photograph.

The pause seemed to last for an eternity and then suddenly, everything began to move again. A light breeze began to blow, background noise began to sound, and the filmstrips below began to shift, first the central one, and then the others all with increasing speed. The shiny flakes dissolved into the atmosphere and the earth's surface closed over losing its transparency. The chess board quivered, the squares merged, and the entire hologram ran smoothly into a single, familiar picture of reality. The mannequins in the square jolted into action and continued along their path as if nothing had happened. The movie was playing again.

A moment later, a cracking noise came from the direction of the Academy, accompanied by a brief flash of light, and then the entire space became bathed in unusually bright sunshine. The lid in the sky dissolved as if it never was.

THE INTENTION PLAIT

In the mall, where we left priestess Itfut and diva Matilda, absolute silence and a literal numbness reigned. The entire space around them had frozen. Glistening flakes hung motionless in the air and mannequins stood in weird poses as if they had been caught off-guard in an instant snapshot.

The scene could have served as an illustration of absolute silence and timelessness if it were not for two living figures, one of whom was spinning about and laughing as she did whenever she was extremely anxious, and the other who was pacing back and forth wildly gesticulating.

"Futi!" she said. "Calm down, will you?! Tell me what you remember?"

Itfut suddenly stopped and froze staring at Matilda with a look of immense seriousness.

"Futi, you're scaring me again!"

The priestess relaxed a moment later and smiled.

"Tili, that thing we call the trigger-jigger, I know what it is now and what it is for."

"Well, go on then, tell me!" said Matilda impatiently.

"It is an archaic vestige, an energy plexus resembling a plait. In its usual state, the plait is invisible, but it becomes visible when the movie stops. You see?" Itfut made a half turn looking at Matilda over her shoulder. “And you have one the same!”

“I could feel that there was something there on my back... like a kind of heavy sensation...” Matilda ran her hands along the back of her head but could not feel anything. “But you can’t feel it, right?” she said in surprise.

“The plait is intangible,” replied Itfut. “You sense it like a phantom limb that feels like it’s there and at the same time, isn’t. It is like when someone has an arm amputated and they can feel it afterwards. At least you had some kind of sensation. I didn’t feel anything at all. I had completely forgotten about it. But I remember now. Imagine that! I can feel my own plait!”

“I don’t feel anything special though,” said Matilda. “It’s just a sensation, or the feeling of the presence of something and it only happens when I focus on it.”

“That’s exactly how it should be!” exclaimed Itfut. “The plait activates when you turn your attention to it. It even lifts slightly at an angle to the spine. You see?” The priestess turned again to show the diva her plait. “I just focused on it and it rose up. Now I take my attention away from it and it goes down again.”

“Got it,” said Matilda. “Look, does the same thing happen with mine?”

“Yes! It’s working really well! Can you see now that your bow has nothing to do with it?”

“My bow taught me to feel my plait!” Matilda said. “I’ll never part with it now, not for anything!”

“Quite right. Don’t!” Itfut agreed. “I can’t imagine you without it. Tili-darling, Tili-Tili-darling!”

“Stop that, Futi. So how does it gets activated and what we need it for?”

"What for? As if you still need to ask. To control reality, that's what for! We have already been using our plaits it's just that we haven't been doing it consciously."

"Yes, and we've stopped filmstrips and shifted between them and provided ourselves with food. And all that is down to our plaits! My plait even saved my life when I first came across the glamrocks."

"There you go then! And what did you do, when were you led to meet with their leader, the glamorc? Remember?"

"I decided that everything would be all right with me, no matter what."

"In essence, you caught the sensation of your plait and declared your intention. You set a different reality in order to escape the one that involved your imminent death."

"But is it really possible to set a new reality?" asked Matilda in surprise.

"Tili, how many times have we talked about this before!" exclaimed Itfut. "Remember, we talked about the fact that you can change the course of events?"

"Yes, you mentioned then that it's impossible to influence a character directly but that you can change the script they are led by."

"It would be more accurate to say that you can't influence the script directly either."

"So, what is it that changes, then?"

"The filmstrip that contains a different script!"

"Futi, can you explain in more detail from the very beginning, what we have to do to set a different reality?"

"Sure. It is really very simple. You focus on the plait and without losing concentration, you imagine in thoughts, words or images the scene you want to have as your reality. In other words, you set your intention, and thereby set your reality. Then you drop the sensation of the plait, basically deactivating it. We have all done this more than once in our lives, the only difference is that we did not know about the plait."

"And so, then what happens? A shift to a different filmstrip?"

"Well done, Matilda, clever you! You can't change the script of the current filmstrip, but you don't need to. As you know, reality consists of many variations of filmstrip, each of which contains its own scenario of events. By lighting up the frame you want with your plait, a frame that may not exist in the current filmstrip but will undoubtedly exist on another, you jump onto that other filmstrip. And then a potential variation of reality is transformed into your current reality, or at they say, the imagined becomes the real."

"So that means that in order to change your reality, you need imagination plus the plait?" asked Matilda.

"Almost," replied Itfut. "It's not just your imagination. It's more like your firm intention - an ***affirmation*** that this is how things will be for you now. You activate the plait and whilst staying focused on the sense of it, you declare your intention to receive such and such. You can do it through thought, words or visualized images, it does not matter which, as long as you do it firmly, confidently and in tandem with the plait. That's the secret. That's why I say that you're not so much changing reality as setting it, composing how you would prefer it to be."

"And will it really be exactly as you imagined it?" Matilda continued to probe Itfut for details.

"Your dreams are unlikely to come true if you just sit around dreaming with your head in the clouds. But once you're using the plait and your intention, almost certainly. Of course, it does not always work straight from the get-go. Sometimes it does not work at all. It all depends on the complexity of the task, as well as how well you've trained your plait. If the task is something particularly hard to achieve, the filmstrip in which that goal manifests will be quite a long way from the current filmstrip and you have to reach it, so, as a rule, big goals are realized in stages by shifting from one filmstrip to another, gradually moving closer to the target strip."

"Are you're saying that the plait can be trained?"

"Of course! Why do you think I called it a vestige? People stopped using it and so it atrophied. Everyone is different of course. Our plaits are more or less still working but many people will have to work quite hard to even get a sense of their plait. For that reason, it's best to set your reality fairly often. There's no point in hoping that something will come true, wondering whether it will or not, or expecting something from reality. It's much better to set your reality, intentionally and systematically."

"Futi! This is a fundamentally different way of thinking and being! Do you realize how different this all is? It is literally like an extraterrestrial worldview! Nothing like ours at all! People have got used to living their lives waiting and hoping! It would never occur to them that rather than worrying and hoping for some manna from heaven, they could just set their own reality! Can you imagine how intense this is! It is even more cool than tracking your attention! You remember how amazed I was when you told me about that?"

"Yes, Tili! And do you remember what I said?" asked Itfut.

"Do I! It returns you to yourself! Basically, you have to tell yourself, 'I will wake up every time something happens, or something gets me down, or when something is going wrong in the world around me'."

"And then what?"

"Then you enter a certain state of awareness. You activate your Witness and begin acting consciously, not like a character, not even as a spectator but as a conscious observer. And then instead of the situation controlling you, you control the situation."

"And do you remember why we need the Witness?"

"To keep track of where you are placing your attention, whether you are owning it or giving it away: whether it is focused on you or on the movie you are immersed in. When you have control over your attention, you have control over yourself and you can be your own person."

"Exactly," said Itfut. "You have to develop the opposite habit: instead of falling asleep, instead of falling into a trance, do the opposite. The moment anything happens, wake up. And another thing, don't forget. When you go to do something, ask yourself: Are you choosing to do this or is something or someone controlling you?"

"Yes, I remember that bit. And, Futi, have I guessed right? I bet there's another opposite habit we have to develop, too right?"

"And what might that be, Tili-Tili?"

"Not to wait for reality to give you something but to set your own reality!"

"You really are smart, Tili-Tili!"

"No, I'm just stunned again by all the things you're telling me! This really is extraterrestrial knowledge!"

"No, Tili, it's most likely that you and I are from the same planet," said Itfut. "My world has a sun and a moon, just as yours does. It is just that our worlds are set far apart in time."

"It is still awesome though! All this stuff is commonplace to you because you were born and brought up with it. You might have forgotten quite a bit, hopefully temporarily, but you'll remember. For me, this kind of Knowledge is incredible! Maybe you'll remember something else just as awesome? Futi!"

"Perhaps, perhaps!"

"By the way, why did you call the vestige archaic?" asked Matilda.

"Because in ancient times, when the Creator had only just created humankind in his own image and likeness, people were capable of controlling reality. They were perfect masters of the plait. But with time, people gradually lost the ability. Why do you think that was?"

"Why was it?"

"They were mired by their own movie. They started to live in the current reality like fish in an aquarium. People stopped trying to control the focus of their own attention. That was the main thing. If you do not control where your attention goes, you forget about the plait. Mastering the plait depends on controlling where your attention goes.

Generally speaking, when we talk about 'controlling' it we do not mean 'owning' it or 'having possession of it' so much as 'having the ability to manage it," Itfut continued. "When people stopped managing their reality, they exchanged their intentions for dreams and cravings. And as you now know, the plait does not work with dreams and desires. It works with intention."

"So, remind me, what's an intention exactly?" asked Matilda.

"An intention is a firm statement that things will be a certain way, '***period!***', as you would say. It is not the desire for a dream that may or may not come true. It is a firm, calm attitude, a certain ***resolve***. Do you understand the difference?"

"Yes, firm, calm resolve. You could say unshakeable resolve."

"Quite. So, our trigger-jigger is not a desire plait, it's an intention plait. That's the only way it will work."

"And another thing, Futi," Matilda continued, "you say that people once had this skill and then they lost it... Well, you have this knowledge, so does that mean that it still exists in your world? What people do you mean?"

"Before our civilization, other more developed civilizations existed. I don't know how many, but they all fell once they reached a certain point in their development. After a period of downfall, development resumed and then declined again. I don't know why this cycle exists or for what purpose but that is how things are. I suspect the reason is that reality will only allow itself to be controlled up to a certain point and whenever that point is reached, reality plunges humankind into a dream."

"As far as our civilization goes, I don't think it has ever woken up and don't think it has any intention of ever doing so."

"We too are far from being developed. We are only just beginning to assimilate this kind of knowledge."

"Where did it originally come from, I wonder?"

"Everything originates in the Supreme Creator. But to whom Knowledge is given and when depends on whether the one it is intended for is ready to receive it."

"Ooh! Futi! This is crazy fascinating. But shouldn't we be getting back to our mannequins? Why do they have plaits do you think if they're not living? What are those rays down their backs, and did we have them too before we became fully aware?"

"I cannot say why they have plaits but the fact they do does not necessarily mean that the owner knows how to use it. The plait most likely has some other function, a control function for instance."

"Do you mean like a kind of rod you would use to control a rag doll and move it around?"

"Yes, probably."

"So, if the plait is in your own hands so to speak, you are your own person. You are self-directed. But if it ends up in the hands of others, then you are not your own person and you can be manipulated by others, right?"

"Precisely, Matilda! That is why it is so essential to own the power of your attention. To be able to control your attention is to be able to control your plait and as a result, yourself. But the blue rays are even more interesting!"

"What are they, Futi?"

"Can you guess? What were we just talking about?"

"About controlling where your attention goes. So?"

"Do you remember what we said the essential difference was between an observer and a character?"

"When I am sleeping and am not aware that I am sleeping, I am a character and I am controlled by the dream."

"Yes, or in other words, you are being led by the movie. The movie owns you! But more precisely, what would we say is really leading you?"

"The script?"

"The blue rays are what bind a character to the script of any particular movie."

"Hela! I get it now! They are like the puppet strings!"

"So, do you understand now why we had them too before we reclaimed our awareness?" asked Itfut.

"Yes, they disappeared when we returned the focus of our attention to ourselves!" said Matilda happily.

"That's it! You become yourself only in the moment that you regain the focus of your attention, when you pull it back from an external movie or from internal pondering. Only then can you say that "you are you." The rest of the time, you are an unconscious character being controlled by the movie. It has you gripped by the plait, by that very same blue ray."

"So, when I free myself from the ray, it is like I am detaching myself from the script and can wander about freely in the movie?"

"And not just that! You can set the scene for a different movie and jump to another filmstrip."

"Wow! Futi! That is so cool!"

"That is the main thing. In dreaming or in waking, it is exactly the same."

"You know, it fills me with horror when I think that just a little while ago, we were trying to kill each other! Futi, my dear friend! I would die without you!"

"Tili-Tili, I couldn't manage without you either!"

And with that, they gave each other a hug.

"What happened to us," said Itfut, "is proof that the power of attention is serious stuff. It is not something that should be left to wander. It is too difficult to constantly hold your attention at the center of your being, but you can tune into it more often and return to it every time the slightest breeze breaks into your space."

"Yes, I understand that now. And what are we going to do about this frozen space?" asked Matilda. "...all these flakes frozen in the air."

"I don't think there's anything we can do here," replied Itfut. "We should shift to a different filmstrip."

"I wonder why these mannequins are so angry with people and what they would do if they caught us?"

"Who knows."

"How are plastic mannequins different from dream mannequins?"

"They're both just bodies, embodied forms lacking a soul and awareness."

"But they wanted something from us, right? That means they must have some element of consciousness."

"It's not consciousness. It's the script of a plot. The same goes for us."

"Where do all these nightmarish plots come from?"

"Partly from our subconscious fears."

"If you remember, the glamrocks did not have plaits or blue rays when they froze," said Matilda. "Then we were able to awaken their consciousness when we made them recall their names."

"Back then, the movie had not stopped. It just slowed down which was probably why it was not so visible. Consciousness is far too complex a subject for us to discuss now. We need to get out of here before the filmstrip starts moving again."

"Futi, why don't we try and get to your world now? Can you take us there?"

"Okay, let's try."

CITY OF TEMPLES AND STATUES

Priestess Itfut leaned forward slightly, lowered her head, threw up her arms bent at the elbow to shoulder level and then straightened them fully with the exclamation, 'OO-OO-OO-OO---LA! In that instant, the space inside the mall became cloudy and began swirling into a whirlwind around the two figures moving with increasing speed.

Then the speed at which the whirlwind span began to slow and turn in the opposite direction unfolding into a static space in which objects of black and white stone gradually began to materialize literally out of thin air. Slowly but inevitably, a complete picture of the scene emerged — a dead city immersed in semi-darkness consisting almost exclusively of temples and statues.

The surface of the ground resembled a huge chessboard on which white statues were arranged on black squares and black ones on white squares. The statues were two to three times the height of a human being. The view to the sides and into the distance was dotted with triumphal arcs and small temples in shades of grey and the main temple with white, stone pillars loomed at the center of a large square. In this monochrome scene, the diva and the priestess stood out as being the only source of color.

Surrounded by huge monuments, the two figures looked like miniature figurines.

The diva and the priestess walked back and forth looking at the sculptures.

“Futi, are you sure this is your city?” asked Matilda. “It looks a bit like it but what’s happened to the beautiful alleys, the houses, trees and flowers?”

“This is not material reality, Tili.” said Itfut. “We are still in meta-reality. There are no people anywhere, see? For some reason, we haven’t managed to get back into physical reality.”

“What are we going to do now?”

“I don’t know. Let’s take a look around.”

“Futi, I think I’m going to cry! Will we ever return to reality?!”

“Come now, Tili, Tili!” The priestess took the diva by the shoulders and gave her a gentle shake. “You may be a darling, but you’ve got get a grip on yourself. Remember to track your attention. Imagine that we’re just taking a stroll through a movie, ok?”

“Okay,” muttered Matilda struggling to hold back the tears. “I’m just so tired of all these nightmares.”

“Let’s start by finding my statue,” suggested Itfut. “That would be interesting, right?”

“Yes, I suppose...”

They joined hands and set out in search of Tufti.

“Who are all these sculptures dedicated to?” asked Matilda.

“They’re all prominent figures of the past and forgotten Gods,” replied Itfut.

"Why forgotten?"

"Because people have a tendency to invent their own Gods as a way of finding some sort of support. They keep on inventing new ones, while the old ones disappear into oblivion."

"Stupid isn't it?"

"People aren't stupid as such, they just don't know how reality works. They don't understand that they can be like Gods in this life. Oh, look, over there, there's one that looks a bit like me."

They approached a plinth on top of which towered an exact copy of Itfut in black granite, only twice her usual size. The inscription pecked out on the plinth below read 'TUFTI. HIGH PRIESTESS'. The two friends circled the statue admiring it succumbing to a sense of awe. Itfut, however, seemed to respond more calmly to the spectacle than one might have expected.

"Not bad work," she said.

"Futi, surely it must freak you out looking at a statue of yourself?" said Matilda in surprise.

"Ha, ha, ha!" responded the priestess in her characteristic light-hearted manner. "It's not like it's a tombstone! And even if it was, what of it? I'm a priestess!"

"It's a good thing you don't have the tradition of showing the dates of birth and death."

"Yes, quite. It's as if there is no death, just eternal memory. But you know, death as such doesn't really exist..."

Itfut did not have time to finish her sentence before she was interrupted by the booming sound of a gong. In that moment, the statues began to move and stepped down from their plinths. Their movements were slow and heavy like the giants they represented, moreover heft from stone. Tufti's statue was the only one to remain standing on the plinth. The diva and the priestess hid behind it watching the giant figures.

The giants, meanwhile, all black and white started moving synchronously, stepping forward and at right angles to the left and to the right until they were all lined up like pieces on a chess board. The largest of them stepped forward front of the row and spoke in a low bass voice.

"I heed and worship!"

"We heed and worship!" the others repeated in a thunderous chorus.

Then they turned intending to walk together in the direction of the main temple but that was not to happen.

"Hey!" shouted Itfut to Matilda's horrified surprise.

"Futi! Are you mad?!" Matilda whispered still squatting behind the plinth. But the priestess had already stepped forwards of the monument, her arms folded. Not wanting to leave her friend alone, Matilda jumped out from behind the plinth, too

"Tili, whatever happens, don't be afraid. They can't hurt us."

"How do you know that?!" Matilda called out to her in a desperate whisper.

"Because that's what I've decided, period!"

The stone statues froze and then they all turned sharply to face the uninvited guests. The head giant extended a finger and thundered in a terrifying voice.

"Drop down, mortals!"

“No living being falls down before the dead,” said Itfut unimpressed.

Furious, the giant stretched out a huge hand and made a grab at the priestess, but his hand passed through her as if through empty space. Unable to understand what was wrong, the stone giant continued to grab at one victim or the other all the time shouting, “Kneel!”

“Right away!” replied Itfut and climbed calmly up onto her plinth, her hands on her hips standing beside her own statue. Matilda stood rooted to the spot petrified.

Now it was the giant’s turn to freeze in shock and horror.

“High priestess Tufti!” shouted the rows of other statues. “Living among the dead!”

“I heed and worship!” the giant boomed and knelt down with his head bowed.

“We heed and worship!” the others repeated going down on one knee.

Itfut climbed down from the plinth and nonchalantly leaned her elbow up against it. Matilda finally took a hold of herself and stood beside her friend.

“You aren’t immortal, so don’t make yourselves out to be Gods.” Itfut said.

“What?” asked the giant in surprise lifting his head.

“You are immortalized in stone but no more than that. And there’s no need for you to bow before me either. Get up!” The statues all stood up again obediently.

“Then lead us, oh great priestess,” said the giant, “into the Supreme Temple!”

"What for?" asked the priestess playfully.

"To worship the Creator!"

"Okay," replied Itfut in the same manner as before. "Let's go."

"We heed and worship!" the statues pronounced majestically and as one they followed the two priestesses as they strode towards the main square, whispering to each other as they went.

When the entire procession had arrived at the temple, Itfut and Matilda made their way up the steps and stood beside the pillars while the giants arranged themselves in a semi-circle below. The main giant stepped into the center of the semicircle and spoke with great pathos.

"Oh, supreme priestess Tufti, heed our appeal! Renew the great solemn ceremony!"

"We heed and worship!" the statues sang in chorus.

"What solemn ceremony?" asked Itfut in an ironic tone.

"The ritual of worshipping the Creator, solemn and holy!" the giant replied.

"Now the chosen one of the Ilit Temple will reveal to you a very solemn message," Itfut announced mysteriously.

The statues froze in breathless anticipation. Matilda stepped forward and then shifting from one foot to another, blurted out her message.

"You don't bloody well need to worship anyone! That's it." And with these words, she stepped to the side.

The stone idols stood open-mouthed in amazement. Then Itfut threw her hands to the side in a gesture as if to say, 'c'est la vie'.

"Us?" Sounds of astonishment sounded along the rows of statues. "Don't bloody well need? Don't need bloody well? What's bloody well?"

"Don't bloody well need, means, what the hell do you need it for?" said Matilda repeating Itfut's hand gesture.

"What the hell?" repeated the statues questioningly. "What the bloody hell? Or hell the bloody? What's hell?"

"What the hell, means that nobody gives a damn about your ritual," Matilda explained.

"We understand!" the main giant declared. "We don't bloody well need it! We heed and worship! What the hell!"

"What the hell do we want that for?!" the statues repeated with enthusiasm. "We heed and worship!"

"No, you don't get it!" Itfut interrupted. "Where do you get the idea that the Creator has to be worshipped?"

"Because He is great and almighty!" replied the giant.

"What are you, slaves?" asked Itfut.

"No!" the statues grumbled. "We aren't slaves! Not us!"

"Maybe you're sloths?" Matilda asked them in a serious tone.

"No! We aren't sloths!" they answered in all seriousness.

"Did the Creator tell you to worship him?" Itfut asked them.

"No, no he didn't," the statues answered.

"Have you ever seen him?"

"No, we've never seen him."

"That's right. He doesn't want to see or talk to you."

"Why? Why?" the statues asked with genuine surprise.

"Because you have cunningly swapped fulfilling His commandments with worshipping Him," replied Itfut. "And have presumptuously raised yourselves to the rank of saints and immortals."

The statues looked puzzled and fell silent for a while.

"But we place ourselves below Him!" the giant objected. "We worship Him!"

"And what makes you think he would find that necessary?"

"Because He is great!"

"You're just hypocrites! You're being hypocritical and have no fear of Him at all!"

"How? How are we being hypocritical?" the statues asked again, genuinely surprised.

"Because you have presumptuously and cunningly decided on His behalf what He needs and what He doesn't. You've become so accustomed to your own deception, that you genuinely think it is the truth."

A grave silence reigned. There was nothing they could say in their defense.

"Then what are we to do, high priestess Tufti?" asked the giant.

"Heed but do not worship. Praise but do not worship. Instead co-create together with the Creator."

"But how can we co-create with Him?" asked the giant in deep surprise. "We are below Him after all!"

"Are you below Him? That's cunning," replied Itfut. "You aren't equal to Him, but you aren't lower than Him either. The Creator created you in the image and likeness of Himself. Why did He do that do you think?"

"So that we would worship Him?"

"I repeat, 'in the image and likeness of Himself.' Why is it expressed in that way? Do children worship their parents? No, they listen to them and respect them. Or maybe the Creator decided to worship Himself? No, because He doesn't waste time. He creates. Unlike you, he's not a slacker."

"Not only are you not creating anything," continued Itfut, "you kill, you cause wars and destruction. You think that by worshipping Him, you will earn His indulgence, so that you can kill and destroy with a clear conscience but that's just hypocrisy and deceit. That's why He doesn't ever show Himself to you.'

"What are we to do, oh great priestess? And how are we to do it?" asked the statues.

"Whether I am great, what you are to do, and how you are to do it, I will show you now. Look at me and at my sculpture."

Right before the eyes of the astonished statues, Itfut carried out her magic gesture with the exclamation 'oo-oo-oo-oo-la!' and in that moment, her statue disappeared from the square along with the plinth on which it had rested.

"So now, I ask you, am I great?"

"No, Mistress," they answered. "But how did you do that, great priestess?"

"First tell me, am I great or am I not?"

"We don't know," the statues answered hesitantly.

"It isn't the individual that is great but their deeds. Get it?"

"What do you mean? What do you mean?" asked the statues bewildered.

"Once you start creating, then you will understand."

"Teach us, great priestess!"

"Back to that again. Luckily for you, in this world you don't have to put in any effort and work. It's enough for you to form an intention and instruct it to happen. Watch how it's done."

Itfut leaned forward in the usual way, and then straightening herself, she threw up her hands exclaiming "By my command, so be it!"

In that very second, in the same spot where previously Tufti's sculpture stood, a fabulous fountain appeared with azure waters falling into a round pool, decorated with exquisite malachite mosaics. The stone idols burst into enthusiastic cheers.

"How did you manage that, oh great priestess?!"

"You're capable of doing just the same," Itfut replied.

"Watch again." This time the diva joined in the magical creation. Matilda straightened her bow, threw up her arms and exclaimed, "By my command, so be it!"

A moment later, the entire city, which had until now been immersed in semi-darkness, was illuminated by the rays of the sun and all the colors of the rainbow shone across the clear blue sky.

"Oh, great priestess Tufti!" cried the statues in admiration. "Oh, great chosen one of the Temple of Ilit! Do another miracle for us!"

"This has nothing to do with miracles," said Itfut. "Now it's your turn. Go ahead, get on with it. Remember, which of you used to have a skill."

"Tell us what we must do, oh great priestess!" exclaimed the giant.

"For a start, get rid of all your 'great' pedestals and instead build yourselves beautiful cozy homes. Then, decorate the entire city."

"I heed and worship!" the giant answered.

"What?! That again?!" said the priestess attacking him.

"Don't be angry, Mistress," he requested. "We'll make everything right and make ourselves right."

The giant turned in the direction of the plinths, threw up his arms, and in a thunderous voice exclaimed,

"By my command, so be it!"

To the amazement of the remaining statues and to the delight of the diva and the priestess, the giant managed it. The plinths disappeared and quaint-looking houses appeared in their place, exactly like the ones in Tufti's real world, only of the size fitting for a giant.

"Honor and praise!" shouted Itfut.

"Bravo!" Matilda shouted.

"O-o-o! A-a-a-a!" the crows sounded.

"Who's next?" asked Itfut. "Don't be shy!"

A brave spirit emerged from the crowd, threw up his arms and exclaimed, "By my command, so be it!"

The chessboard disappeared replaced everywhere by inviting walkways and boulevards.

Then the next volunteer stepped forward.

"By my command, so be it!"

Paths, alleys and squares appeared all overgrown with shrubs and trees. Then a female statue stepped forward.

"By my command, so be it!"

In addition to the vegetation, the entire district was tastefully decorated with flowers. Each in turn came forward and proclaimed, 'by my command, so be it!' and added some new detail to the space. Eventually, the city was transformed into the same blessed place that Matilda so admired when she had observed what was happening in Tufti's world.

"So, what will your slogan be now?" asked Itfut.

"I heed, praise, create!" answered the main giant.

"We heed, praise and create!" the others repeated.

Immediately after these cries, the temple began to shine with a bright radiance that was coming from inside the building. The glow continued to shimmer for about a minute, while everyone silently observed the divine phenomenon with unprecedented delight.

"The Creator has appeared to you in the form of a blessing!" exclaimed Itfut.

The giants lifted both their benefactors up above their heads and carried them ecstatically throughout the city streets. This was a real triumph for priestess Tufti and the new recruit of the Ilit Temple in whose honor the sacred building in the city was subsequently named. Nonetheless, the friends' most outstanding achievements still lay ahead of them...

For now, their most important task was to escape metareality and return to the reality of physical phenomenon. When exactly this was destined to happen, only Threshold could say.

WALKING BENEATH THE LID

"Hooray-hooray-hooray!" shouted Submarine.

The friends jumped about, clapped their hands and then hugged each other.

"The self-destruct mechanism worked!"

"That's the pend of the sciend experiment!"

"The end to end all ends!"

"A catty-cappy end!"

"Happy!"

"Our mission is complete!"

The people below were also shouting in excitement now and then lifting their arms upwards. People were flocking down the streets towards the city hall and soon the square was filled with a jubilant crowd. Members of the administration lost no time in appearing before the people, crowding onto the balcony wherever there was space. One of them raised their arms signally for quiet and the crowd gradually calmed down.

"Fellow citizens!" the representative shouted. "Our society was trapped behind a veil of darkness and for a long time our souls knew no peace! But the government took action! Finally, the lid is lifted!"

"Glory to the authorities!" came a shout from the crowd.

"Curtains for the lid!" other members of the crowd were shouting.

Meanwhile, on the opposite side of the square, the sciendologists poured out onto the balcony of the Academy building. The head sciendologist decided to make his own appeal to the city's residents.

"Fellow citizens!" The crowd turned as one staring in the direction of the Academy.

"As you all know, sciend is the light and non-sciend is the darkness! Wandering through the darkness never slumbering, our valiant sciendologists searched tirelessly for the tunnel to the end of the world! And now, as a result of their immense sciendific efforts, the luminary of sciend rises above the horizon once again!"

"Glory to sciend!" came a cry from the crowd.

"Curtains for the lid!" voices in the crowd joined in.

The friends observed the proceedings from above with curiosity.

"What are they shouting?" asked Submarine.

"They don't understand it themselves," answered Eejit.

"Have you noticed that our catty-plaits have disappeared?" asked Puscilla.

"They're probably only visible when the movie pauses," Cow suggested. "But they're probably still there."

"Do you think human beings still have blue rays, too, like threads but invisible ones?" asked Submarine.

"It would seem so, yes," said the queen.

"The question is, who has a tighter hold on the threads, the movie or those in power," Beast added.

The head of City Administration addressed the crowd again.

"Fellow citizens!" he cried straining his vocal cords to the limit.

The crowd immediately turned to face the city hall.

"Guided exclusively by the interests of society, we have taken measures to strengthen our leadership by introducing a fresh current into a muddy flow! Day and night, barely shutting our eyes for we a moment, we have thought endlessly of the people and the well-being of the people! Daily and nightly, we have rushed about in modest, official cars from one end of the city to another and from that end to a third, never ceasing to carry out urgent telephone negotiations! And as a result of our skillful leadership, we succeeded. We pulled through!"

"Glory to the authorities!" came a shout from the crowd.

"Curtains to the lid!" the others joined in.

"Fellow citizens!" the head sciendologist said taking the initiative.

The audience of fellow citizens turned obediently once again.

"It gives me deep satisfaction to note that advanced sciend has gained the totalitarian confidence of the masses, delving into its authoritarianism further in depth and expansively in breadth! We must never underestimate or even overestimate the driving force of sciend, which has crushed the lid and plunged it back from whence it came, subsequently growing in metastases, into the deep abyss of insanity! And now, having emerged from the abyss victorious, sciend finally emerges shining with viability and competence!"

"Experiment-sciend-abscess!" chanted the sciendologists on the balcony.

"Glory to sciend!" came a cry from the crowd again.
"Curtains for the lid!" voices in the crowd joined in.

Our friends moved away from the edge of the viewing platform and gathered in a circle.

"Okay, so it's all very clear," said Eejit.

"They're still walking beneath the lid as they did before," said Beast.

"That's nothing to do with us, though. We've done our job," said Puscilla.

"It's time for us to leave," said the queen. "While the meeting is in progress, we can disappear in the crowd without drawing attention to ourselves."

"But where will we go?" asked Submarine.

"Let's go to Caramilla's first and then home," replied the queen.

"Great!" said Submarine. "We're going to the good old Villa Maravilla!"

"Yes, to our dear Caramilla," added Eejit.

THE LIVE AMONG THE LIVING

While speeches were being given on both sides of the square and the public were turning back and forth, our friends went down to the street below unnoticed and dived into one of the side streets. For obvious reasons, no-one was intent on pursuing them. A few blocks later, they reached Villa Maravilla and rang the bell. Caramilla greeted them overflowing with enthusiasm.

"Oh! My dear ones! My dear ones! You did it!" Caramilla gave a crushing hug to each of them in turn.

Her former extravagant hairdo had been replaced by a more convenient, elegant style.

"Without your intelligence and your help, dear Caramilla, we would never have been able to do anything," said Eejit.

"The world did not want to be saved but we saved it anyway," said Submarine.

"And the whole moggy-world is now happy celebrating," said Puscilla.

"You won't believe what is happening on the square, Caramilla," said Cow.

"I know, I know, my dears! All the city people are there but I wanted to wait for you, and here you are! Now then, let me bring you something to eat while you settle down and relax!"

The guests arranged themselves at the table in the living room while the hostess busied herself.

"Caramilla, we are very grateful to you for everything," said Brunhilda "especially for your help in lifting the lid."

"I don't know what I would have done without you!" said Caramilla bursting with happiness. "Tuck in, tuck in, my dears. Eat first and afterwards you can tell me all about it!"

The friends tried all the different dishes that Caramilla had so lovingly prepared and over dessert they all jumped in sharing their adventures and amazing transformations within reality.

"Caramilla, did you notice any changes when the movie stopped?" asked the queen.

"No, I didn't feel a pause at all," answered Caramilla. "Everything was the same as usual."

"It seems as if those who freeze in the movie never know afterwards that the movie stopped," said Eejit. "Each pause could last an eternity but as soon as the movie gets going again, the lives of its inhabitants continue as if nothing had happened."

"Everything you've told me is extraordinary!" exclaimed Caramilla. "Clearly reality is not constructed quite as we imagined it."

"If it wasn't for the lid, we would not have found out about any of this!" said Submarine.

"And we would never have met!" added Cow.

"And we wouldn't have been transformed," said Beast. "I would probably still be a beast at any rate."

"And I have to confess, I thought our efforts were in vain," said Eejit. "I thought we'd get rid of that damned machine and they would just build a new one."

"They won't restore it now," said Caramilla. "The authorities and the sciendologists have been forced to join the mainstream of public opinion."

"They worked that one out pretty quick!" said Submarine.

"They had no choice," said Cow. "How did they put it? 'Bring a fresh current to a muddy flow'. Only it would have been more accurate if they had swapped the place of the adjectives in that phrase."

"I suppose it's quite possible the sciendologists will invent some other poisonous machine," Puscilla surmised.

"They'll have another abscess with its subsequent insanity and another invention will find its way into being. No matter what they invent, it'll always be a bomb in one form or another. It is not just a cat-trocity, it is terrorism in its moggiest form."

"And then we'll have to come and save the world again!" shouted Submarine.

"Or perhaps we won't," said Cow. "The people know that life is better without the lid now and are genuinely rejoicing at the clear sky. So, they're not completely lacking in awareness."

"They just don't understand fully. They have not fully understood the essence of the lid," Beast commented.

"Oh yes! That's the trouble with society," Caramilla lamented.

"We were not completely consciously aware before, either," said Submarine. "Eejit and I, for example, went out setting mammoth traps."

"There's no point in bringing all that up!" said Eejit, waving his hand to show his displeasure.

"We were asleep then," said the queen. "It's only because of the adventures we had to go through that we woke up."

"Not to mention our wonderful transformations!" exclaimed Submarine.

"Transfigurations!" added Cow.

"I can transform back and forth now at will!" declared Submarine.

"Me too," said Cow. "What about you Beast?"

"I don't know," he replied. "I'm not sure whether I would want to. What would be the point?"

"Well, Puscilla looks fabulous with or without transformation," said Eejit throwing her a complement.

"Catty-fab! I look catty-fab!" said Puscilla happily. "It's true, isn't it, my lord," she said turning to Beast. "Don't I look great?"

"Yes, Puscilla, you look great," replied Beast as sparing with his words as always.

Under the subtle shadow of jealousy, Brunhilda gave them both a side-long glance while trying to maintain a calm composure. But everyone could sense that she felt far from calm.

"Caramilla, why did you behave so... um, shall we say strangely at first?" asked Cow trying to diffuse the tension.

"How else is one to behave in the company of the characters of a dream?" Caramilla replied. "Until you started talking about the lid, I took you for being asleep. You have no doubt experienced for yourselves what it is like to talk to the living, who might look vibrant enough but are in fact asleep, living in a waking dream."

"Yes, it really is like being in a dream," agreed Submarine. "When you suddenly realize that it's a dream and that none of the characters inside it are real, you tend to talk to them as if they were fictional characters and remain a certain detachment watching how they will react."

"I used to talk to my dolls like that when I was little," said the queen.

"Teddy bears were more my specialty," Eejit broke in. "Only they weren't very communicative."

"Ha, ha, ha!" Cow laughed. "I bet they were your most devoted listeners!"

"Being in a movie is probably just like dreaming," supposed Submarine. "I wonder what it would be like if you woke up inside a movie and tried to talk to the main characters?"

"Most likely, you would play with them in their own roles according to the plot, only you'd be doing it consciously, knowing that they are fictional characters playing a given role and that you are playing a role, too, only you're playing for fun," replied Cow.

"We've already been doing that essentially!" said Eejit.

"Yes, that's what we were doing when we were communicating with the local characters," the queen stated.

"We felt it most acutely when we were watching events from the tower," said Beast.

"So, what's the difference between those who are alive and those who are living in the movie?" asked Submarine.

"They are living here to the extent that they are connected by threads to a given script, like puppets," replied Eejit, "whereas we can wander about anywhere because those threads have been released."

"Here's another question for you, then. Are we only able to wander through a movie when it has stopped playing?" asked Submarine. "And are tied by threads, too, the rest of the time?"

"No, I don't think so," replied Puscilla. "We can say, 'I am me' whereas the other characters can't."

"That takes us back to the question of 'where are we'?" said Cow.

"I still get the impression that we aren't in everyday reality," said Submarine.

"So, in your opinion, am I real or not?" asked Caramilla with indignation.

"Caramilla! Of course, you are real!" they all replied.

"So that brings me back to the same old dilemma: What is the difference between genuine reality and non-reality? Can you define it?"

"Genuine reality does not stop."

"Have you ever tried?"

"Caramilla, are you saying that all the filmstrips, plaits and blue threads exist in genuine reality, too?"

"Who knows? Maybe one day you'll be able to answer that question with certainty."

There was a short pause. They all understood that mission 'expedition lid' was complete and that the time had come for them to return to their own paths.

"Well, Caramilla, thank you so much for everything!" said the queen.

"For everything and each single thing!" added Submarine.

"It's time for us to go home," said Eejit. "Right, Your Majesty?"

"Yes," replied Brunhilda.

"Caramilla, would you like to come with us at least for a short while?" asked Cow.

"I would like to very much, my dears, but I have no-one with whom I can leave Villa Maravilla in safe hands."

"Our Villa-Maravilla!" exclaimed Submarine. "We liked it here so much it's sad to leave and to part company with you."

"My home is your home, my dears!"

"The gates of my castle will always be open to you," said the queen.

Caramilla shed a tear and nodded silently.

"What about you, Puscilla, are you coming with us?" asked Beast.

"You promised that you wouldn't abandon me!" said Puscilla alarmed.

"We have no intention of abandoning you."

"Then it ought to be completely pussy-clear that I'm coming with you. I don't belong here."

The friends began preparing for their journey. Caramilla saw them off with tears in her eyes.

"Oh, my dears, shall we ever see each other again?"

"Definitely, dear Caramilla," Eejit assured her.

"You'd better catty bet on it!" added Puscilla.

"We will definitely, definitely see each other again!" Cow, too, was struggling to hold back tears.

"We will return to our Villa-Maravilla!" promised Beast.

"That a cast-iron promise!" said Submarine.

"We'll see you again soon!" said the queen.

"I'll be expecting you!"

JUST THE BEGINNING

The friends walked toward the object in the direction that Caramilla had shown them. They were happy that their mission was successful, but at the same time they were a little sad that their amazing adventures had come to an end. The unsuspecting pursuers of adventure could not have imagined what surprises still lay ahead of them. The reality in which they found themselves was so unpredictable, it would have been at the very least naive to hope for any level of certainty.

In the meantime, in their happy ignorance our travelers were busy making plans for how they would return home, how they would celebrate and how they would begin living a new life of harmonious abundance. They had become great friends during the time of their travels although recent events had come at them so thick and fast, there had not been a moment to work out how the relationships between them stood.

Once they went beyond the outskirts of the city, they were just a stone's throw from the mirror-like object.

"I just hope that once we arrive at this strange place, we'll understand where to go next," said Submarine. "We knew how we got there before, didn't we?"

"Hoping is for girls," said Eejit in an ironic tone.

"No, it's the girls who are the hope of men," retorted Submarine.

"I don't know who is for whom over there but I'm really looking forward to seeing this object of yours," said Puscilla. "Is it catty-cosmic?"

"Oh yes, Puscilla, it's so catty-cosmic that you'll be completely cattified," answered Eejit.

"It's moggy-mazing," said Cow in turn.

"Or even night-moggy-marish," added Submarine.

Eventually, they arrived at the site of the strange object. As before, the view opened out onto a stunning azure sea with grass, sand and palm trees lining the shore.

"Miaow! How luxurious!" exclaimed Puscilla in admiration. "I'll wet my tail there with pleasure, and possibly my paws, too, if not everything else!"

"Slow down, Puscilla," Beast warned her. "Don't you think it's strange that one landscape shifts so sharply into another?"

Puscilla looked puzzled. The area through which they were walking changed radically as if two different landscape photographs had been pushed together.

"You really could get cattified here," said Puscilla in surprise, fumbling her way along the invisible wall. "It is a mirror, right?"

"Well, yes and no," replied Eejit. "See how everything around us is reflected whereas our silhouettes are sketchy?"

"And there's no end or edge to this wall? Have you checked?"

"It could either be a screen, which is unlikely, or a border between two worlds or aspects of reality as Caramilla suggested," said Brunhilda. "But we haven't found any edges to it."

"Whatever the case, this is sheer moggy-mockery!" said Puscilla in indignation. "What monstrous catty-trickery! Can we study it?"

"We've already tried from every possible angle," replied Eejit, "but it is not the kind of object that can be researched. It just... exists."

"Out sciendologists would say the opposite, wouldn't they? They would conclude that if an object is not subject to research, it cannot in fact exist," said Cow. "A very convenient approach!"

"Whatever that may be, if can't make any headway here, all we can do is go home. At least for now," said the queen.

"I think when we were first here, we approached from over there," said Cow pointing in one direction.

"No, we approached from over there," said Submarine pointing in the opposite direction.

"Let's try over there first," said Eejit pointing in another direction altogether.

"Okay, let's go where your mind-boggling intuition leads us," agreed the queen.

"Your Majesty, my intuition is entirely educational, enlightening and very much to the point," replied Eejit in his old-style manner.

And with that they set off in the direction Eejit had indicated. They walked some distance from the object and eventually it disappeared from view. But even though they tried to go strictly in one direction, familiar features of the landscape soon reappeared, and they ended up where they had first started.

"Right," said the queen.

"Right," echoed Submarine.

"Looks like we're going around in circles," said Puscilla.

"That's not possible!" said Cow.

"That can't be!" repeated Eejit.

"I have a great sense of direction. We can't have gone in a circle," said Beast.

"Then let's try going in a different direction," the queen suggested.

The friends set off in the direction Cow had originally chosen. Again, they stayed in a neat line and after a while the contours of a town appeared in the distance. Once they were a little closer, they all exclaimed in chorus, "Pomponius!"

"It's our town!"

"Look! Over there is the tower of the town hall!"

"What are we going to do now?" Submarine said asking her favorite question.

"First of all, we should go back to the site of the strange mirror-like object," the queen decided.

Eventually, they found themselves back where they had started again. Behind the invisible wall, just as before, the sea methodically drove its much-longed-for waves towards the shore and the palm trees swayed their wide leaves indifferently in the breeze.

"Maybe I should get up into the sky and take a look around like before?" Cow suggested.

"Yes, try it. Good for you, Cow," said the queen.

Cow stopped to concentrate for a moment, shook her wings and shape-shifted into her former appearance, — a winged orange cow. Having straightened her feathers, Cow gave her wings a quick flap and rose upwards into the sky drawing spiraling circles in the air. Having turned this way and that, she landed safely instantly regaining her human form. The friends all looked at her in questioning expectation.

"Your Majesty," she said addressing the queen, "there is nothing in the area of any note except for the city. Although I did spot something resembling a patch of woodland."

"Yes! We passed through an area of rare species of tree when we were here the first time!" said Eejit enthusiastically.

"Then that's the direction we'll take," decided the queen.

"I'll go ahead," said Beast

And they all followed him.

A quarter of an hour later, they entered the woodland area, which was truly very small and so it was not long before they emerged on the other side. After that the landscape became hilly and thick with grasses and shrubs. Heading consistently straight ahead, the friends began to notice that the distinctive features of the landscape which they were navigating by began to be repeated creating the impression that they were turning back on themselves. And indeed, they soon found themselves back where they had started beside the mirror-like object and in the distance, they could still make out the outlines of the same city. Throwing themselves onto the ground with exhaustion, the friends fell silent completely flummoxed.

Submarine, who had become highly agitated rushed from left to right shoving her hands up against the invisible wall.

"What is this punishment?" she wailed. "There must be a way through somewhere! Why won't anyone answer me?"

No sooner had she spoken than a muffled whisper rose up out of the silence and darted from one direction to another like a jumping wind.

"Who's there?" asked Submarine.

"Threshold... Threshold..." came the whispering response.

"Threshold of what?"

"Time... time..."

"Where are you?"

"I am everywhere and all about you... everywhere and all about you..."

"Oh, can you tell me, could you just tell me," asked Submarine, "where are we? What is this invisible wall? How can we get out of here?"

"Too many questions... questions..."

"Can you at least tell us how to get home?"

"Find the synthetic maid and the little red queen... They will help you..."

"But how? Where are we supposed to find them?"

"You'll learn... Find them..."

"Can't you tell me, just tell me..."

But the whispering wind dissipated as suddenly as it had appeared.

The friends sat in silence staring at each other in amazement.

Eejit was the first to break the silence.

"Threshold of time? Sounds a bit mystical…"

"This is all way beyond me," said Cow.

"And my pussy-vision," added Puscilla.

"And who are the synthetic maid and red queen?" asked Beast. "Have any of you ever heard of them?" The others shook their heads.

"Don't worry. We'll find out who they are somehow, and we'll find them," said Submarine encouragingly. "Threshold promised that at least!"

"And you believe him?" asked Eejit.

"Do we really have a choice?" replied Submarine.

"At least we have something to go on now," said Brunhilda, "thanks to your persistence, Submarine, we now have some clues."

"Thank you, Your Majesty. You will always be our queen but now it looks like we need to find another, a little red queen."

"Yes, and a maid… a synthetic maid."

"What can all this mean?"

"Ho hum," sighed Cow, "and there we all were thinking it was over."

"It looks like things are only just beginning," said the queen.